NOISE CONTROL FOR ENGINEERS

NOISE CONTROL
FOR ENGINEERS

Harold W. Lord
Michigan Technological University

William S. Gatley
Portable Products Division, Motorola, Inc.

Harold A. Evensen
Michigan Technological University

Krieger Publishing Company
Malabar, Florida

Original Edition 1980
Reprint Edition 1987

Printed and Published by
ROBERT E. KRIEGER PUBLISHING COMPANY, INC.
KRIEGER DRIVE
MALABAR, FLORIDA 32950

Library of Congress Cataloging-in-Publication Data

Lord, Harold W.
        Noise control for engineers.

        Reprint. Originally published: New York :
McGraw-Hill, 1980.
        Includes index.
        1. Noise control   2. Acoustical engineering.
I. Gatley, William S.   II. Evensen, Harold A.
III. Title.
[TD892.L67   1987]   620.2'3   87-22611
ISBN 0-89464-255-3

10   9   8   7

CONTENTS

Part 2   Practical Aspects of Noise Control

Part 3   Laboratory and Field Experiments

PREFACE

This book has been written to fill the need for an introductory textbook on noise control. There are already a number of excellent textbooks on acoustics which deal with sound per se, developing the physical laws governing its propagation and providing extensive mathematical analysis of sound as vibration of an elastic medium. Although these books provide superior treatments of the theory of sound, they do not attempt to develop the techniques needed to solve noise problems: the elimination of *unwanted* sound. At the other extreme are several authoritative texts which treat noise control at the level of the professional. These texts presuppose a basic understanding of noise control techniques and, therefore, devote relatively little space to developing an understanding of how sound is generated, propagated, and controlled. Neither type of text presents the fundamentals of noise control at the introductory, elementary level required by the aspiring newcomer in noise control—namely, *the engineer* who has no formal background in noise control, yet whose duties now include the evaluation and control of noise; *the student* who needs to acquire a basic understanding of noise control principles and their application; and *the teacher* who must provide a first course in noise control to undergraduate engineering students, yet who may not have had the opportunity to fully develop his or her own experience in this area of instruction. It is toward these individuals that this book is directed.

The objective of this book is to develop readers' skills to the point where they can initiate and implement an effective program in noise control. To do this, it is necessary to raise their basic understanding to the level required to undertake further study in the more advanced texts in noise control and to comprehend the available journals dealing with noise control. The book strives specifically to develop the reader's capabilities to perform the following tasks:

1. Select and use the basic instruments employed in most noise control work.
2. Conduct basic measurements of noise in plant and community environments.

3. Evaluate the noise environment in light of standards and known human response to noise.
4. Identify the sources, paths, and receivers associated with typical noise problems.
5. Initiate basic measures to control and improve the quality of the noise environment.

The level of presentation of material has been designed so that this book will serve either as a text for an introductory course in noise control or as a means of self-study. A heuristic approach is taken in developing the fundamental concepts of sound propagation, transmission, reflection, and absorption. The authors draw upon the reader's experience with related wave phenomena such as the motion of a string, water and light waves, and the analogy between heat conduction and sound absorption in developing these concepts. A model of the hearing mechanism is developed and related to hearing damage, speech interference, and subjective responses of man to noise. Noise control regulations and standards are discussed in light of what is known about the effects of noise on human beings.

Worked examples are used to illustrate and reinforce principles of sound propagation and to demonstrate noise control techniques and applications. They serve as guides in problem-solving techniques and as references for later use. The problems are posed in terms of the tasks which the reader may be expected to perform in real situations. A set of problems with answers is included at the end of each chapter, so that readers can test their understanding of the material presented.

Case studies are provided which deal with assessment and solution of real problems. Although the fundamental principles of noise control can be learned from tutorial material, their applications are better understood after dissecting and evaluating an actual solution to a real problem. The case studies provide a means to impart "instant experience" on a variety of typical noise problems and can, with prudent application, serve as reference solutions for the reader.

Control of noise is intimately related to its measurement. It is impossible to become proficient in noise control without knowledge of both measurement and control techniques. For this reason, this introductory text emphasizes and encourages hands-on experience with the instruments used in noise control and provides a workout in techniques and in data analysis. This is accomplished through a set of *laboratory experiments* which are provided at the end of the book. These experiments are oriented toward selection, familiarization, and use of basic instrumentation used in noise control, as well as illustration of control techniques. Instruments are discussed as "black boxes," that is, in terms of their functions rather than their operation. This approach enables the reader to master the use of any instrument of like function with the aid of the appropriate instrument manual.

The material in this book has been divided into three parts. Part 1 contains four chapters in which the fundamental concepts of sound needed in noise control engineering are presented. The basic concepts are developed in a straightforward manner in this section of the book. Precautions which must be exercised when applying these concepts to practical situations are reserved for later chapters.

Part 2 presents the practical aspects of noise control and deals with the applications of concepts presented in Part 1 to field situations. The measurement and evaluation of noise environments in light of standards and regulations are discussed. Case studies are presented which consider noise control procedures applied to actual noise problems. These studies emphasize criteria used to evaluate problems, the approach taken in establishing noise control treatments, and evaluation of the completed noise control projects.

Part 3 of the text is devoted to laboratory and field experiments. The chapters in this section should be read concurrently with Parts 1 and 2. The experiments outlined at the end of each of these chapters serve the very important function of giving the reader some practical experience in using sound-measuring equipment and in evaluating measured data. Many of the experiments are directed toward practical applications often encountered by the noise control engineer.

Parts 1 and 2 alone will serve readers whose main interest is to obtain an understanding of the basic concepts and principles of sound propagation, as applied in noise control engineering. Even if readers are unable to carry out the experiments outlined in Part 3, they will find this part of value in learning to understand and use measured data.

Harold W. Lord
William S. Gatley
Harold A. Evensen

ONE

FUNDAMENTAL CONCEPTS
OF SOUND

THE NATURE OF SOUND AND ITS MEASUREMENT

1.1 INTRODUCTION

The word "noise" carries the meaning of *unwanted sound*. This interpretation implies a value judgment of the sound, which in turn generally implies the response of a human being to a noise environment. In our study we will be concerned with noise environments which have an adverse effect on human beings.

We are all aware that a very intense noise can cause permanent hearing loss, but perhaps we have less appreciation for the fact that the same type of hearing damage can accrue after exposure to more moderate noise environments over an extended period of time. The intensity of sound around airports, along assembly lines of many plants, and in the operator's position of a pneumatic drill, a snowmobile, or a motorcycle all are examples of such noise environments. The use of high-powered electronic amplifiers by "rock" bands provides "music" of an intensity which most certainly will lead to premature hearing loss of many of the young people who play in the bands and who enjoy listening to this form of music for long periods of time.

Our health and sense of well-being can be affected in other ways by noise which interferes with our sleep, our work, and our recreation. Many of us who have lived in modern apartment buildings lacking proper sound isolation or acoustical treatment have been irritated by a neighbor's air-conditioning unit, TV, or other appliance which keeps us awake at night. Even the noisy ballast of a fluorescent lamp is bothersome in a quiet room when we are trying to read or make calculations. The noise from a canning factory or a drop forging plant or the hum of an electrical power transformer can be a source of annoyance to neighboring residential areas.

Noise which masks other sounds that communicate information to us can be bothersome, and it may even endanger our lives; for example, serious accidents can result when the din of a power lawnmower drowns out the warning sound of a horn as we step onto a busy street, or when the rush of air from a large fan in a factory muffles the warning shout of a co-worker. People working underground in mines are very sensitive to the sudden sounds of bursting or falling rocks, which forewarn them of impending danger. For this reason, it is very difficult to get miners who operate noisy equipment to wear protective earplugs, even though these plugs may be designed to let desired sounds through. On the other hand, it may be difficult to sell a "quiet" vacuum cleaner, because the operator associates noise with power to suck up dirt from a floor.

Three adverse effects of noise on human beings have been demonstrated in the examples given above: (1) hearing loss, (2) annoyance, and (3) speech interference. Our ultimate goal in this study will be to learn to measure and evaluate a given noise environment based on specific criteria which relate to these three effects on people, and to apply standard noise control techniques to problem environments in order to bring them up to acceptable standards. The remainder of this chapter will be devoted to laying the groundwork needed to achieve these goals. We will develop the basic concepts of sound, define terms and build the vocabulary needed to describe noise problems, and specify and quantify noise criteria related to the effects of noise on humans.

1.2 GENERATION AND PROPAGATION OF SOUND

The manner in which sound is generated and propagated can be demonstrated by considering simple experiences which most of us have encountered. Consider a small inflated balloon, suspended by a string from the ceiling in the middle of a large room. If the excess pressure inside the balloon were applied to a piston, it could do work. Hence, there is potential energy associated with the pressurized air in the balloon. If the balloon is ruptured, there is a sudden expansion of the air which was in the balloon, and the potential energy of the air is transformed into kinetic energy. The air in the immediate vicinity of the balloon, which was initially in a state of equilibrium, is suddenly pushed outward, compressing neighboring particles of air, which in turn push outward against their neighbors, and so on. Thus, a spherical compressive wave expands outward from the burst balloon until it finally reaches the boundaries of the room. The ear, which is a pressure-sensing device, perceives the compressive wave as sound as it passes by. If none of the energy carried by the compressive wave is reflected back from the walls of the room, the sudden "pop" of the balloon as the wave passes is all that is heard.

A similar experience is encountered if the balloon is replaced by a tuning fork whose prongs vibrate at a fixed frequency characteristic of the fork. As the prongs move back and forth, the air in the immediate vicinity of the prongs experiences periodic compression and rarefaction. These disturbances propagate out from the tuning fork in the same way the compression wave moved out from the balloon, except that now there is a continuous train of periodically varying compression and rarefaction disturbances, as indicated in Fig. 1.1. The ear perceives this as a continuous sound having a tonal quality determined by the frequency of vibration of the prongs of the tuning fork.

It is not difficult to extend this last experiment to that of several tuning forks vibrating simultaneously, each at a different frequency. The sound which our ear perceives is no longer a pure tone but rather has several frequency components. In general, the sounds which reach our ears have an infinite number of frequency components. However, the normal human ear is sensitive only to the components in the range from about 20 to 20,000 cycles per second (or Hertz). The ear does not "hear" the components of a sound if they fall outside this range of frequencies.

If sound is defined as *a disturbance that propagates through an elastic medium at a speed characteristic of that medium,* it becomes evident that the same type of phenomenon which occurred with the balloon in air can occur in a steel rod. When the end of a rod is struck with a hammer, a compressional disturbance propagates along the rod. Individual particles vibrate about fixed equilibrium

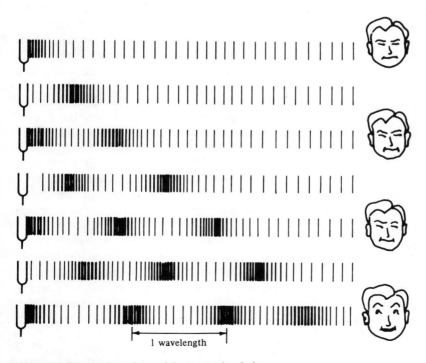

1 wavelength

Figure 1.1 Propagation of sound from a tuning fork.

positions within the rod as the compression wave passes. Compressional waves in the rod propagate at a much higher speed than disturbances in air. Similarly, sound can be generated in liquids, the basis for "sonar" used in fishing boats and submarines to locate objects under water.

In the above discussions the basic elements of sound propagation have been discussed in a very intuitive manner. In each case, there was a noise *source* which caused a disturbance in an elastic medium. The elastic medium provided a *path* for propagation of the sound (acoustic energy), which finally reached a *receiver*. The receiver could be someone's ear, a microphone, or a panel which is set into vibration. The source-path-receiver concept is used extensively in noise control problems and will be dealt with in detail later in this text.

1.3 WAVE NATURE OF SOUND

Sound is a wave-type phenomenon by which vibrational energy is propagated through elastic media. Sound can propagate in gases, liquids, and solids, but it cannot propagate in a vacuum. Normally, two types of waves can be generated in an elastic medium: *transverse waves* and *longitudinal waves*.

Wave propagation in a wire or string held taut between two supports is a common occurrence. If one end of the wire is plucked, a disturbance is seen to propagate along the wire. Propagation of the wave imparts motion (kinetic energy) to elements of the wire which is transverse to the direction in which the wave propagates, hence the name *transverse waves*. As the disturbance passes, elements of the wire move back and forth in a direction perpendicular to it, about some equilibrium configuration. However, the energy is propagated along the length of the wire with the motion of the wave.

A similar phenomenon occurs with a long coil spring (a "Slinky") stretched between two supports. If one end of the spring is suddenly displaced in a direction parallel to the longitudinal axis of the spring, a compression of the coils occurs which propagates along the length of the spring. If a small piece of paper is attached to the spring, the paper will move back and forth in a longitudinal direction about some fixed equilibrium position as the disturbance propagates along the length of the spring. In this case, the motion of particles in the elastic medium is in the direction of wave propagation. Hence, these waves are called *longitudinal waves*.

Shearing forces are required to cause motion of particles transverse to the direction of wave propagation. Hence, transverse waves are sometimes referred to as *shear waves*. On the other hand, normal forces, or pressures, are required to cause motion of particles in the direction of wave propagation, and for this reason longitudinal waves are sometimes called *pressure waves*. A viscous fluid, such as water, can sustain both shearing and compressional forces, so that both types of waves exist for sound in water. However, gases can sustain very little shearing forces, so that sound propagation in air is predominantly the result of pressure waves.

1.4 TRANSMISSION, REFLECTION, AND ABSORPTION OF SOUND BY BOUNDARIES

When a sound wave strikes a boundary of the medium in which it propagates, the energy in the wave can be *transmitted*, *absorbed*, or *reflected* by the boundary. In general, all three of the above occur in varying degrees depending upon the type of boundary encountered.

As an example, consider the taut strings shown in Fig. 1.2. Two collinear strings are attached to a very light (massless) sleeve, which can slide freely on a support rod. Various constraints are applied to the sleeve at the support, as indicated in the figure:

1. The sleeve is free to slide on the rod.
2. Motion of the sleeve is constrained by a linear elastic spring.
3. Motion of the sleeve is constrained by a viscous dashpot.
4. Motion of the sleeve is constrained by a combination spring and dashpot.
5. The sleeve is rigidly welded to the support rod.

In this "paper" experiment we wish to observe what happens to a wave pulse, propagating toward the support from the left, as it encounters the support. In case 1 there is no resistance to the string's transverse motion at the support, and all the energy is *transmitted* to the second string on the right, as though the support were not there. In the other extreme, case 5, no motion can occur at the support, and all the energy is *reflected* back into the string on the left. In case 2 the elastic spring resists displacement, but the sleeve can move. Consequently, some energy is transmitted to the string on the right and some is reflected back to the left. Since the ideal spring cannot dissipate energy, all the energy that is not transmitted is reflected. In case 3 the transverse motion of the sleeve is resisted by a viscous force which is proportional to the velocity. Since sleeve motion can occur, energy will be transmitted to the string on the right. However, the resisting force will reflect energy back into the string on the left. Moreover, since the dashpot dissipates energy, there will be *absorption* of energy at the support. The reflected energy will be equal to the total incoming energy minus the sum of the transmitted and absorbed energies. Case 4 is a combination of cases 2 and 3 and will also result in transmission, reflection, and absorption of energy at the support.

The example of transverse waves in a string was chosen here because it is easy to visualize this type of wave motion. Similar phenomena occur with compressional waves in air. Instead of two strings separated by a support, consider two rooms of air separated by a partition, with an acoustic wave approaching the partition from the left. In the first case the partition is assumed to be a very thin, flexible sheet of material. As the pressure wave impinges upon the sheet, the thin (massless) material offers no resistance. Consequently, the disturbance (sound) will propagate through the partition into the room on the right with no loss in energy. That is, there will be 100 percent transmission, just

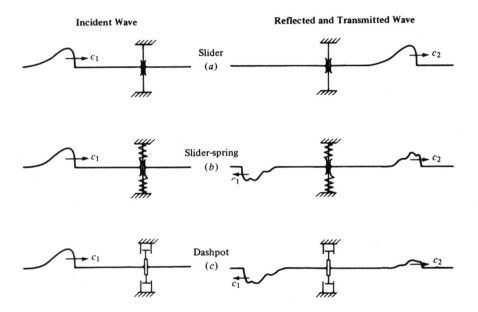

Incident Wave   **Reflected and Transmitted Wave**

Slider
(a)

Slider-spring
(b)

Dashpot
(c)

Figure 1.2 Transmission, reflection, and absorption of wave energy.

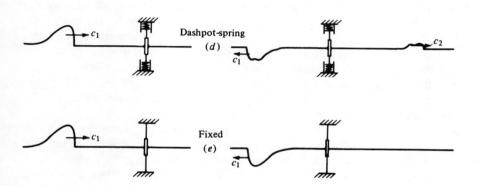

Figure 1.2 Transmission, reflection, and absorption of wave energy (continued).

as there was in case 1 of the strings. On the other hand, if the thin sheet is replaced by a perfectly rigid wall, all the acoustic energy will be reflected back to the left, as in case 5 above. Now consider the thin sheet to be stretched so that it behaves like an elastic membrane. As the pressure wave impinges upon the membrane, the latter will deflect a certain amount due to the increase in pressure, causing a disturbance to propagate into the room on the right. However, some of the energy will be reflected back into the first room when the elasticity of the membrane causes it to return toward its initial configuration. Since no energy is dissipated in an elastic membrane, the total acoustic energy will be equal to the sum of the transmitted and reflected energies, as in case 2 of the strings. Consider next a panel which is rigid but has small perforations. When a compressional wave impinges upon this panel, some of the energy will excite the particles of air in the perforations of the panel, and some will be reflected back by the rigid wall. The motion of particles in the small holes of the panel will cause a disturbance to be transmitted through to the room on the right. We note, however, that there will be a viscous or shearing resistance as the air particles vibrate back and forth in the fine pores of the panel, so that some of the energy is dissipated, or absorbed, during this transmission. Consequently, this panel corresponds to case 3, with sound being reflected, transmitted, and absorbed by the panel. Case 4 above is like having an elastically flexible panel which is also porous.

A wall made of almost any material will exhibit to some degree the ability to reflect, transmit, and absorb acoustic energy. For example, brick and smooth masonry walls reflect about 98 percent of the acoustic energy impinging upon them. As one might expect, the sound field generated by any given source will vary considerably depending upon the room in which it is placed and upon other objects located in its vicinity from which reflections can occur.

Whenever there are walls or objects in the neighborhood of a sound source, the sound field generated will consist of sound waves radiating directly from the source and of sound reflected from neighboring surfaces. There will be regions around the source where the level* of sound at any point in that region is established by the sound radiating directly from the source. This region is called the *direct sound field*. The remaining region, where the level is established by reflected sound waves, is called the *reverberant field*.

Whenever reflecting surfaces exist in the vicinity of a noise source, a *standing wave* can occur. This phenomenon is of interest in noise control engineering and will be discussed further.

Consider a sound wave, consisting of a single frequency (a "pure tone"), impinging upon a reflecting surface. The reflected wave will have the same frequency as the incident wave, but the phase relationship between them will vary. At locations where the two traveling waves are in phase they will reinforce one another, and at locations where they are out of phase they will partially, or

---

* A precise definition of the word "level," as used here, is given in the following section of the text.

completely, cancel one another. However, at any given location, the traveling waves combine to form a pure tone of constant amplitude. If you were to scan the resulting sound field with a microphone (or your ear) while moving away from the reflecting surface, you would find that the amplitude of the combined sound increases at locations where the two waves reinforce and decreases where they cancel. In fact, the amplitude periodically increases and decreases like a wave that is fixed, or standing, in space; hence the term "standing wave."

The standing-wave phenomenon can also occur when waves reflect obliquely off a surface. Consequently, when sound is generated in a space that has highly reflective surfaces, the sound will reflect many times off many surfaces, and the resulting standing-wave pattern will be very complex. The sound field is a function not only of the source but also of the characteristics of the room in which it is located.

Another phenomenon of interest can occur whenever there are several reflecting boundaries located so that the path of the wave repeats itself as it is reflected from surface to surface. If the length of this circuitous path is such that it is equal to some multiple of the wavelength* of the wave being generated, a phenomenon called *resonance* can occur. Resonance is readily demonstrated with a rope stretched between two rigid supports. A wave pulse propagating along the rope will strike the rigid support at one end and be reflected. The reflected wave has the same shape as the incident wave but is inverted, as shown in Fig. 1.2e. Theoretically, a wave pulse would be reflected continuously back and forth between the two supports, being inverted with each reflection. The length of the circuitous path of the wave is twice the length of the rope. Next, consider a half-sine pulse propagating in the rope. If the distance between supports is just equal to the length of the half-sine pulse, the rope would vibrate continuously between the upright and inverted half-sine shape, with no apparent propagational motion occurring; that is, a standing wave would occur having zero displacements (nodes) at the supports and maximum displacement (antinode) midway between supports. In the absence of energy losses, once set in motion the rope would continue to vibrate in this mode forever. This is called a *natural* (or resonance) *mode* of vibration of the rope; it can persist even after the source is shut off.

If additional energy were applied, forcing the rope to vibrate in this mode, the amplitude of the standing wave would grow, or *resonate*. We could generate yet another natural mode of vibration of the rope by using a full-sine pulse and placing the supports one wavelength apart. The standing wave which would result in this case would have a node at the center of the rope with half-sine lobes on each side of the node (see Fig. 1.3a).

Similar phenomena occur with sound waves in a closed tube, where the sound can reflect back and forth between the ends of the tube. Unlike standing displacement waves in a rope, the standing sound-pressure waves for resonance in the tube will have antinodes (points of maximum pressure) at the boundaries, as shown in Fig. 1.3b.

* See Sec. 1.5 for a definition of wavelength of a continuous wave.

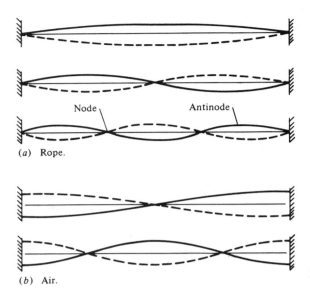

(a) Rope.

(b) Air.

Figure 1.3 Standing-wave patterns.

For the reverberant rectangular room, where there are many complicated circuitous paths which the reflecting sound may take (the simplest being back and forth between two parallel walls), the resonant modes of vibration of the room associated with these complicated paths will be quite complex. Since there is a direct relationship between wavelength and frequency of a sound wave, as will be shown in Sec. 1.5, a sound source having many frequency components will, in general, excite many of the resonant modes of a room, causing buildup of sound associated with these modes. The phenomenon of resonance is of interest to the noise control engineer when evaluating the sound field generated in a room or enclosure, particularly when the source has a dominant single frequency.

1.5 MATHEMATICAL DESCRIPTION OF SOUND WAVES

The physical description of a sound wave is a disturbance that propagates through an elastic material at a speed characteristic of that medium. Consequently, sound has both spatial and temporal characteristics which we would like to describe mathematically.

Consider first the experiment of the single tuning fork which generates a continuous pure tone. A microphone measuring the pressure variation in the air at a fixed location in space would allow one to observe the temporal characteristics of the sound. An oscilloscope display of the time-varying signal would show that the *sound pressure* (the deviation from atmospheric or equilibrium pressure, sometimes called excess pressure) varies sinusoidally with time, as shown in Fig. 1.4.

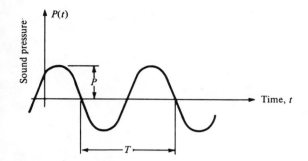

Figure 1.4 Temporal characteristics of a pure tone (time domain).

The pressure variation is *periodic*, i.e., the pressure-time history repeats itself in equal time intervals. One complete variation in pressure is called a *cycle*. The time T required for one complete cycle is called the *period* of pressure oscillation. The *frequency* of the pressure change f is defined as the number of cycles per unit of time.

$$f = \frac{1}{T} \tag{1.1}$$

Frequency is usually given in cycles per second or Hertz (Hz), the latter being synonymous with cycles per second. We shall use Hertz throughout this text.

A mathematical description of the pressure variation with time is given by the equation

$$p(t) = P_R \sin(\omega t + \phi_1) \tag{1.2}$$

where P_R = amplitude of the pressure fluctuation

ϕ = phase of the sound signal being measured relative to some reference

ω = circular frequency (rad/s)

The third of these is related to the frequency f by the expression

$$\omega = \frac{2\pi}{T} = 2\pi f \tag{1.3}$$

Now suppose a "flash picture" could be taken, showing how the sound pressure varies in space at a given instant of time. For the example of a tuning fork the pressure would vary sinusoidally in space, as shown in Fig. 1.5. If another picture were taken at a time Δt later, the disturbance would have moved a distance Δx, as shown by the dashed curve. The *velocity of propagation* c of the sound is given by $c = \Delta x / \Delta t$. The *wavelength* of the periodic sound-pressure wave is defined as the distance through which the wave propagates during time T. During the time T required for one oscillation of the sound pressure in Fig. 1.4, the pressure wave in Fig. 1.5 would have moved one wavelength, λ. Hence, for a constant velocity c, the wave moves a distance $\lambda = cT$ during the time period T. Making use of Eq. (1.1) we obtain the very important result

$$\lambda = \frac{c}{f} \tag{1.4}$$

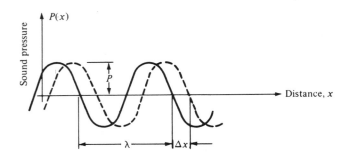

Figure 1.5 Spatial characteristics of a pure tone (space domain).

which relates wavelength and frequency of sound. For example, the velocity of sound in air at sea level and 60°F is approximately 1100 ft/s. Hence, the wavelength of a 1000-Hz sound in air is about 1.1 ft. The same sound signal in water, which has a velocity of sound equal to 4500 ft/s, would have a wavelength of 4.5 ft.

A mathematical description of the spatial variation in sound pressure is given by the equation

$$p(x) = P_R \sin(kx + \phi_2) \tag{1.5}$$

where k is called the *wave number* (radians per unit of length) and is related to wavelength and frequency by the expressions

$$k = \frac{2\pi}{\lambda} = \frac{2\pi f}{c} = \frac{\omega}{c} \tag{1.6}$$

The combined spatial and temporal characteristics of a sound wave propagating at constant speed and without change in shape can be simply described mathematically. Consider the function $f(x)$, which would represent the spatial variation of sound pressure. Then $f(x - h)$ represents the same function displaced in the positive x direction by an amount h. During time t, a sound wave traveling in the positive x direction would be displaced an amount $h = ct$. Thus, the combined spatial and temporal behavior of the propagation of a single-frequency sound (pure tone) in the positive x direction is obtained by replacing x by $x - ct$ in Eq. (1.5):

$$p(x, t) = P_R \sin[k(x - ct) + \phi]$$

or $$p(x, t) = P_R \sin(kx - \omega t + \phi) \tag{1.7}$$

A similar expression can be obtained for propagation of sound in the negative x direction by replacing x by $x + ct$.

The concepts of frequency and wavelength are important in predicting the behavior of a wave impinging on obstacles in its path. If the dimensions of the object are small compared with the wavelength of the sound, the object will have little influence on the sound field or wave pattern. On the other hand, if the object's dimensions are of the same order of magnitude as or larger than the wavelength λ, the object will interact with the sound wave causing reflection and absorption near its leading face and a region of reduced sound pressure (an "acoustical shadow") behind its trailing face. These effects can be readily observed on the shore of a pond, where water ripples pass unimpeded through the small-diameter reeds, but reflect from and bend (diffract) around relatively large boulders in the water. In the latter case, the reflected and diffracted waves interact with the incoming waves to significantly alter the wave pattern near the boulders. It is known from experience that similar phenomena occur in the case of airborne sound waves. Because of this fact, it is easier to use barriers and absorbers to control high-frequency (small-wavelength) sound components than it is to control the low-frequency (large-wavelength) components.

1.6 PHYSICAL DESCRIPTORS OF SOUND

In preceding sections we have discussed several descriptors which are used to characterize a sound wave of one frequency. These are amplitude, frequency, period, wavelength, and propagation velocity. In this section, additional descriptors will be introduced so that elementary sound fields can be discussed. (More complex sound fields are discussed in Chap. 3.) We will begin our task by reviewing the physics of sound generation and propagation from a somewhat more precise viewpoint than was used in Secs. 1.2 and 1.3.

Consider an open space in which no acoustic energy is present. Individual air molecules move about in this space with random thermal motion and frequently collide with other molecules without loss of energy. The net result is an equilibrium condition of the air, which is characterized by an absolute pressure and temperature. Now suppose that a small pulsating sphere whose surface is vibrating with frequency ω is introduced into the space. As individual molecules collide with the vibrating surface of the sphere, they acquire additional momentum in the direction of motion of the surface. In subsequent collisions with neighboring molecules, this additional momentum is transferred, and a disturbance propagates into the space with a velocity essentially equal to the thermal speed of individual molecules. This disturbance manifests itself as a spherically spreading sound wave of single frequency.

As this disturbance propagates outward, through momentum transfer, individual particles of the medium experience net displacements and velocities in the direction of propagation, as well as changes in absolute pressure and temperature. These small changes in equilibrium pressure, displacement, and particle velocity of elements of the medium can be positive or negative, depending on whether the motion of the surface of the sphere is outward (in the direction of propagation) or inward (opposite to the direction of propagation). When these pressure variations occur at the eardrum or the diaphragm or a microphone, sound is perceived.

Let us investigate some further characteristics of sound waves propagating through a medium. A spherical sound wave (of frequency ω) generated by the surface of a pulsating sphere (of radius R_0) will have a pressure amplitude and phase at radius r given by

$$p(r, t) = \frac{R_0 A}{r} \sin\left[k(r - R) - \omega t + \phi \right] \tag{1.8}$$

where A denotes the amplitude of the pressure wave at the surface of the sphere. The sound wave "spreads out" in a spherical manner as it moves through the medium, in much the same way as light waves illuminate the space surrounding a light source. As the wave propagates from the sphere, its amplitude diminishes in direct proportion to its distance from the center of the sphere.

A sound wave at any given frequency is said to be *freely propagating* when the particle velocity is in the direction of wave propagation and when the pressure and particle velocity reach their maximum or minimum values simultaneously.* Under these conditions, the acoustic pressure p and particle velocity u at a given distance r from the source are related according to

$$\rho_0 c = \frac{p(r, t)}{u(r, t)} \tag{1.9}$$

The term $\rho_0 c$ is the product of the equilibrium mass density of the medium (ρ_0) and the propagation velocity of sound waves (c) through the medium. It is the ratio of the pressure and the particle velocity associated with a freely propagating sound wave and is termed the *characteristic impedance* of the medium. Expressed in units of kilograms per square meter per second (called mks rayls in honor of Lord Rayleigh), the characteristic impedance of air at standard temperature and pressure is 415 mks rayls, where $\rho_0 = 1.21$ kg/m^3 and $c = 343$ m/s.

Now consider a freely propagating sound wave which is confined to a long tube of diameter D. If D is less than about 1.2 λ, the wave will be "plane." This means that all properties of the sound wave (including pressure, displacement, and particle velocity) are uniform in a plane perpendicular to the direction of sound propagation (the longitudinal axis of the tube). In this case, the acoustic pressure is

$$p(x, t) = A \sin(kx - \omega t) \tag{1.10}$$

for a sound wave of frequency ω generated by a vibrating piston located at $x = 0$. The expression $\rho_0 c = p(x, t)/u(x, t)$ is also valid in this case.

The *intensity* of the sound wave is defined as the average amount of acoustic power passing through a unit area of the medium that is perpendicular to the

---

* This occurs when $k^2 r^2 \gg 1$ and $r \gg a$, where k is the wave number, r is the distance from the center of the source, and a is a characteristic dimension of the source (such as the radius of a loudspeaker cone). As a practical matter, these conditions are satisfied for most sources of sound at distances from the source greater than two or three principal source dimensions, and greater than two or three wavelengths of the frequency of interest.

direction of sound propagation. For a freely propagating spherical sound wave of single frequency,

$$I = \frac{1}{T} \int_0^T p(r, t) \cdot u(r, t) \, dt$$

$$= \frac{1}{T} \int_0^T p(r, t) \cdot \frac{p(r, t)}{\rho_0 c} \, dt \qquad (1.11)$$

where T is the time interval of integration. Defining the *effective pressure* as the root mean square (rms) acoustic pressure,

$$p = p_{rms} = \sqrt{\frac{1}{T} \int_0^T p^2(r, t) \, dt} \qquad (1.12)$$

the intensity becomes

$$I = \frac{p_{rms}^2}{\rho_0 c} \qquad (1.13)$$

Since p_{rms} is the effective pressure measured by a sound meter, Eq. (1.13) gives a means for determining the intensity of sound from sound measurements.

Equation (1.13) is valid for both spherical and plane freely propagating waves. Putting Eq. (1.8) into (1.13) indicates that the intensity of the spherical wave diminishes with distance, varying inversely with the square of the distance from the source. This is called the *inverse-square law*. On the other hand, substitution of Eq. (1.10) into (1.13) shows that the intensity of a plane wave remains constant as it moves away from the source. This is why we can hear the whisper of a child talking into a garden hose, or the heartbeat in a stethoscope. The acoustic energy is confined to propagate without spreading, so that the intensity of the sound remains practically constant as it moves along the tube.

If a sound field is being generated by several freely propagating sound waves, the intensity of the sound at any point in the sound field is the sum of the intensities of the individual sources at that point.

$$I_{total} = I_1 + I_2 + I_3 + \cdots + I_n = \frac{p_{total}^2}{\rho_0 c} \qquad (1.14)$$

Except for those cases where reinforcement or cancellation effects are significant, Eq. (1.13) can be substituted in (1.14) to give the total effective pressure at any point in the sound field:

$$p_{total} = p_1^2 + p_2^2 + p_3^2 + \cdots + p_n^2 \qquad (1.15)$$

Equation (1.15) can be used to calculate the total acoustic pressure resulting from the combination of several sound sources whenever the sources are broadband and, for pure tones, whenever the sources have different frequencies. However, if two of the sources are pure tones and of the same frequency, they will first have to be combined in a special way as indicated below.

Let the instantaneous acoustic pressures of the two tones at some fixed point in space be

$$p_1(t) = P_1 \cos(\omega t + \theta_1)$$
$$p_2(t) = P_2 \cos(\omega t + \theta_2)$$

where ω represents their angular frequencies and θ_1 and θ_2 are their respective phases. The two sources will combine to produce a total rms pressure of

$$p = \sqrt{p_1^2 + p_2^2 + 2p_1 p_2 \cos(\theta_1 - \theta_2)} \qquad (1.16)$$

where p_1 and p_2 are the rms pressures of the individual components.

Now, suppose we wish to find the rms sound pressure for a number of sources all of which are broadband or tones of different frequencies, except, say, two which are tones of the same frequency. These two sources should be added together first, using Eq. (1.16), to obtain a new rms pressure. This pressure and the rms pressures of the remainder of the sources are then combined according to Eq. (1.15).

The *acoustic power* (or *sound power*) of a source is defined as the acoustic energy being generated per second by the source. As you might expect, this is a very important quantity in specifying the acoustical characteristics of any product which generates noise. The sound power is measured in watts (newton-meters per second or joules per second) and is represented by the symbol W.

The acoustic power of a source radiating into an open space (without reflection of sound waves) can be obtained by summing all energy radiating through the surface of an imaginary sphere enclosing the source. For a spherical source, the energy is spread uniformly over any such sphere. Hence, the total energy radiated across a sphere of radius r centered at the source will be the intensity of the sound at that radius times the surface area of the sphere, that is, $W = I 4\pi r^2$. Using Eq. (1.13) for the intensity, we obtain the following expression for sound power in terms of the effective pressure:

$$W = \frac{p_{\text{rms}}^2}{\rho_0 c} 4\pi R^2 \qquad (1.17)$$

for a spherical source, where R is the radius of the sphere at the point where p_{rms} is measured.

The acoustic power of a freely propagating plane sound wave in a tube is obtained by multiplying the intensity and the cross-sectional area of the tube:

$$W = \frac{p_{\text{rms}}^2}{\rho_0 c} \frac{\pi D^2}{4} \qquad (1.18)$$

(This relation assumes that no energy losses occur at the tube walls.)

The acoustic power of an arbitrary source radiating nonuniformly into an open space can be obtained in a similar manner by considering the spherical surface to be broken into N surface elements. Thus,

$$W = \frac{\bar{p}_1^2 S_1 + \bar{p}_2^2 S_2 + \cdots}{\rho_0 c} = \sum_{n=1}^{N} \frac{(\bar{p}^2)_n S_n}{\rho_0 c} \tag{1.19}$$

where N = number of surface elements
$\qquad S_n$ = area of each surface element
$\qquad (\bar{p}^2)_n$ = rms acoustic pressure averaged over S_n

Energy density is the average acoustic energy present in a unit volume of the medium. The energy density is obtained by summing the average potential and kinetic energies represented by the passage of a sound wave at a given point in the medium. Each element of the medium acts as a spring which is extended or compressed by acoustic pressure; hence, the element possesses potential energy. Each element also has a particle velocity which results from an acoustic pressure differential across the element; hence, the element has kinetic energy. The energy density of a freely propagating spherical wave of frequency ω is given by

$$\bar{\varepsilon} = \frac{p_{rms}^2}{\rho_0 c^2} \left(1 + \frac{1}{2k^2 r^2} \right) \tag{1.20}$$

where k is ω/c, the wave number, and r is the distance from the source. Note that when $kr \gg 1$, $\bar{\varepsilon}$ is proportional to p_{rms}^2. Since the acoustic pressure decreases with increasing radius, the energy density decreases as the square of the radius.

In the case of a freely propagating plane wave, p_{rms} is constant and the energy density is given by

$$\bar{\varepsilon} = \frac{p_{rms}^2}{\rho_0 c^2} \tag{1.21}$$

A freely propagating sound wave consisting of many frequencies can be analyzed in the same way, on a frequency-by-frequency basis, using the principle of superposition. The same result will be obtained; that is, the intensity and energy density are proportional to the square of the rms acoustic pressure.

All the discussion presented so far is based on "elementary" or "linear" acoustic theory. Simply stated, the equations of linear acoustics are derived from the general equations of fluid dynamics by assuming that the disturbances resulting from propagation of sound waves are sufficiently small for the deviations from equilibrium conditions to be approximated by linear relationships. Further assumptions are that the medium is a perfect gas and that the passage of the sound wave through the medium is an adiabatic process.

The advantage of elementary theory is that the equations of motion, and solutions to them, are simplified. In most practical situations, the restrictions imposed by elementary theory present little, if any, difficulty. These are

$$p \ll p_0 \qquad \text{(the equilibrium pressure)}$$
$$u \ll c$$
$$\rho \ll \rho_0$$
$$v \ll c$$

where v is the steady-flow velocity. Under these conditions, the propagation velocity c is a function of temperature only:

$$c \sim \sqrt{T}$$

where T is the absolute temperature. The approximate upper limit for p, to satisfy these restrictions, is 10 N/m². This corresponds to the peak rms sound pressures produced by a loud rock band, or by a jet aircraft at 300 ft. The corresponding peak particle velocity is 0.024 m/s. Steady-flow velocity (in ductwork or automotive exhaust systems, for example) does not materially affect the propagation of sound if the velocity is less than about 5 percent of the propagation velocity c.

Representative values of rms acoustic pressures produced by various sources are listed in Table 1.1. Observe both the range of pressures typically encountered (on the order of 10^6) and the small amplitudes associated with even loud sounds. Although there is no direct relationship between sound pressure (which depends on surroundings) and source power (which usually does not), it is apparent that the acoustic powers generated by common noise sources are very small. Representative values are listed in Table 1.2.

In this section we have introduced and discussed the physical descriptors commonly used to characterize freely propagating spherical and plane acoustic waves. We will reserve discussion of more complex cases (reflected sound waves, multiple and directional sources, sound fields close to a source) for Chap. 3.

1.7 LEVELS AND THE DECIBEL

It is sometimes argued that the perceived intensities of nearly all the sensations we experience in nature are proportional to the logarithm of the external stimuli causing the sensations. Experiments show this to be accurate for hearing over the frequency range 100 to 400 Hz, and approximately so over the remainder of the audible frequencies of sound, 20 to 20,000 Hz. For this reason, a logarithmic unit is used to describe and measure the intensity of sound. The logarithmic unit is further justified because it compresses the tremendous range of audible sound pressures to a convenient scale.

It is convenient when talking about energy-related characteristics of sound to compare these quantities with some reference quantity. Consider the sound power W produced by a source and an arbitrary reference power W_{ref}. We introduce the concept of level by considering the ratio W/W_{ref}. If the ratio is greater than 1, we say that W is at a level above W_{ref}; if the ratio is less than 1, W is at a level below W_{ref}; and if the ratio is equal to 1, we say W is at the reference level. Next, consider the tremendous range of powers associated with common sounds. The sound power of a very soft whisper is about 10^{-9} W, while that of a large jet aircraft at takeoff is about 10^6 W. Consequently, a very large linear scale would be required to record these extreme ratios of powers. This tremendous range can be compressed if we express the power in terms of the

Table 1.1 Common sounds and sound-pressure levels

Sound pressure — psi	Sound pressure — N/m²	Sound-pressure level, dBA	Typical environment	Average subjective evaluation
3×10^{-2}	200	140	Near jet engine	Intolerable or deafening
		130	Threshold of pain Pneumatic chipping	
3×10^{-3}	20	120	Boiler shop (maximum levels); "hard rock" band	Very noisy
		110	Automatic punch press; hand grinding; near motorcycle	
3×10^{-4}	2	100	Loud auto horn at 10 ft	
		90	Construction site with pneumatic drilling; noisy urban area	
3×10^{-5}	2×10^{-1}	80	Curbside of busy street; school cafeteria	Loud
		70	Loud radio; stenographic room	
3×10^{-6}	2×10^{-2}	60	Restaurant; department store	Moderate to quiet
		50	Conversation at 1 m; average office	
3×10^{-7}	2×10^{-3}	40	Soft radio music in home; residential area at night	Faint
		30	Average residence without stereo playing	
3×10^{-8}	2×10^{-4}	20	Background in TV studios	Very faint
		10	Rustle of leaves	
3×10^{-9}	2×10^{-5}	0	Normal threshold of hearing	

Table 1.2 Typical sound sources and sound-power levels

Power, W	Sound-power level, dB	Source
24–40 million	— 195	Saturn rocket
1,000,000	— 180	Ram jet, turbo jet with afterburner
100,000	— 170	
10,000	— 160	
1,000	— 150	
		4-propeller airplane
100	— 140	
10	— 130	75-piece orchestra ⎫ peak rms levels in 1/8-s intervals Pipe organ ⎭
1.0	— 120	Large chipping hammer
0.1	— 110	Radio blaring
0.01	— 100	Car on highway
0.001	— 90	Voice, shouting (average long-time rms)
0.0001	— 80	
0.00001	— 70	Voice, conversational level
0.000001	— 60	
0.0000001	— 50	
0.00000001	— 40	
0.000000001	— 30	Voice, very soft whisper

logarithm of the ratios. To do this, we define the level as the *logarithm of the ratio of two power-related quantities*. This logarithmic ratio has been designated the Bel, in honor of Alexander Graham Bell. For more practical purposes a unit which is one-tenth of the Bel is more convenient than the Bel. This unit is called the *decibel* and is designated by dB. Thus, the *level of the sound power W in decibles* is defined as:

$$L_W = 10 \log_{10} \frac{W}{W_{ref}} \qquad \text{dB Re } W_{ref} \qquad (1.22a)$$

or, conversely, the sound power is

$$W = W_{ref} \text{ antilog}_{10} \frac{L_W}{10} = W_{ref} \times 10^{L_W/10} \qquad (1.22b)$$

Four things should be kept in mind when expressing levels in decibels:

1. Level indicates the logarithmic ratio of *power-related* quantities (W, I, p^2).
2. The decibel is defined as 10 times the logarithm (base ten) of this ratio.
3. The level expressed in decibels *always* implies a reference quantity. Since many acoustical data have been recorded in the literature using reference quantities which differ from currently accepted international standards, it is important when reporting levels in decibels to indicate the reference quantity used. In this way, errors will be avoided when your data are compared with other published results.

4. Since the level is the logarithm of a ratio, it is a dimensionless quantity. Hence, the value obtained for the level will be independent of the system of units used.

International agreement has been achieved on reference quantities for acoustical measurements. These reference quantities are based upon levels associated with the threshold of hearing of a 1000-Hz pure tone. The American National Standards Institute (ANSI Standard SI.8-1969) gives the following preferred reference quantities for sound power, sound intensity, and sound pressure:

$$W_{ref} = 10^{-12} \text{ W*}$$
$$I_{ref} = 10^{-12} \text{ W/m}^2 \tag{1.23}$$
$$p_{ref} = 2 \times 10^{-5} \text{ N/m}^2 \text{ (00.0002 } \mu \text{ bars)}$$

Using these standard reference quantities, we now define the level in decibels of the following important acoustical parameters characterizing sound waves in air:

Sound-power level

$$L_W = 10 \log_{10} \left(\frac{W}{W_{ref}} \right) \qquad \text{Re } 10^{-12} \text{ W} \tag{1.24a}$$

Sound-intensity level

$$L_I = 10 \log_{10} \left(\frac{I}{I_{ref}} \right) \qquad \text{Re } 10^{-12} \text{ W/m}^2 \tag{1.24b}$$

Sound-pressure level

$$L_P = \text{SPL} = 10 \log_{10} \left(\frac{p}{p_{ref}} \right)^2 \qquad \text{Re } 2 \times 10^{-5} \text{ N/m}^2 \tag{1.24c}$$

where L denotes the level and the subscript denotes the powerlike quantity. The last expression for sound-pressure level is often written in the equivalent form

$$L_p = \text{SPL} = 20 \log_{10} \left(\frac{p}{p_{ref}} \right) \qquad \text{Re } 2 \times 10^{-5} \text{ N/m}^2 \tag{1.24d}$$

Use of this form for the definition of SPL sometimes gives rise to confusion regarding the factor of 20 in front of the logarithm. If we remember that the basic definition of the level is based on *power-related* quantities (that is, p^2), this confusion can be avoided.

---

* A value used in the past in the United States for reference power was 10^{-13} W. Values of sound-power level computed using this value of reference power are 10 dB higher than those obtained using the standard 10^{-12} W.

In many practical situations it is necessary to determine the combined effect of several sources. For example, assume that a machine produces a sound-pressure level L_{p_1} at a specified location in a room. A second machine is then brought into the room and operated with the first machine shut off, producing a sound-pressure level L_{p_2} at the same specified location. What will be the combined level L_{p_c} with both machines operating? Conversely, consider the case of a noisy machine which has a sound-power output L_{W_1}. A vibrating panel on the machine is suspected of contributing significantly to this output. In order to determine its contribution, the panel is removed and the new sound-power level L_{W_2} determined. What is the power contribution of the panel?

Since levels are logarithmic quantities, they cannot be combined by simply adding or subtracting the individual levels. Instead, the actual acoustic intensities represented by the logarithmic expressions must be determined by taking antilogs of the level readings. In the absence of dominant pure tones, their intensities can usually be added together directly and the new levels determined from the logarithm.

Example Consider the effect of adding another machine in an area where other equipment is operating. Assume that the ambient sound level due to other equipment is L_{p_1} = 90 dB and the level from the machine to be added is L_{p_2} = 88 dB. Estimate the combined level.

SOLUTION

$$L_p = 10 \log\left(\frac{p}{p_{\text{ref}}}\right)^2 \quad \text{or} \quad \left(\frac{p}{p_{\text{ref}}}\right)^2 = \text{antilog}\,\frac{L_p}{10}$$

Thus,

$$\left(\frac{p_1}{p_{\text{ref}}}\right)^2 = \text{antilog}\,\frac{90}{10} = 10 \times 10^8$$

$$\left(\frac{p_2}{p_{\text{ref}}}\right)^2 = \text{antilog}\,\frac{88}{10} = 6.31 \times 10^8$$

$$\left(\frac{p_{\text{total}}}{p_{\text{ref}}}\right)^2 = \left(\frac{p_1}{p_{\text{ref}}}\right)^2 + \left(\frac{p_2}{p_{\text{ref}}}\right)^2 = 10 \times 10^8 + 6.31 \times 10^8$$

$$L_{p_{\text{total}}} = 10 \log(16.31 \times 10^8) = 92.12 \text{ dB}$$

Rather than going through this cumbersome procedure each time we are required to combine decibels, a graphic procedure using Figs. 1.6 and 1.7 is recommended.

Example 1.1 One motor on a dual-motor shop vacuum cleaner is turned on, and a sound-pressure level of 89 dB is measured at a position 8 ft from the unit. The first motor is turned off and the second motor turned on. The sound pressure at the same location is now 90 dB. What will be the level be at this location when both motors are turned on?

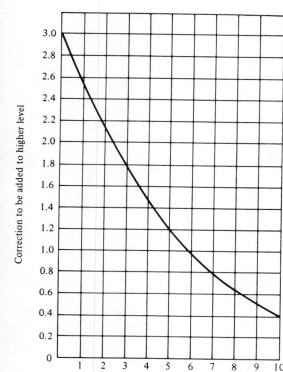

Difference in decibels between two levels being added   **Figure 1.6** Adding levels.

SOLUTION In this case we know the levels in decibels of two separate sources and wish to determine the combined level when the source intensities are added. Using Fig. 1.6, and noting that the difference in the two levels to be added is 1 dB, the graph indicates that about 2.5 dB should be added to the highest level. Thus, the combined sound-pressure level would be 92.5 dB with both motors operating. The precision of the sound-level meter used to obtain these measurements does not warrant precision better than ±0.5 dB; moreover, the human ear is incapable of distinguishing sound-level differences less than 1 dB, even under optimum conditions.

Example 1.2 The sound-pressure level at the operator's position, near a commercial cutoff saw, is measured at 98 dB. It is suspected that most of the sound is being generated by air turbulence around the teeth of the circular saw blade. When the saw is operated with a toothless blade, a new level of 91 dB is measured. What is the sound-pressure level of the sound being generated by air turbulence?

SOLUTION In this case we know the level both before and after one source was removed, and we wish to determine the level of the source which was

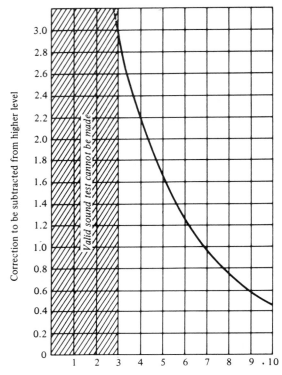

Difference in decibels between two levels being subtracted

Figure 1.7 Subtracting levels.

removed. The difference in the two levels is 7 dB. Using this difference, Fig. 1.7 indicates that about 1 dB should be subtracted from the higher level. Hence, the contribution due to air turbulence is approximately 97 dB.

We can check our results by asking what the sound-pressure level would be if the original saw blade were returned. In this case, we combine two levels: 97 dB due to air turbulence and 91 dB due to the machine without the turbulence. The difference between these levels is 6 dB. Figure 1.6 indicates that about 1 dB should be added to the higher of the levels in order to determine the combined level of the saw plus blade. Adding this quantity to the higher level gives approximately 98 dB.

The same procedures demonstrated in these examples are used for combining sound-pressure levels at a point, sound-intensity levels at a point, and sound-power levels, since all are power-related quantities. An exception to this rule occurs when combining levels from two sources of the same frequency, which must be combined in accordance with Eq. (1.16), as discussed in Sec. 1.6.

When the difference in two levels is 3 dB after one source is shut off, the contribution of the source being eliminated is equal to the combined contributions from all other sources. A 3-dB change is barely noticeable to our ears under most circumstances, yet it represents a 50 percent decrease in acoustic intensity.

When the difference in the levels is less than 3 dB, this means that the source removed is less intense than those that remain. It then becomes more difficult to determine the contribution of that source, due to the steep slope of Fig. 1.7. Since measurement accuracy of ± 0.5 dB is typical, the validity of evaluations made in the shaded zone is doubtful.

1.8 MEASURING AND DISPLAYING ACOUSTICAL DATA

Sound spectra In our earlier discussion we considered an experiment in which a sound field was generated by the simultaneous action of several tuning forks, each having different frequencies of vibration. The resulting sound field had several frequency components. From this it was inferred that a sound source could in general have an infinitely large number of frequency components. Since a sound wave's interaction with a given object depends upon its frequency content, it becomes very important to characterize a sound in terms of its frequency content in order to control it. Determination of the frequency content of a sound is called *spectral* or *frequency analysis*.

Consider the tuning fork experiment again. A microphone placed in the sound field would sense a pressure-time variation similar to that shown in Fig. 1.5. The frequency characteristics of this sound field can be represented by the line graph shown in Fig. 1.8a. The length of the line represents the sound-pressure level, while the location of the bar on the horizontal axis represents the frequency of the sound-pressure variation. Such a frequency-domain plot is called the *sound spectrum* or *frequency spectrum* of the sound. Figure 1.8b shows the frequency spectrum of the sound field produced by six tuning forks, each vibrating at a different frequency. This results in six *discrete-frequency* or *pure-tone* components. The last figure, 1.8c, shows the continuous-frequency spectrum representative of noise produced by an actual sound source, such as the exhaust from an automobile engine.

Use of filters in obtaining sound spectra Ideally, the frequency spectra of the sound shown in Fig. 1.8 would give us precisely the frequency content of each of the sound fields being measured. However, there are limits on the instrumentation used to record this information. A good microphone is equally sensitive to all frequency components of interest and acts as a transducer which changes the sound-pressure signal into an equivalent time-varying electrical signal. Now suppose that this signal were fed into an electrical filter which would block all frequency components of the signal except one. The rms amplitude of the signal passed could be measured and recorded. If we had 19,980 filters, one for each frequency in the audio range, we could systematically record the rms value of the pressure amplitude of each frequency component of the electrical signal and, by proper scaling, plot the frequency spectrum of the sound over this range.

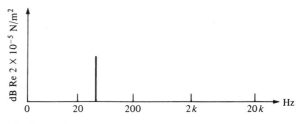

(*a*) One single-frequency source

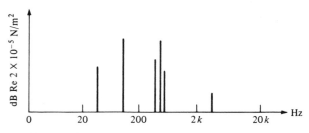

(*b*) Six single-frequency sources

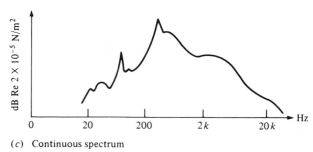

(*c*) Continuous spectrum

Figure 1.8 Frequency character-istics of sound (frequency domain).

Obtaining such detailed information about the sound would be prohibitively time-consuming, and a bank of filters with such fine resolution would carry an astronomical price tag! Instead of passing the signal through single-frequency filters, broader filters are used which allow a range, or band, of frequency components to pass. One of the most common types of filters used is the *octave-band filter*, where the highest frequency passed is twice the value of the lowest frequency passed. A set of octave-band filters has the highest frequency passed by one filter equal to the lowest frequency passed by the succeeding filter. In this way, the entire audible spectrum can be covered by relatively few filters. The value of the amplitude of the effective pressure of each octave band of frequencies can then be recorded to give an *octave-band spectrum* of the sound. Very often the data recorded are the sound-pressure levels of each band of frequencies, called the *band levels*.

Many other types of filters are available, differing in their bandwidths and the way in which these bandwidths vary with tuning frequency. Examples are

1/3-octave-band filter sets, from which we obtain 1/3-*octave-band spectra,* and continuously tunable* narrow-band filters, from which we get *narrow-band spectra* of sound.

The advantages of making a broadband analysis of sound are that (1) less time is needed to obtain data, and (2) the instrumentation required to measure the data is less expensive. The main disadvantage is loss of the detailed information about the sound which is available from narrow-band analysis.

Figure 1.9 shows an example of machinery noise displayed in the three forms of sound spectra. In Fig. 1.9c, a *narrow-band analysis,* using a very narrow

* The center frequency of a continuously tunable filter can be set at (tuned to) all possible values within a range of frequencies specified for the filter.

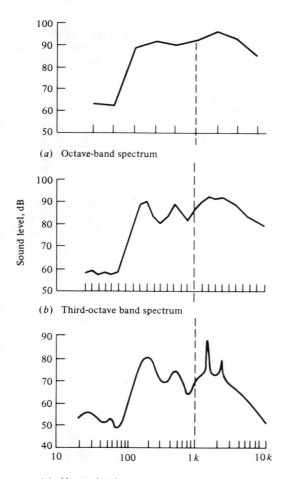

(a) Octave-band spectrum

(b) Third-octave band spectrum

(c) Narrow-band spectrum

Figure 1.9 Effect of bandwidth on frequency spectrum.

tunable filter, shows detailed peaks at specific frequencies which can often be related to a particular source. For example, if the number of blades on a fan multiplied by its rotational speed yields a blade passage frequency which corresponds to the frequency at which a peak in the sound spectrum occurs, then the fan blade is suspected of being the source of that part of the noise spectrum. It may be possible to ascertain whether the fan blade is indeed the source by removing the blade from the system and again recording the sound spectrum. If the peak is missing in the new record, the source of the peak has been identified. This approach is a common method of identifying noise sources in a complex system.

It is customary to plot *octave* (Fig. 1.9*a*) or 1/3-*octave* (Fig. 1.9*b*) spectra by recording the band level (in decibels) at the center frequency of each band. A continuous line is then constructed, joining the values obtained at each center frequency, as shown in Fig. 1.9. Despite this convention one must understand that the level recorded for each center frequency represents the total rms value associated with all the components contained in the band of frequencies being measured. An alternate, more correct way of plotting this information is shown in Fig. 1.10, where the value at each center frequency is extended to cover its corresponding band of frequencies.

Two more points should be noted about the frequency-domain plot: (1) The instantaneous variations of sound pressure from atmospheric or reference pressure are not usually presented. Instead, the effective (rms) pressure is recorded. Very often, the band level in decibels is plotted in lieu of effective pressure (see Sec. 1.7). (2) It is conventional to use a logarithmic scale on the frequency axis of the plot in order to conveniently cover the wide frequency range (20 to 20,000 Hz) of human audibility.

The frequency-domain representation of sound is the one most commonly encountered in noise control work. Since the acoustical absorption and transmission properties of materials are frequency-dependent, their selection and use in noise control problems are based largely on information available from the frequency spectrum of the sound being considered.

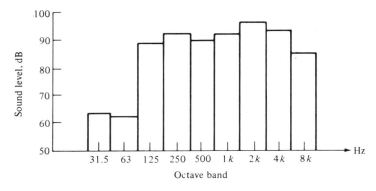

Figure 1.10 Octave-band spectrum of sound.

1.9 SOUND LEVEL METER, WEIGHTING SCALES, OCTAVE BANDS

Sound level meter The basic elements of a typical sound level meter are: (1) a microphone, (2) a preamplifier, (3) special weighting networks, (4) an amplifier, (5) a meter, and (6) an output terminal. These elements are shown in Fig. 1.11.

The microphone is a transducer which transforms pressure variations in air to a corresponding electrical signal. Since the electrical signal generated by the microphone is relatively small in magnitude, a preamplifier is needed to boost the signal before it is analyzed, measured, or displayed. The special weighting networks are used to shape the signal spectrum in much the same way that the human ear responds to sounds of different amplitudes. Details of the weighting networks will be discussed later. The "weighted" signal then passes through a second (output) amplifier into a meter. The meter and associated circuitry detect the approximate rms value of the signal and display it on a logarithmic scale, laid out to read the signal level in decibels.

Weighting networks Three weighting networks, denoted A, B, and C, are commonly incorporated in most sound level meters. These networks were designed to provide a response that approximates the way in which the human ear responds to the loudness of pure tones (see Chap. 2). The B weighting is rarely used in practice. The C scale is essentially linear over the frequency range of greatest interest. The A-weighted sound level has found much use in noise evaluation, since it correlates reasonably well with hearing-damage risk in industry and with subjective annoyance for a wide category of industrial, transportation, and community noises. Noise limits are specified in A-weighted

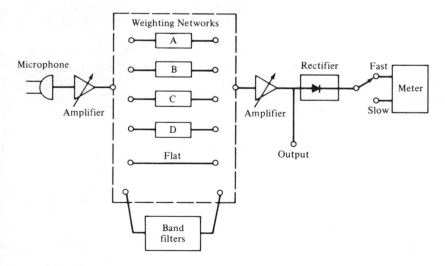

Figure 1.11 Block diagram of a sound-level meter.

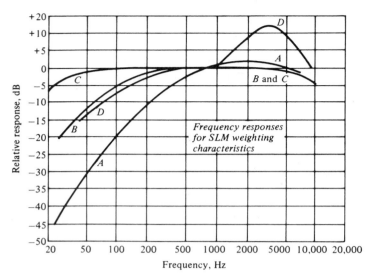

Figure 1.12 Frequency characteristics of the A, B, C, and D weighting networks.

sound levels in the Occupational Safety and Health Act (OSHA) and in many state and local noise regulations. In addition, a D-weighting network is found on some sound-level meters. This network was designed specifically to give an indication of annoyance associated with aircraft flyover noise. The frequency-response characteristics of these four weighting networks are shown in Fig. 1.12.

We see in Fig. 1.12 that a 30-Hz pure tone having a sound-pressure level of 73 dB would produce a response of approximately 33 dB on the A-weighted scale, corresponding to the fact that the human ear is less sensitive to frequencies in the lower portion of the audible range than is the microphone of the sound-level meter.

The readings obtained using any of the above weighting networks are designated *sound levels*, rather than *sound-pressure* levels. When reporting sound-level readings, always indicate the weighting employed. For example, a suitable way of giving the weighting is, "The sound level is 77 dBA," or "The A-weighted sound level is 77 dB."

IMPORTANT TERMS AND FORMULAS

Period: T s

Frequency: $f = 1/T$ Hz

Wavelength: $\lambda = c/f$

Speed of sound: $c = \sqrt{\dfrac{\gamma p_0}{\rho_0}} = k\sqrt{T} \approx 1100$ ft/s

Characteristic impedance: $\rho_0 c = 415$ mks rayls   (at standard temperature and pressure)

Sound intensity for a freely propagating plane wave: $\quad I = p^2/\rho_0 c$

Intensity of point source in a free field: $\quad I = W/4\pi r^2$

Multiple sources: $\quad I_{total} = I_1 + I_2 + \ldots + I_n$

$$P_{total} = \sqrt{p_1^2 + p_2^2 + \ldots + p_n^2}$$

$$P_{total} = \sqrt{p_1^2 + p_2^2 + p_1 p_2 \cos(\theta_1 - \theta_2)} \qquad \text{(tones of same frequency)}$$

Sound-power level: $\quad \text{PWL} = L_W = 10 \log \dfrac{W}{W_{ref}} \qquad \text{Re } 10^{-12} \text{ W}$

Sound-intensity level: $\quad L_I = 10 \log_{10} \dfrac{I}{I_{ref}} \qquad \text{Re } 10^{-12} \text{ W/m}^2$

Sound-pressure level: $\quad \text{SPL} = L_p = 10 \log_{10} \left(\dfrac{p}{p_{ref}}\right)^2 \qquad \text{Re } 2 \times .10^{-5} \text{ N/m}^2$

PROBLEMS

$p^2 = \text{antilog}\left[\dfrac{SPL}{10}\right] \cdot p_{ref}^2$

1.1 Calculate the intensity and SPL (sound-pressure level) at a distance of 10 m from a uniformly radiating source of 1-W power.

   Answer: SPL = 89 dB, $I = 7.96 \times 10^{-4}$ W/m^2

1.2 The noise level from a power station with 10 identical transformers measured near some residential property line was found to be 54 dB. The maximum permitted in this area is 50 dB at night. How many machines could be used during the night?

   Answer: 4 machines

1.3 Determine the sound-power-level range (Re 10^{-12} W) of the human voice, which has an acoustical-power output of about 10 to 50 μW.

   Answer: 70–77 dB

1.4 The SPL of noise emitted from an engine without a muffler was measured at 100 dB. Attaching a muffler to the engine reduced the SPL at the microphone to 80 dB.

   (*a*) What was the percentage reduction in rms acoustic-pressure amplitude?

   Answer: Reduced to 10 percent of original value

   (*b*) What was the rms acoustic pressure before the muffler was attached?

   Answer: 2 N/m^2

1.5 The sound-level meter has various weighting networks that are designed to simulate different types of response to sound. The more important of these are the A, D, and "linear" networks. Which would be most desirable when making noise measurements in response to the following situations? Explain if necessary.

   (*a*) Prevention of deafness among employees in a ball mill.

   Answer: A network.

   (*b*) Reduction of complaints against aircraft flyover noise.

   Answer: D network.

   (*c*) Reduction of fatigue damage to walls and panels in a jet-engine test facility.

   Answer: Linear network.

1.6 You have available to you two pump styles: pump A at 1000 gal/min produces a 100-dBA sound-pressure level at a given point, and pump B at 500 gal/min produces 90 dBA at that same point. From a noise control standpoint, which combination of pumps would be most acceptable for developing a flow rate of 2000 gal/min? Explain.

1.7 What is the change in sound-pressure level from a uniformly radiating source:

(a) If the intensity is doubled?

Answer: +3 dB

(b) If the pressure is doubled?

Answer: +6 dB

(c) If the distance from the source is doubled?

Answer: −6 dB

(d) If two more identical sources are added in locations equivalent to the first?

Answer: +4.8 dB

1.8 What is the wavelength of:

(a) A 1000-Hz pure tone in air under standard conditions and in a typical automotive exhaust system (air at 1000°F)?

(b) A 125-Hz pure tone in air under standard conditions and in a typical automotive exhaust system (air at 1000°F)?

1.9 Representative sound-pressure levels for typical sources and environments are:

Source	Sound-pressure level, dB	Sound pressure		
		N/m^2	μ bars	psia
(a) Library	30			
(b) Quiet neighborhood at night	40			
(c) Normal conversation	60			
(d) Noisy street corner	80			
(e) Typical manufacturing area	100	(2)	(20)	(2.9×10^{-4})
(f) Pneumatic chipper, 4 ft	110			
(g) Loud rock band, discomfort threshold	120			
(h) Near jet engine, pain threshold	140			

Convert these levels to rms sound pressures in newtons per square meter, microbars, and pounds per square inch absolute. Refer to Table 1.3 for conversion factors.

1.10 Calculate the percentage of acoustical energy that must be removed to reduce a given sound-pressure level by 1, 2, 3, 4, 5, 6, 7, 8, 9, and 10 dB.

Answer: Reduce energy to 50 percent of its original value to achieve a 3-dB reduction in sound-pressure level.

Table 1.3 Conversion factors

To convert	Into	Multiply by	Conversely, multiply by
atm	lb/in^2	14.70	6.805×10^{-2}
	N/m^2	1.0132×10^5	9.872×10^{-6}
°C	°F	$(°C \times 9/5) + 32$	$(°F - 32) \times 5/9$
cm	in	0.3937	2.540
	ft	3.281×10^{-2}	30.48
cm^2	in^2	0.1550	6.452
	ft^2	1.0764×10^{-3}	929

Table 1.3 Conversion factors (continued)

To convert	Into	Multiply by	Conversely, multiply by
cm^3	in^3	0.06102	16.387
	ft^3	3.531×10^{-5}	2.832×10^4
dyn	lb (force)	2.248×10^{-6}	4.448×10^5
	N	10^{-5}	10^5
dyn/cm^2	lb/ft^2 (force)	2.090×10^{-3}	478.5
	N/m^2	10^{-1}	10
erg	ft · lb (force)	7.376×10^{-8}	1.356×10^7
	J	10^{-7}	10^7
erg/s	W	10^{-7}	10^7
	ft · lb/s	7.376×10^{-8}	1.356×10^7
ft	in	12	0.08333
	cm	30.48	3.281×10^{-2}
	m	0.3048	3.281
hp (550 ft · lb/s)	ft · lb/min	3.3×10^4	3.030×10^{-5}
	W	745.7	1.341×10^{-3}
	kW	0.7457	1.341
in	ft	0.0833	12
	cm	2.540	0.3937
	m	0.0254	39.37
$\log_e n$, or $\ln n$	$\log_{10} n$	0.4343	2.303
m	in	39.371	0.02540
	ft	3.2808	0.30481
	yd	1.0936	0.9144
	cm	10^2	10^{-2}
μbars (dyn/cm^2)	lb/in^2	1.4513×10^{-5}	6.890×10^4
	lb/ft^2	2.090×10^{-3}	478.5
	N/m^2	10^{-1}	10
mi (statute)	ft	5280	1.894×10^{-4}
	km	1.6093	0.6214
mi/h	ft/min	88	1.136×10^{-2}
	km/min	2.682×10^{-2}	37.28
	km/h	1.6093	0.6214
N	lb (force)	0.2248	4.448
	dyn	10^5	10^{-5}
N/m^2	lb/in^2 (force)	1.4513×10^{-4}	6.890×10^3
	lb/ft^2 (force)	2.090×10^{-2}	47.85
	dyn/cm^2	10	10^{-1}
lb (force)	N	4.448	0.2248
lb/in^2 (force)	lb/ft^2 (force)	144	6.945×10^{-3}
	N/m^2	6894	1.4506×10^{-4}
W	erg/s	10^7	10^{-7}
	hp (550 ft · lb/s)	1.341×10^{-3}	745.7

EFFECTS OF NOISE ON PEOPLE

2.1 INTRODUCTION

Excessive noise has been blamed not only for hearing damage and community annoyance but also for hypertension, fatigue, heart trouble, and reduced motor efficiency. Despite the latter allegations, most researchers in the US feel that the deleterious effects of noise are confined to damage of the hearing mechanism and to masking of auditory information. In general, it is felt that the nonauditory effects attributed to noise are related to the *information* carried by the sound rather than the sound itself. In this chapter we will concentrate on *proved* measurable effects of noise on people, with the understanding that action taken to reduce these effects will probably lead to reductions of the other nonauditory effects.

Hearing damage, speech masking, and annoyance are the best-documented effects of noise on human beings. Since the ear's sole function is to "hear," i.e., to receive acoustical waves and convert them for interpretation by the brain, any action which interferes with this function is undesirable. Therefore, noise affects the hearing function of the ear in two ways: (1) It may cause permanent physical damage to the hearing mechanism, rendering it insensitive to important components of sound; and (2) it may mask or drown out desirable sound. The former is a permanent effect; the latter is a short-term effect. Both can be evaluated by objective testing, and both can be induced by pleasant as well as unpleasant sounds. By contrast, annoyance is a highly subjective, unfavorable response to noise which interferes with human activity or sense of well-being. It has been evaluated only in qualitative terms on the basis of interviews and complaints.

Much work has been done in an effort to understand the effects of noise on human beings and to establish suitable *criteria* for relating the unfavorable effects to specific measurements of the sound field [2]. These criteria are then used to develop *standards* which describe noise environments considered acceptable in a given situation. These standards then form the basis for *regulations* which are adopted by communities or federal agencies to prescribe acceptable noise environments in the community and workplace. The noise control engineer must understand these standards and their underlying criteria in order to determine the appropriate measurements and control procedures needed to solve a particular noise problem. This chapter will discuss the relationships between the human response to noise and some of the related criteria needed for evaluating noise environments, while standards and regulations will be discussed later, in Chap. 7.

2.2 ANATOMY OF THE EAR

The ear is an extremely intricate and delicate mechanism consisting of three main divisions, as depicted in Fig. 2.1: (1) the outer ear, which includes the visible pinna, the auditory canal, and the eardrum; (2) the middle ear, which is an air-filled chamber containing three tiny bones (ossicles) that transmit the vibrations of the eardrum to the inner ear; and (3) the inner ear, a liquid-filled cavity which lies within the bony structure of the skull and contains the nerve endings by which aural information is detected and transmitted to the auditory nerve.

The ear mechanism begins to function when sound, traveling down the auditory canal, strikes the eardrum and causes it to move back and forth. The motion of the eardrum is transmitted through the ossicles of the middle ear to an

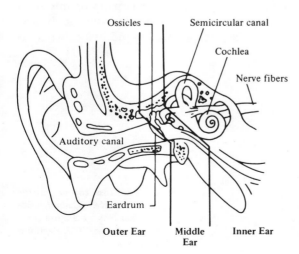

Figure 2.1 Cross section of the ear. *(Source: J. T. Broch,* Acoustic Noise Measurements, *B & K Instruments, Inc., January 1971. With permission.)*

opening in the inner ear, setting up pressure fluctuations in the incompressible liquid filling the inner ear. This fluid pressure excites the membranes in the cochlea, a section of the inner ear shaped like a snail shell, and a signal is generated for transmission along the auditory nerve to the brain. Damage sustained at any point along the described path can result in changes in both the perceived loudness and the character of the sound.

A cross section of the cochlea (Fig. 2.2) reveals two membranes, the basilar membrane and the tectorial membrane, running the full length of the cochlea. The basilar membrane is covered with many (about 23,000) tiny hair cells distributed over its length. These hair cells, which are actually the nerve endings of the auditory nerve, project from the outer surface of the basilar membrane and either touch or are imbedded in the tectorial membrane. The hair cells are known to be piezoelectric; when stressed they develop a measurable voltage in the inner ear. Thus, when the basilar membrane is set into motion by the fluid-pressure fluctuations, the hair cells along the length of the membrane are stressed, creating a voltage distribution along its length which is sensed and (somehow) interpreted by the brain. Since the distribution of motion along the basilar membrane is affected by the frequency of the incoming sound wave, the voltage distribution along the basilar membrane will depend upon the frequency of the sound. Figure 2.3 shows the relationship between basilar-membrane activity and the frequency of the incoming tone. The basilar membrane is shown here "unrolled" for convenience. Note that as the frequency of the incoming sound is increased from 50 Hz toward 10 kHz, the position of peak activity shifts toward the stapes (ossicles) end.

Although the foregoing description provides a rather crude model of the ear's behavior, it is sufficient to enable us to understand the phenomena of noise-induced hearing loss and masking. It is generally accepted that the brain's perception of the pitch of the sound is related to the position of maximum activity on the basilar membrane, while its perception of loudness is related to the amplitude of this activity. Moreover, anything which impairs or interferes with the response of the hair cells at a particular location on the basilar membrane also interferes with the brain's perception of sound associated with that location.

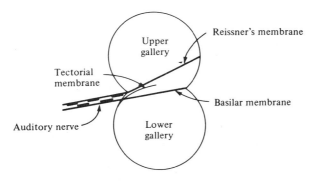

Figure 2.2 Cross section of the cochlea. *(Source: Cunniff, En-vironmental Noise Pollution, John Wiley & Sons, Inc., 1977. Reprinted by permission.)*

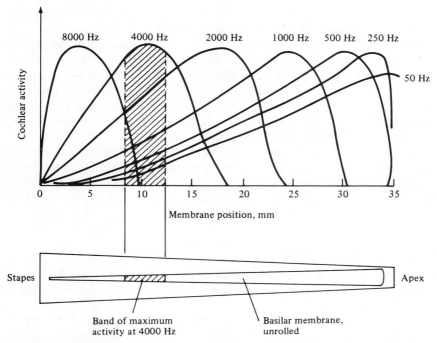

Figure 2.3 Effect of frequency on nerve activity along the basilar membrane. Sound is of constant amplitude. The maximum-activity region continues to move toward the stapes as the frequency is increased. *(Source: Békésy, JASA 21, pp. 245–259, 1949.)*

2.3 NORMAL HEARING RESPONSE

Loudness Level—Phons

The sensitivity of the hearing mechanism is highly dependent upon the frequency content of the received sound. Although it would appear difficult to quantize this sensitivity, in view of individual variations, a remarkable degree of agreement has been found between healthy subjects in evaluating the relative loudness of sounds. Figure 2.4 summarizes one such result, based on experiments with thousands of young people with undamaged ears. Subjects placed in a free sound field with frontal incidence were asked to listen to a reference tone at 1000 Hz, then to adjust the loudness of a second tone to equal the loudness of the reference. Each contour in Fig. 2.4 represents sound-pressure levels producing equal loudness over the audible frequency range for 1000-Hz reference tones ranging from 0 to 140 dB. The sound-pressure level of the 1000-Hz tone for each equal-loudness contour is defined as the *loudness level*, in phons. Figure 2.4 shows that a 50-Hz tone at 78 dB falls on the same contour as a 1000-Hz tone at 60 dB; both are rated at a loudness level of 60 phons. It should be evident from the figure that the human *perception* of loudness is highly dependent on frequency, and that the frequency dependency itself varies with loudness level.

The equal-loudness contours permit us to deduce several other characteristics of the ear. The *hearing threshold* defines the level at which the ear barely perceives the sound. This threshold is frequency-dependent, corresponding to the 0-phon curve in Fig. 2.4. The *threshold of feeling* defines the level at which a tickling sensation is produced in the ear. This threshold corresponds to the 120-phon curve in Fig. 2.4, representing sound pressures approximately one million times as large as the hearing-threshold pressures.

Damage to the hearing mechanism has the effect of raising the hearing threshold, indicating that higher sound levels are required in order to be heard. The degree of shift in the hearing threshold is used as an index of the amount of hearing impairment incurred; criteria for hearing damage are usually based on shifts in this threshold.

Subjective Loudness—Sones

Subjective tests, where the subject is asked to rate the relative loudness of two sounds of the same frequency but different level, have shown that the ear's

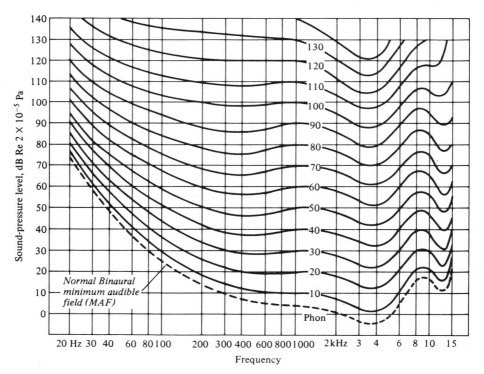

Figure 2.4 Internationally standardized set of equal-loudness-level contours. *(Source: J. T. Broch, Acoustic Noise Measurements, B & K Instruments, Inc., January 1971. With permission.)*

judgment of loudness does not correspond directly with the level of either sound pressure or loudness. For example, doubling the number of identical sources producing 40 dB at the observer's ear raises the sound level to 43 dB but is not perceived as a doubling, only as a "noticeable" increase in loudness. In order to produce a sound subjectively twice as loud as the single source, tests have shown that approximately *10* identical sources would be needed, corresponding to a 50-dB combined sound-preessure level. A redoubling of loudness would require *100* identical sources, resulting in a 60-dB combined sound-pressure level. It is evident that the equal-loudness contours provide information on tones of *equal* loudness but do not indicate the subjective loudness of one loudness level relative to another. Somewhat arbitrarily, a sone has been defined as the subjective loudness of a 40-phon sound, and a sound judged by normal subjects to be N times as loud as a 1-sone sound has a subjective loudness of N sones. Numerous experiments have been performed to relate the *loudness level* (phons) to the *subjective loudness* (sones). Figure 2.5 describes this relationship, and shows that for loudness levels above 40 phons each 10-phon increase is perceived as an approximate doubling of subjective loudness, although below 40 phons the loudness increases more rapidly with loudness level. The rough approximation of a 10-dB level increase per doubling of loudness is a useful rule of thumb for evaluating the subjective effects of changes in sound levels.

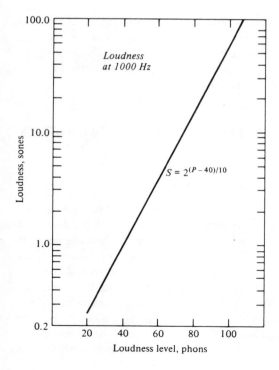

$$S = 2^{(P-40)/10}$$

Figure 2.5 Graphic relationship between loudness in sones and loudness level in phons. *(Source: Cunniff,* Environmental Noise Pollution, *John Wiley and Sons, Inc., 1977. Reprinted by permission.)*

Loudness of Broadband Noise

Typical speech and environmental sounds contain components from most of the audible spectrum, and it is not correct to estimate overall loudness using Fig. 2.4, which is based on pure tones. A practical method of evaluating broadband noise consists of determining loudness on a frequency-band by frequency-band basis, then combining to determine overall loudness in sones. A procedure for determining loudness, using equal-loudness contours for octave-band-limited noise, is outlined in ANSI S3.4-1968. Often called the Stevens Mark VI method, it is employed as follows:

1. Octave-band levels from 31.5- to 8000-Hz center frequencies are tabulated.
2. The band loudness index S for each band level is determined from Table 2.1, which is a tabular equivalent to Figs. 2.4 and 2.5.
3. The total loudness in sones is computed, using the formula

$$\text{Loudness} = 0.7 S_{\text{max}} + 0.3 \sum_i (S_i)$$

   where S_{max} is the highest loudness index and ΣS_i is the sum of all the loudness indices.
4. The corresponding loudness *level* in phons can also be determined, using the right-hand column in Table 2.1. (An application of Steven's Mark VI method is illustrated in Lab 2 at the end of this book.)

The sone has not found widespread use in noise control, partly because of the complexity of determining loudness in sones, and partly because the sone has not been shown to be a good index of hearing damage, speech masking, or annoyance. Nevertheless, the sone is occasionally used by manufacturers as an index for rating the noisiness of household products.

2.4 NOISE-INDUCED HEARING LOSS—HEALTH AND SAFETY STANDARDS

Hearing Loss from Prolonged Exposure to Noise

Most of the hearing difficulties associated with the outer ear and middle ear can be relieved by mechanical means. Eardrums can be replaced, and the bones of the middle ear can be freed, or even replaced, to complete the hearing path. If surgical means fail, the inner ear can still be excited by means of bone-conduction hearing aids. Occupational noise standards are *not* directed toward controlling hearing problems of this type, since they could be incurred by disease or physical injury quite independently of sound and the hearing process, and since they are correctable. However, hearing loss originating in the delicate inner ear results from nerve and cell damage. This damage and its effects are irreversible, and the associated hearing loss has so far proved irrecoverable, even with the use

Table 2-1 Band-level conversion to loudness index

Band level, dB	Band loudness index									Loudness, sones	Loudness level, phons
	i31.5	63	125	250	500	1000	2000	4000	8000		
20						.18	.30	.45	.61	.25	20
21						.22	.35	.50	.67	.27	21
22					.07	.26	.40	.55	.73	.29	22
23					.12	.30	.45	.61	.80	.31	23
24					.16	.35	.50	.67	.87	.33	24
25					.21	.40	.55	.73	.94	.35	25
26					.26	.45	.61	.80	1.02	.38	26
27					.31	.50	.67	.87	1.10	.41	27
28				.07	.37	.55	.73	.94	1.18	.44	28
29				.12	.43	.61	.80	1.02	1.27	.47	29
30				.16	.49	.67	.87	1.10	1.35	.50	30
31				.21	.55	.73	.94	1.18	1.44	.54	31
32				.26	.61	.80	1.02	1.27	1.54	.57	32
33				.31	.67	.87	1.10	1.35	1.64	.62	33
34			.07	.37	.73	.94	1.18	1.44	1.75	.66	34
35			.12	.43	.80	1.02	1.27	1.54	1.87	.71	35
36			.16	.49	.87	1.10	1.35	1.64	1.99	.76	36
37			.21	.55	.94	1.18	1.44	1.75	2.11	.81	37
38			.26	.62	1.02	1.27	1.54	1.87	2.24	.87	38
39			.31	.69	1.10	1.35	1.64	1.99	2.38	.93	39
40		.07	.37	.77	1.18	1.44	1.75	2.11	2.53	1.00	40
41		.12	.43	.85	1.27	1.54	1.87	2.24	2.68	1.07	41
42		.16	.49	.94	1.35	1.64	1.99	2.38	2.84	1.15	42
43		.21	.55	1.04	1.44	1.75	2.11	2.53	3.0	1.23	43
44		.26	.62	1.13	1.54	1.87	2.24	2.68	3.2	1.32	44
45		.31	.69	1.23	1.64	1.99	2.38	2.84	3.4	1.41	45
46	.07	.37	.77	1.33	1.75	2.11	2.53	3.0	3.6	1.52	46
47	.12	.43	.85	1.44	1.87	2.24	2.68	3.2	3.8	1.62	47
48	.16	.49	.94	1.56	1.99	2.38	2.84	3.4	4.1	1.74	48
49	.21	.55	1.04	1.69	2.11	2.53	3.0	3.6	4.3	1.87	49
50	.26	.62	1.13	1.82	2.24	2.68	3.2	3.8	4.6	2.00	50
51	.31	.69	1.23	1.96	2.38	2.84	3.4	4.1	4.9	2.14	51
52	.37	.77	1.33	2.11	2.53	3.0	3.6	4.3	5.2	2.30	52
53	.43	.85	1.44	2.24	2.68	3.2	3.8	4.6	5.5	2.46	53
54	.49	.94	1.56	2.38	2.84	3.4	4.1	4.9	5.8	2.64	54
55	.55	1.04	1.69	2.53	3.0	3.6	4.3	5.2	6.2	2.83	55
56	.62	1.13	1.82	2.68	3.2	3.8	4.6	5.5	6.6	3.03	56
57	.69	1.23	1.96	2.84	3.4	4.1	4.9	5.8	7.0	3.25	57
58	.77	1.33	2.11	3.0	3.6	4.3	5.2	6.2	7.4	3.48	58
59	.85	1.44	2.27	3.2	3.8	4.6	5.5	6.6	7.8	3.73	59
60	.94	1.56	2.44	3.4	4.1	4.9	5.8	7.0	8.3	4.00	60
61	1.04	1.69	2.62	3.6	4.3	5.2	6.2	7.4	8.8	4.29	61
62	1.13	1.82	2.81	3.8	4.6	5.5	6.6	7.8	9.3	4.59	62
63	1.23	1.96	3.0	4.1	4.9	5.8	7.0	8.3	9.9	4.92	63
64	1.33	2.11	3.2	4.3	5.2	6.2	7.4	8.8	10.5	5.28	64
65	1.44	2.27	3.5	4.6	5.5	6.6	7.8	9.3	11.1	5.66	65
66	1.56	2.44	3.7	4.9	5.8	7.0	8.3	9.9	11.8	6.06	66
67	1.69	2.62	4.0	5.2	6.2	7.4	8.8	10.5	12.6	6.50	67
68	1.82	2.81	4.3	5.5	6.6	7.8	9.3	11.1	13.5	6.96	68
69	1.96	3.0	4.7	5.8	7.0	8.3	9.9	11.8	14.4	7.46	69
70	2.11	3.2	5.0	6.2	7.4	8.8	10.5	12.6	15.3	8.00	70
71	2.27	3.5	5.4	6.6	7.8	9.3	11.1	13.5	16.4	8.6	71
72	2.44	3.7	5.8	7.0	8.3	9.9	11.8	14.4	17.5	9.2	72
73	2.62	4.0	6.2	7.4	8.8	10.5	12.6	15.3	18.7	9.8	73
74	2.81	4.3	6.6	7.8	9.3	11.1	13.5	16.4	20.0	10.6	74

Table 2-1 (Continued)

Band level, dB	Band loudness index									Loudness, sones	Loudness level, phons
	i31.5	63	125	250	500	1000	2000	4000	8000		
75	3.0	4.7	7.0	8.3	9.9	11.8	14.4	17.5	21.4	11.3	75
76	3.2	5.0	7.4	8.8	10.5	12.6	15.3	18.7	23.0	12.1	76
77	3.5	5.4	7.8	9.3	11.1	13.5	16.4	20.0	24.7	13.0	77
78	3.7	5.8	8.3	9.9	11.8	14.4	17.5	21.4	26.5	13.9	78
79	4.0	6.2	8.8	10.5	12.6	15.3	18.7	23.0	28.5	14.9	79
80	4.3	6.7	9.3	11.1	13.5	16.4	20.0	24.7	30.5	16.0	80
81	4.7	7.2	9.9	11.8	14.4	17.5	21.4	26.5	32.9	17.1	81
82	5.0	7.7	10.5	12.6	15.3	18.7	23.0	28.5	35.3	18.4	82
83	5.4	8.2	11.1	13.5	16.4	20.0	24.7	30.5	38.	19.7	83
84	5.8	8.8	11.8	14.4	17.5	21.4	26.5	32.9	41.	21.1	84
85	6.2	9.4	12.6	15.3	18.7	23.0	28.5	35.3	44.	22.6	85
86	6.7	10.1	13.5	16.4	20.0	24.7	30.5	38.	48.	24.3	86
87	7.2	10.9	14.4	17.5	21.4	26.5	32.9	41.	52.	26.0	87
88	7.7	11.7	15.3	18.7	23.0	28.5	35.3	44.	56.	27.9	88
89	8.2	12.6	16.4	20.0	24.7	30.5	38.	48.	61.	29.9	89
90	8.8	13.6	17.5	21.4	26.5	32.9	41.	52.	66.	32.0	90
91	9.4	14.8	18.7	23.0	28.5	35.3	44.	56.	71.	34.3	91
92	10.1	16.0	20.0	24.7	30.5	38.	48.	61.	77.	36.8	92
93	10.9	17.3	21.4	26.5	32.9	41.	52.	66.	83.	39.4	93
94	11.7	18.7	23.0	28.5	35.3	44.	56.	71.	90.	42.2	94
95	12.6	20.0	24.7	30.5	38.	48.	61.	77.	97.	45.3	95
96	13.6	21.4	26.5	32.9	41.	52.	66.	83.	105.	48.5	96
97	14.8	23.0	28.5	35.3	44.	56.	71.	90.	113.	52.0	97
98	16.0	24.7	30.5	38.	48.	61.	77.	97.	121.	55.7	98
99	17.3	26.5	32.9	41.	52.	66.	83.	105.	130.	59.7	99
100	18.7	28.5	35.3	44.	56.	71.	90.	113.	139.	64.0	100
101	20.3	30.5	38.	48.	61.	77.	97.	121.	149.	68.6	101
102	22.1	32.9	41.	52.	66.	83.	105.	130.	160.	73.5	102
103	24.0	35.3	44.	56.	71.	90.	113.	139.	171.	78.8	103
104	26.1	38.	48.	61.	77.	97.	121.	149.	184.	84.4	104
105	28.5	41.	52.	66.	83.	105.	130.	160.	197.	90.5	105
106	31.0	44.	56.	71.	90.	113.	139.	171.	211.	97.	106
107	33.9	48.	61.	77.	97.	121.	149.	184.	226.	104.	107
108	36.9	52.	66.	83.	105.	130.	160.	197.	242.	111.	108
109	40.3	56.	71.	90.	113.	139.	171.	211.	260.	119.	109
110	44.	61.	77.	97.	121.	149.	184.	226.	278.	128.	110
111	49.	66.	83.	105.	130.	160.	197.	242.	298.	137.	111
112	54.	71.	90.	113.	139.	171.	211.	260.	320.	147.	112
113	59.	77.	97.	121.	149.	184.	226.	278.	343.	158.	113
114	65.	83.	105.	130.	160.	197.	242.	298.	367.	169.	114
115	71.	90.	113.	139.	171.	211.	260.	320.		181.	115
116	77.	97.	121.	149.	184.	226.	278.	343.		194.	116
117	83.	105.	130.	160.	197.	242.	298.	367.		208.	117
118	90.	113.	139.	171.	211.	260.	320.			233.	118
119	97.	121.	149.	184.	226.	278.	343.			239.	119
120	105.	130.	160.	197.	242.	298.	367.			256.	120
121	113.	139.	171.	211.	260.	320.				274.	121
122	121.	149.	184.	266.	278.	343.				294.	122
123	130.	160.	197.	242.	298.	367.				315.	123
124	139.	171.	211.	260.	320.					338.	124
125	149.	184.	226.	278.	343.					362.	125

Source: A. P. G. Peterson and E. E. Gross, *Handbook of Noise Measurement*, 7th ed., General Radio Company, Concord, Mass., pp. 25–26. The method used here is that standardized in ANSI S 3.4 - 1968.

of hearing aids. Control of this type of damage, *commonly incurred through prolonged exposure to intense sound*, is the object of the occupational noise standards promulgated by the Occupational Safety and Health Administration (OSHA).

It used to be the general belief that hearing loss was a phenomenon associated with aging, and that such loss was as inevitable as the aging process itself. This loss was given the same *presbycusis*. In 1962 Rosen [3] reported that people living in a relatively noise-free environment in the Sudan exhibited little of this so-called presbycusis, and he suggested that much of the loss attributed to presbycusis in modern societies may actually be *sociocusis*, or noise-induced hearing loss. The handicap which hearing loss imposes on a person is determined by the degree to which the loss affects his or her ability to respond to human speech. Table 2.2 indicates this handicap as defined by the Committee on Hearing of the American Academy of Ophthalmology and Otolaryngology, based on the average hearing threshold level for tones at 500, 1000, and 2000 Hz. A hearing loss greater than 25 dB, averaged over these frequencies, is considered detrimental to the ability to understand speech.

Figure 2.6 depicts a person's chances of incurring a hearing handicap when working in a background of sustained noise. On the age axis, the working life is assumed to begin at age 20; thus, age 65 characterizes people who have spent 45 years at the occupation in question. Each curve corresponds to the continuous

Table 2.2 Guideline for the relations between the average hearing threshold level for 500, 1000, and 2000 Hz and degree of handicap as defined by the Committee on Hearing of the American Academy of Ophthalmology and Otolaryngology

Class	Degree of handicap	Average hearing threshold level for 500, 1000, and 2000 Hz in the better ear		Ability to understand speech
		More than dB	Not more than dB	
A	Not significant		25	No significant difficulty with faint speech
B	Slight handicap	25	40	Difficulty only with faint speech
C	Mild handicap	40	55	Frequent difficulty with normal speech
D	Marked handicap	55	70	Frequent difficulty with loud speech
E	Severe handicap	70	90	Can understand only shouted or amplified speech
F	Extreme handicap	90		Usually cannot understand amplified speech

Source: Davis, *Trans. Am. Acad. Ophthalmol. Otolaryngol.*, 1965. With permission.

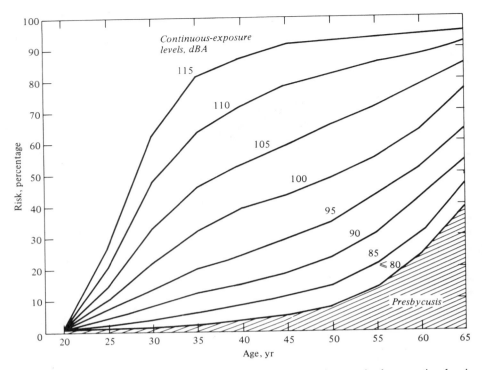

Figure 2.6 Percentage risk associated with hearing handicap under sustained occupational noise exposure.

exposure level, in dBA, incurred in this work environment. A person with, say, 30 years of work experience (average age 50 years) in a 90-dBA work environment has a 23 percent chance of incurring a hearing handicap; in other words, 23 out of 100 in this group will exhibit a hearing handicap at age 50. In Fig. 2.6 the impairment-risk curves for exposure levels below 80 dBA coincide with the 80-dBA curves. Consequently, hearing impairment associated with exposure levels below 80 dBA is apparently the result of other factors, such as aging. For this reason the risk attributable to noise-induced hearing loss is associated with the unshaded area, while the risk attributable to presbycusis is confined to the shaded area. From these curves, one can conclude that workers in a 90-dBA work environment increase their chances of impairment (upon retirement) by approximately 14 percent over those working in quiet environments below 80 dBA. As Table 1.1 reveals, the sound levels in Fig. 2.6 are not unusual. In fact, many of the sounds normally accepted away from the job environment could be damaging if sustained continuously over extended periods of time.

One model describing the mechanism by which sustained, intense noise causes damage to the inner ear makes use of the fact that different sound frequencies are sensed in different regions of the basilar membrane and that the voltages along the basilar membrane are generated by stressing the hair cells. If the hair cells in any region of the basilar membrane are destroyed, the ability of the ear to perceive a frequency associated with that region is likewise destroyed. Since the hair cells are extremely delicate, it is very likely that sustained exposure to intense noise results in a fatigue-type failure (similar to the failure of a thin rod subjected to cyclic flexing for a prolonged period of time) and that the hair cells begin to degenerate and lose their function. Over the years, as more and more of the hair cells in a region of the basilar membrane cease to function, the ability to perceive the associated frequencies likewise declines. If one looks at the cochlear activity at different frequencies (Fig. 2.3), one sees not only that the stapes end of the basilar membrane shows activity at *all* frequencies, but also that the higher the frequency the more intense the activity at that end. As a result, the ear would be expected to lose its ability to hear the higher frequencies first. The test data in Fig. 2.7 show that this is indeed the case. The ability to perceive higher frequencies diminishes more rapidly as the subject ages. This is not serious in the early stages for most people, since the frequencies above 8,000 Hz contribute little to the understanding of speech. However, as the damage progresses, lower frequencies lying in the speech range become affected, and the intelligibility of speech becomes progressively reduced.

The frequency content and relative loudness of common speech sounds are shown in Fig. 2.8. Note that the vowels are spoken at relatively high power levels, so that a moderate impairment in their frequency ranges does not seriously affect the ability to hear them. On the other hand, the consonants, which actually carry most of the information of speech, are spoken at relatively low power levels and would be more difficult to perceive if an impairment existed. Because of the relatively low power of some consonants (such as v, f, th) coupled with their high-frequency content, a person suffering progressive, noise-induced hearing loss would first lose the ability to hear these sounds. Since much of a voice's information is carried in consonants such as these, the intelligibility of the speaker will be greatly diminished.

A hearing aid may be of help in restoring intelligibility, but since it performs through *amplification* in the impaired frequency range, it could also hasten the degeneration of the hair cells in the afflicted region of the basilar membrane. If used on the job, for example, a hearing aid would in effect move the worker onto a higher risk curve (Fig. 2.6).

Occupational Noise Standards—OSHA Criteria

Occupational standards for permissible average noise levels are the results of tradeoffs between the risks associated with a given occupational noise level (Fig. 2.6) and the benefit gained by the individual and society from work performed in that environment. Obviously, this is not a straightforward decision based on purely biological considerations. Many value judgments must be made on the basis of medical, legal, sociological, and economic factors. One such judgment has been prepared by the National Academy of Sciences—National Research Council, Committee on Hearing, Bioacoustics, and Biomechanics, commonly known as CHABA. Its recommendations, based on data similar to those in Fig. 2.6, are listed in Table 2.3 below [5].

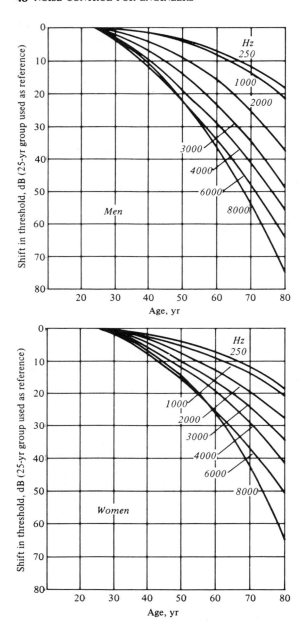

Figure 2.7 Average shifts with age (in persons with "normal" hearing) of threshold of hearing for pure tones. *(Source: Spoor,* International Audiology, *vol. 6, no. 1, July 1967.)*

In this table, a *permissible exposure* is defined as one which increases the risk of hearing handicap by no more than 10 percent over that attributable to presbycusis. As this table indicates, a given cumulative exposure is potentially less damaging when distributed over the entire working day, rather than occurring in a single exposure period. For example, a 99-dBA sound level can be tolerated for up to 4 h per day if exposure occurs in 75 short time-intervals, while only 1 h

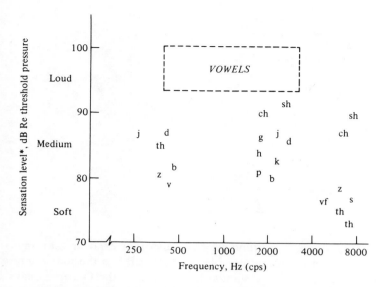

Figure 2.8 Frequency and loudness characteristics of some speech sounds. *(Source: H. Fletcher, Speech and Hearing, D. Van Nostrand, Co., 1929. With permission.)*

Table 2.3 Permissible average noise levels, in dBA, for steady and interrupted noise exposures

To use this table, select the column headed by the number of times the noise occurs per 8-h workday, read down to the average A-weighted sound level of the noise, and locate directly to the left in the first column the total duration of dangerous noise for any 24-h period.

Cumulative exposure	Number of noise interval exposures per 8-h workday						
	1	3	7	15	35	75	150 or more
8 h	90						
6 h	91	92	93	94	94	94	94
4 h	93	94	95	96	98	99	100
2 h	96	98	100	103	106	109	112
1 h	99	102	105	109	114	(115)	
30 min	102	106	110	114	(115)		
15 min	105	110	115				
8 min	108	115					
4 min	111						

Note: Noise intervals are periods of time during which the noise remains above 80 dBA. The *average noise level* is the mean A-weighted SPL during this time. An *interruption* of exposure occurs when the noise drops below 80 dBA for either (1) more than 5 min, or (2) a length of time equal to one-fifth of the average noise interval duration.

Source: L. L. Beranek (ed.), *Noise and Vibration Control*, McGraw-Hill, New York, 1971, p. 544. With permission.

Table G-16 Permissible noise exposures

Duration per day, h	Sound level, dBA, slow
8	90
6	92
4	95
3	97
2	100
$1\frac{1}{2}$	102
1	105
$\frac{1}{2}$	110
$\frac{1}{4}$	115

is tolerable when the exposure is continuous. Note also that exposures to any levels over 115 dBA are considered intolerable, while 90 dBA is the maximum recommended 8-h exposure level. The standard employed in the Occupational Safety and Health Act is based on this table, with the assumption of seven exposure intervals per workday.

It is important to note that some people are more susceptible to noise-induced damage than others. Rather than requiring zero damage due to occupational noise, the CHABA recommendations and the standards promulgated from them are designed to keep damage risk within *acceptable* limits, while acknowledging that some individuals will suffer hearing loss in even mild noise environments. The OSHA noise regulations [6], for example, specify permissible noise exposures which are considered to be the upper limit of a daily noise dose that will not produce hearing impairment in more than 20 percent of a population exposed through a working lifetime of 35 years.

Shown above is the often-quoted "Table G-16" of the Occupational Safety and Health regulation on noise, which corresponds to the CHABA recommendations of Table 2.3 for the case of seven intervals per 8-h day. The OSHA regulations will be discussed at length in Chap. 7.

2.5 SPEECH INTERFERENCE

Masking of Sound

Speech perception can be impaired not only by damage to the hair cells, but also by the presence of sounds which *compete* for the attention of the listener. The ear itself is only a transducer; it does not discriminate between sources of sound. Separation and identification of sources occurs in the brain after it receives signals from the hearing mechanism. The brain seems to respond to hair-cell activity only in a narrow region about each position of maximum activity in the basilar membrane (see Fig. 2.9). Thus, if two narrow-band sounds of equal spectrum level are received simultaneously, the ear will recognize them as distinct sounds only so long as the two basilar activity regions do not overlap. As the center frequencies of the two sounds approach one another and the two activity regions begin to overlap, the two sounds are no longer perceived separately.

The effect described above is illustrated in Fig. 2.9, which shows regions of hair-cell activity for several different sounds. Note that since a low-frequency sound creates activity along much of the basilar membrane, it could interfere with the ability to hear higher-frequency tones, while a high-frequency tone would not interfere as strongly with the perception of low-frequency tones. This interference between two sounds is called *masking*. The undesirable tone is said to mask the desirable tone. The *degree of masking* is defined as the extent to which the masking sound raises the threshold of audibility of the desired sound. Thus, if a 1000-Hz tone, with audibility threshold normally at 0 dB, cannot be heard in the presence of the masking tone until it is raised to 50 dB, we say that the masking is 50 dB. Typical results of masking experiments for pure tones are shown in Fig. 2.10, where the threshold shift is plotted as a function of frequency and masking-tone level. Note in this figure that the masking tone causes the highest degree of masking against tones of higher frequency. When the masking sound is broadband noise, rather than a pure tone, it has been found that [1]:

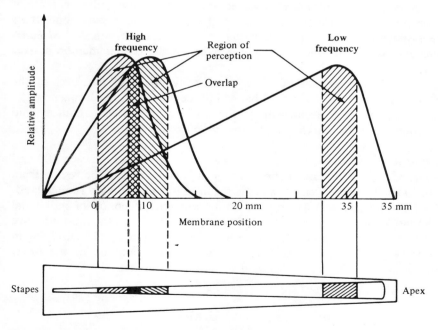

Figure 2.9 Activity in the basilar membrane for narrow-band noise signals at constant intensity. Note the competition for hair-cell activity in the overlap region.

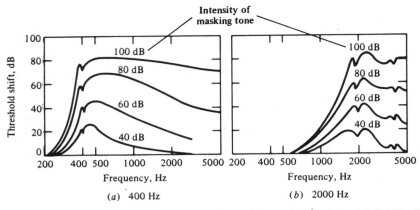

Figure 2.10 Masking of one pure tone by another. *(Source: L. E. Kinsler and A. R. Frey*, Fundamentals of Acoustics, *2d ed., John Wiley and Sons, Inc., 1962. Reprinted by permission.)*

1. Narrow-band noise causes greater masking around its center frequency than does a pure tone of that frequency. This should be evident, since a larger portion of the basilar membrane is excited by the noise.
2. Narrow-band noise is more effective than pure tones in masking frequencies above its center frequency.
3. A noise bandwidth is ultimately reached above which any further increase of bandwidth has no further influence on the masking of a pure tone at its center frequency. This implies that the ear recognizes certain *critical bandwidths* associated with the regions of activity on the basilar membrane (see Fig. 2.9).
4. The threshold of the masked tone is normally raised to the level of the masking noise only in the critical bandwidth centered on that frequency.
5. A tone which is a few decibels above the masking noise seems about as loud as it would be *if the masking noise were not present.*

Although the human voice produces sounds in the range between 100 and 10,000 Hz, nearly all the information in speech is contained in the region from 200 to 6000 Hz [9]. Moreover, the sounds required for intelligibility (understanding of words and phrases) as opposed to articulation (reception of individual speech sounds) are contained between 500 and 2500 Hz. Thus, the most effective masking of speech will be obtained with tones and noise at frequencies lying in this latter range. The most effective masking noise would lie in the lower frequencies, around 500 Hz, and should be rich in components.

Evaluation of Speech Interference—PSIL, dBA

Extensive data on the intelligibiltiy of speech and the effects of masking have led to procedures whereby one can, from physical measurements, calculate an index of speech intelligibility. This index is called the *Articulation Index*, or AI. The detailed procedure is laid out in ANSI S3.5-1969 and will not be discussed here.

A simplified version of AI is proposed by Beranek [10] for predicting effectiveness of person-to-person speech communication in the presence of noise. In this procedure, the arithmetic average of the 500-, 1000-, and 2000-Hz octave-band levels of the interfering noise is determined. This average, called the *preferred speech-interference level* (PSIL), is compared with subjective data to determine whether speech communication will be easy or difficult in the environment being considered. It can also be used to determine the changes in band levels needed to improve the ease of communication. As an example, the PSIL of a factory noise environment was determined by measuring the octave-band levels at the three critical center frequencies to obtain $(81 + 80 + 80) \div 3 \doteq 80$ dB. Examination of the rating chart shown in Fig. 2.11 shows that 80 dB is a high figure for a PSIL; verbal communication is possible only at less than 2 ft, and then only if special effort is made to communicate.

As Fig. 2.11 indicates, the A-weighted sound-pressure level L_A (dBA) can be used as a simplified alternative index when octave-band readings cannot be made. For surveys and preliminary studies, the PSIL method can be employed with reasonable reliability, while the level based on dBA is somewhat less reliable. Since the PSIL and L_A indices either ignore or deemphasize sound outside the 500- to 2500-Hz range, neither should be used when intense low-frequency (below 500 hz) or high-frequency (above 2500 Hz) noise is present. However, most practical situations requiring evaluation of speech intelligibility are covered by these procedures.

The criterion based on PSIL is, like all criteria, derived from observation of human responses. It should be considered a *statistical* estimate of response, suitable as a guideline for design and evaluation purposes.

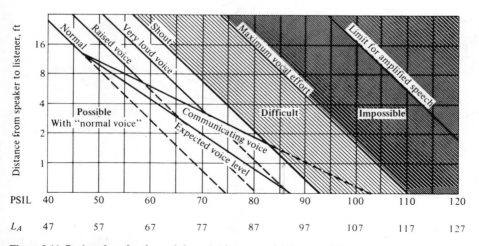

Figure 2.11 Rating chart for determining speech communication capability from speech-interference levels. (*Source: J. C. Webster, Proc Conference Noise as a Public Health Hazard, 1979. Reprinted by permission.*)

2.6 ANNOYANCE—PERCEIVED NOISINESS

In contrast with the concepts of speech masking and hearing damage, which can be evaluated with some statistical reliability, annoyance or perceived noisiness is a highly subjective impression of the *unwantedness* of a sound. Experimenters have found it difficult to evaluate or quantitatively define noisiness because it appears to involve the listener's subjective notions of loudness, acceptability, and intrusiveness, as well as annoyance. Although it seems that noisiness will continue to elude exact definition, it is essential to identify the measurable physical aspects of a sound which contribute most to perceived noisiness. Five such features of sound have been identified: (1) spectrum content and level; (2) spectrum complexity and existence of pure tones; (3) duration; (4) amplitude and frequency of level fluctuations; and (5) rise time of impulsive sounds.

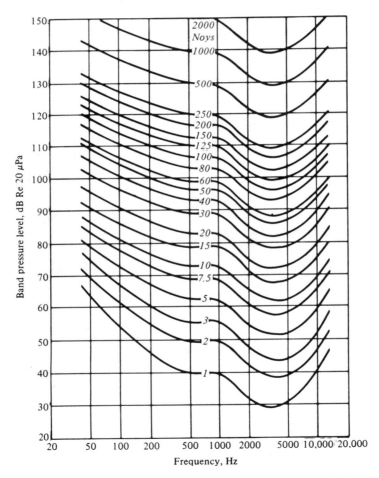

Figure 2.12 Contours of equal perceived noisiness of octave-band noise. *(Source: E. B. Magrab, Environmental Noise Control, John Wiley and Sons, Inc. 1975. Reprinted by permission.)*

Experiments investigating the effects of these five features have led to the development of *equal-noisiness* contours, whose application is similar to that of the equal-loudness contours. Figure 2.12 summarizes the data. The subjective unit of noisiness is called the *noy*, in parallel with the *sone* for loudness. A sound of 2, 4, 10, or 20 noys would be judged 2, 4, 10, or 20 times as noisy as a sound of 1 noy, where a noy is defined as the noisiness of a 1000-Hz tone at a 40-dB sound-pressure level.

In this chapter we have dealt with the effects of noise on humans. An understanding of the relationships between noise and hearing-damage risk, speech interference, and annoyance has led to the development of criteria for evaluating noise environments, such as those given in Fig. 2.11. These criteria form the basis for standards which are used in the regulation of noise. A discussion of noise rating criteria, standards, and regulations is given in Chap. 7.

REFERENCES

1. Kryter, K. D., *The Effects of Noise on Man*, Academic, New York, 1970.
2. Glorig, A., "Non-Auditory Effects of Noise Exposure," 5(5):28–29 (1971).
3. Rosen, S., M. Bergman, D. Plestor, A. El-Mofty, and M. Satti, "Presbycusis Study of a Relatively Noise-Free Population in the Sudan," *Ann. Otol. Rhinol. Laryngol.* 71:727–743 (1962).
4. Glorig, A., W. D. Ward, and J. Nixon, "Damage-Risk Criteria and Noise-induced Hearing Loss," *Arch. Otolaryngol.* 74:413–423 (October 1961).
5. CHABA, "Hazardous Exposure to Intermittent and Steady-State Noise," *J. Acoust. Soc. Amer.* 39:451–464 (1966).
6. Sec. 1910.95 of Federal Register, May 20, 1969.
7. Sec. 1910.95 of Federal Register, Oct. 24, 1974.
8. Peterson, A. P. G., and E. E. Gross, *Handbook of Noise Measurement*, 7th ed., General Radio Company, Concord, Mass., 1972.
9. Zwicker, E., G. Flottorp, and S. S. Stevens, "Critical Bandwidth in Loudness Summation," *J. Acoust. Soc. Amer.* 29(5):548–557 (1959).
10. Beranek, L. L., "Noise Control in Office and Factory Spaces," 15th Annual Mtg. of the Chemical Engineering Conference, *Trans. Bull.* 18:26–33 (1950).

IMPORTANT TERMS AND FORMULAS

Noise: Sound that is *unwanted* because of hearing damage, signal masking, or annoyance

Phon: Unit of loudness *level*, logarithmic

Sone: Unit of subjective loudness, linear

Noy: Unit of subjective noisiness, linear

PSIL: Preferred-octave speech-interference level, arithmetic average of 500, 1000, and 2000-Hz octave-band levels

Threshold of hearing

Threshold of feeling

Threshold of pain

OSHA: Occupational Safety and Health Administration, concerned with hearing *damage*

Human voice range: 100 to 10,000 Hz

Speech articulation range: 200 to 6000 Hz

Speech intelligibility range: 500 to 2500 Hz

Audible range: 20 to 20,000 Hz

Hearing damage and masking: related to cochlear activity

Hearing handicap: Greater than 25-dB hearing loss, averaged over measured 500-, 1000-, and 2000-Hz hearing losses

Critical bandwidths

ANSI: American National Standards Institute

Loudness index

PROBLEMS

2.1 Given a 50-Hz tone at 78 dB, a 10,000-Hz tone at 65 dB, and a 1000-Hz tone at 65 dB, which tone is louder to the normal ear?

   Answer: 1000-Hz tone

2.2 Given a 20-phon tone and a 30-phon tone, which is louder? How much louder?

   Answer: 30-phon tone; twice as loud, subjectively

2.3 Given a sound generator operating at 1000 Hz and producing a 40-dB sound pressure level at a given point, how many similar generators operating simultaneously would generate a sound twice as loud?

   Answer: 10

2.4 The noise environment in the work area near a metal cutting saw is analyzed by octave bands, yielding the octave-band levels listed in the table below:

Center frequency, Hz	Band level, dB
31.5	74
63	79
125	80
250	87
500	83
1000	83
2000	93
4000	98
8000	91
16000	86

(*a*) What is the subjective loudness, in sones, near the saw?
Answer: 155.5 sones
(*b*) What is the overall sound-pressure level, in decibels?
Answer: 100 dB

(c) What is the A-weighted sound-pressure level in dBA?

Answer: 100.5 dBA

(d) What is the PSIL?

Answer: 86 dB

(e) Which octave bands are of most concern when attempting to reduce the loudness?

Answer: 4000, then 8000, then 2000

(f) Will two people standing near the saw be able to converse? At what distance?

(g) Can they converse without being overheard by someone 10 ft away?

Answer: Yes, even if shouting.

(h) Will reduction of the 4000-Hz band level to 90 dB reduce the loudness?

Answer: (Yes)

Significantly?

Answer: No; to 136 sones

2.5 What do the letters OSHA stand for? What aspect of noise is OSHA intended to regulate?

2.6 Your company is considering purchase of a new machine to be installed in a work area where its noise may be objectionable. There are two contenders, A and B, which satisfy price and performance requirements. The choice between the two machines is to be based on noise considerations. The octave-band sound-pressure spectra of the two machines are listed below:

Band, Hz	Machine A, dB	Machine B, dB
31.5	88	96
63	89	91
125	90	86
250	90	81
500	90	76
1000	87	71
2000	86	66
4000	81	61
8000	77	56

Which machine would you select? Why?

2.7 What is the risk that a heavy-equipment operator with 20 years' experience at levels of 100 to 110 dBA will exhibit a hearing handicap?

Answer: Excellent chance, 40 to 70 percent; that is, out of every 100 people in this category, 40 to 70 will show impairment.

2.8 A pure tone of frequency 200 Hz has an intensity level of 60 dB. Determine its loudness level and loudness. To what intensity level must this pure tone be raised in order to increase its loudness to twice the original value?

2.9 The frequencies and sound-pressure levels of three pure tones are 200 Hz at 64 dB, 500 Hz at 70 dB, and 1000 Hz at 74 dB.

(a) Which tone is the loudest?

(b) What is their total loudness level in phons?

2.10 Given three pure tones with the following frequencies and intensity levels: 100 Hz at 60 dB, 500 Hz at 70 dB, and 1000 Hz at 80 dB.

(a) Compute the total loudness in sones of these three pure tones.

(b) What is the combined intensity level of the three?

(c) Find the intensity level of a single 2000-Hz pure tone which has the same loudness as all the three pure tones combined.

THREE

DESCRIPTION OF SOUND FIELDS

3.1 INTRODUCTION

Sound has been defined earlier as vibrations in an elastic medium. If a fluctuating disturbance is created at some point in an elastic medium, the vibrational energy (sound) generated at this point will spread as waves to fill the surrounding medium. Airborne vibrational energy is characterized by longitudinal waves in which the particle velocity is in the same direction as the propagation of radiated acoustical energy. The fluctuating mechanism causing the disturbance is called the *sound source*, and the resulting disturbance in the medium is called the *sound field*. A quantitative measure of the sound at any point in the field is the sound-pressure level in decibels. In order to obtain a complete description of the sound field it is necessary to know the sound-pressure level at every point in the field. Fortunately, in many practical situations it is possible to predict the sound field generated by particular types of sound sources within a region of interest around the source. Alternatively, if the sound field can be characterized by making a reasonable survey of sound-pressure levels in the region of interest, it may be possible to predict the type of source and its location and to compute the sound power being radiated.

The remainder of this chapter deals with ways of relating noise measurements to source identification and sound-power computation, and introduces terminology commonly used in describing particular types of sound fields. The concepts presented will be of importance to the noise control engineer in relating sound-level measurements to acoustical output and location of an unknown source, or in predicting sound fields caused by a specified sound source when placed in a known environment.

3.2 SOUND SOURCES AND RADIATED SOUND FIELDS

The basic instrument used to evaluate a sound field is the sound-level meter, which obtains a quantitative measure of the effective root-mean-square (rms) sound pressure at any point in the field. This quantity can be related to the sound intensity I at the point under certain conditions. If in addition we know how the sound energy is radiated from the source, it is possible to relate the measured sound-pressure levels to the sound power W of the source. In this section, we will look briefly at some of the basic physical concepts and mathematical models needed in order to establish relationships between sound-level measurements and sound-power output for several basic types of sources and their resulting sound fields.

Consider the sound source of sound power W shown in Fig. 3.1. Let S be the surface of a sound wave radiating from the source and $p(r, t)$ be the instantaneous sound pressure at point O on the surface. Then the average acoustic intensity at O is the time-averaged rate of flow of energy through a unit area normal to the direction of wave propagation,

$$I = \overline{pu_n} \tag{3.1}$$

where $u_n(r, t)$ is the normal component of particle velocity and the bar over the product pu_n indicates time-averaged. The total sound power radiated through the surface S enclosing the source is given by the integral

$$W = \iint_S \overline{pu_n} \, dS \tag{3.2}$$

Plane Sound Field—One-dimensional Source

We begin our study by considering the simplest type of wave motion propagated in a fluid medium, namely, plane sound waves. A sound wave that propagates in such a way that the acoustic pressures, particle velocities, density changes, etc. each have uniform phases and amplitudes at all points on any given plane perpendicular to the direction of wave propagation is called a *plane wave*. The

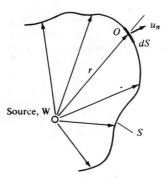

Figure 3.1 Sound radiation.

resulting sound is called a *plane sound field*. Plane waves occur in ducts and pipes where the cross-sectional dimensions of the path are small compared with the wavelength of the sound. In addition, the subregion of any divergent sound field takes on the characteristics of a plane sound field if we move to large distances from the source, and if the dimensions of the region of interest are small compared with the distance from the source.

Only one coordinate, x, in the direction of wave propagation is needed to describe the plane-wave motion. Let $p(x, t)$ be the excess pressure or acoustic pressure, ρ_0 the constant equilibrium density of the undisturbed fluid, δ the change in density caused by the acoustic pressure, and $u(x, t)$ the particle velocity in the x direction at any point in the fluid. In most practical cases the acoustic pressures are small compared with the equilibrium pressure (see Table 1.1), and the resulting changes in density are much less than the equilibrium density. Under these conditions the acoustic-pressure fluctuations occur adiabatically, and the first-order approximation of the equation of motion (Newton's Second Law) for the element of fluid shown in Fig. 3.2 reduces to

$$\frac{\partial p}{\partial x} = -\rho_0 \frac{\partial u}{\partial t} \qquad \text{equation of motion} \qquad (3.3)$$

If in addition we consider the conservation of mass flowing through the spatial element of fluid, we obtain the continuity equation for an adiabatic fluid

$$\frac{\partial p}{\partial t} = -\rho_0 c_0^2 \frac{\partial u}{\partial x} \qquad \text{continuity equation} \qquad (3.4)$$

where c_0 is the propagation velocity of the acoustic wave.

The velocity terms can be eliminated from the two equations above, by taking the time derivative of Eq. (3.4) and the spatial derivative of Eq. (3.3), to obtain the one-dimensional wave equation

$$\frac{1}{c_0^2} \frac{\partial^2 p}{\partial t^2} - \frac{\partial^2 p}{\partial x^2} = 0 \qquad \text{wave equation} \qquad (3.5)$$

The general solution for this equation is given by

$$p(x, t) = f_1\left(t - \frac{x}{c_0}\right) + f_2\left(t + \frac{x}{c_0}\right) \qquad (3.6)$$

where the first term represents a pressure wave propagating in the positive x direction at a constant velocity c_0, and with no change in shape as it propagates. The second term represents a similar pressure wave propagating in the opposite direction.

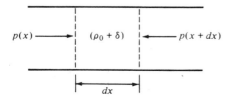

$p(x) \longrightarrow \quad (\rho_0 + \delta) \quad \longleftarrow p(x + dx)$

dx

Figure 3.2 Plane sound field.

If we are close enough to the sound source and far enough away from reflecting surfaces, only the first term in Eq. (3.6) is of interest in describing a plane sound field. Substituting f_1 for p in the equation of motion (3.3) and integrating yields an expression for the particle velocity field

$$u(x, t) = \frac{1}{\rho_0 c_0} p(x, t) \tag{3.7}$$

Hence, the particle velocity at any point in a plane-progressive (no reflections) sound field is directly proportional to and in phase with the pressure at that point.

The acoustic intensity at any point in a plane sound wave is obtained from Eq. (3.1):

$$I = \overline{pu} = \frac{p^2}{\rho_0 c_0} \tag{3.8}$$

where p is the rms value of the acoustic pressure, as defined by Eq. (1.12). The sound power radiated through any area S perpendicular to the direction of wave propagation is obtained from Eq. (3.2) to give

$$W = IS = \frac{p^2}{\rho_0 c_0} S \tag{3.9}$$

The sound intensity and sound power of the sound field are related to the measured sound-pressure level L_p through the equation

$$L_p = 10 \log_{10} \left(\frac{p}{p_{\text{ref}}} \right)^2$$

Thus, we obtain

$$I = \frac{p^2}{\rho_0 c_0} = \frac{p_{\text{ref}}^2}{\rho_0 c_0} \text{antilog}_{10} \left(\frac{L_p}{10} \right) \approx 10^{\left(\frac{L_p}{10} - 8 \right)} \tag{3.10}$$

and

$$W = IS = \frac{p_{\text{ref}}^2}{\rho_0 c_0} S \, \text{antilog}_{10} \left(\frac{L_p}{10} \right) \approx S \times 10^{\left(\frac{L_p}{10} - 8 \right)} \tag{3.11}$$

Now consider a source of noise which produces sound at a continuous steady level at one end of a long duct with rigid walls. The dimensions of the duct are such that plane waves are propagated along its length. Equation (3.6) indicates that, in the absence of relfected waves* and losses through the duct wall, the pressure wave will propagate along the duct without change. This concept is the basis for the design of the stethoscope and for systems used to "pipe" music to passengers in modern aircraft. Moreover, Eqs. (3.10) and (3.11) indicate that the sound intensity and sound power radiated in the duct can be determined from a single pressure-level measurement.

---

* The acoustic pressure resulting from incident and reflected waves is derived in Sec. 4.4.

Spherical Sound Field—Point Source

The governing equations derived above for one-dimensional plane waves can be extended to cover the general three-dimensional wave propagation. The general three-dimensional vector equations are:

$$\frac{\partial \mathbf{u}}{\partial t} = -\frac{1}{\rho_0}\,\text{grad}\, p \qquad \textit{equation of motion} \qquad (3.12)$$

$$\text{div}\, \mathbf{u} = -\frac{1}{\rho_0 c_0^2}\frac{\partial p}{\partial t} \qquad \textit{continuity equation} \qquad (3.13)$$

$$\frac{1}{c_0^2}\frac{\partial^2 p}{\partial t^2} - \nabla^2 p = 0 \qquad \textit{wave equation} \qquad (3.14)$$

where $\mathbf{u}$ is a vector quantity representing the particle velocity at a point.

Spherical waves, such as would radiate from a small central sound source, are the first type of three-dimensional wave which we will consider. The acoustic pressure, particle velocity, density change, etc. for this type of wave are functions only of time and of radial distance from the source. Hence, the wave equation reduces to

$$\frac{1}{c_0^2}\frac{\partial^2 (rp)}{\partial t^2} - \frac{\partial^2 (rp)}{\partial r^2} = 0$$

which is of the same form as Eq. (3.5) for the plane wave. The general solution for rp will have the same form as that given by Eq. (3.6). Dividing through by r gives the expression for acoustic pressure

$$p(r, t) = \frac{1}{r}f_1\!\left(t - \frac{r}{c_0}\right) + \frac{1}{r}f_2\!\left(t + \frac{r}{c_0}\right) \qquad (3.15)$$

The first term of this equation represents a spherical wave propagating outward from a point source with a constant velocity c_0. Unlike that of the plane wave, the pressure amplitude of the spherical wave diminishes with distance from the source, since the disturbance must spread itself out over an ever-increasing surface area as the wave propagates outward. The second term of Eq. (3.15) represents a spherical wave which converges on the source center and has little practical significance.

The particle velocity field can be obtained using the equation of motion which, for a spherical wave, reduces to

$$\frac{\partial u}{\partial t} = -\frac{1}{\rho_0}\frac{\partial p}{\partial r}$$

where u now represents the radial velocity of a fluid particle. Using the first term from Eq. (3.15) for pressure and integrating gives the radial particle velocity

$$u(r, t) = \frac{1}{\rho_0 r^2}\int_0^t f_1\, dt + \frac{p(r, t)}{\rho_0 c_0} \qquad (3.16)$$

The first term in Eq. (3.16) becomes negligible for large values of r, and the equation for particle velocity reduces to that derived for a plane wave. This behavior is to be expected, since the wave front of all spherical waves becomes essentially plane at large distances from the source. On the other hand, the first term dominates when we move in close to the source. Consequently, we say that the first term represents the *near-field* behavior and the second term the *far-field* behavior of the propagating wave. Near-field effects will occur whenever a sound source generates nonplanar waves, which is the case for most practical situations. The practical aspects of the near- and far-field characteristics of sound are discussed in a later section of this chapter.

One of the most important types of spherical waves is one whose vibrations are harmonic. It can be shown that the acoustic intensity of a harmonic spherical wave is related to the sound pressure in the same way as for a plane wave,* that is, $I = p^2/\rho_0 c_0$. However, in this case the pressure is proportional to I/r. Consequently, the intensity obeys the inverse-square law with distance, as discussed in Chap. 1, and the sound-pressure level drops off at a rate of 6 dB per doubling of distance from the source.

The sound-power output through any closed spherical surface of radius r surrounding the source is obtained from

$$W = 4\pi r^2\left(\frac{p^2}{\rho_0 c_0}\right) = \frac{4\pi r^2 p_{\text{ref}}^2}{\rho_0 c_0}\,\text{antilog}_{10}\left(\frac{L_p}{10}\right) \qquad (3.17)$$

Hence, the sound power of a point source causing a spherical sound field can be predicted from the sound-pressure level measured at a radius r using Eq. (3.17). This equation is valid provided the source is located far enough from reflecting surfaces and the sound level measured close enough to the source, so that the sound radiating directly from the source dominates the sound field. These conditions will be satisfied if field measurements show that the sound-pressure levels decrease at a rate of 6 dB per doubling of distance in the region around the source.

Cylindrical Sound Field—Line Source

Consider a series of point sources equally spaced along a straight line, such as cars in a line of traffic or a string of moving railroad cars. We assume that the sources are closely spaced and that the sound radiating from each source is unrelated to any of the other sources, i.e., uncorrelated. If all the sources are of equal strength, the acoustical energy will radiate uniformly from the line as cylindrical waves. The intensity of the sound in the far field of the line source will be related to the mean square pressure, as in a plane wave:

$$I = \frac{p^2}{\rho_0 c_0}$$

---

* See Lawrence E. Kinsler and Austin R. Frey, *Fundamentals of Acoustics*, Wiley, 1962, chap. 7.

Consider the line source in Fig. 3.3. Let W' be the sound power per unit length (in watts per meter). Then the sound power generated by a length of line dx will be $W'\,dx$. Since the acoustic energy spreads out uniformly over the cylindrical wave as it propagates outward from the line, the intensity of sound on the cylindrical strip of width dx will be

$$I = \frac{W'\,dx}{2\pi r\,dx} = \frac{W'}{2\pi r} \tag{3.18}$$

The intensity and the mean square pressure diminish by one-half with doubling of the distance r. This will result in a 3-dB decrease in sound-pressure level with each doubling of distance from a line source in a free field. The sound power per unit length of a line source can be estimated from a single sound-level measurement:

$$W' = I2\pi r = \frac{p^2}{\rho_0 c_0}(2\pi r) = \frac{p_{\text{ref}}^2}{\rho_0 c_0}(2\pi r)\,\text{antilog}_{10}\!\left(\frac{L_p}{10}\right) \tag{3.19}$$

The concept of a line source can be used to explain the preferred orientation of column speakers. Consider a bank of speakers placed one on top of the other. If we treat the speakers as a line source, cylindrical sound waves will radiate transverse to the vertical line source. However, when we view the speakers from above, they appear as a point, so that we would expect spherical spreading in the direction along the line of speakers. Consequently, there would be a 6-dB drop in sound level with doubling of distance along the axis of the speakers, but only a 3-dB drop with doubling of radial distance. For this reason, the speakers radiate sound more efficiently radially, and the column of speakers is more effective when placed vertically in a large room.

Fundamental Source Mechanisms—Monopole, Dipole, Quadrupole

Several basic types of sound sources have been discussed in a general way. Emphasis was placed on identifying far-field characteristics of the sound fields which were generated and on relating sound-pressure levels of the fields to

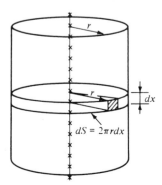

Figure 3.3 Line source.

sound power of the sources. In this section, we take a closer look at the fundamental mechanisms by which noise is generated and at the physical and mathematical models used to describe these mechanisms. The mathematical model chosen to describe an actual noise source is often a matter of convenience. Sometimes several models must be combined to bring out all features of a sound field. Emphasis will be placed on developing a physical understanding of how sound is generated in a fluid and why the different models are needed to bring out special features of a sound field.

Source models Fundamental to any type of sound generation in a fluid is the requirement that fluid particles at some point or region of the fluid must be set into fluctuating motion. This can be accomplished in several basic ways: (1) by a fluctuating flow of mass into the fluid, (2) by applying fluctuating forces to the fluid, (3) by applying fluctuating couples or moments to the fluid, and (4) by applying a fluctuating "squeezing" action to the fluid.

A small pulsating sphere, as in Fig. 3.4, is the simplest model which can be used to describe motion caused by a fluctuating mass flow. As the sphere expands, it has the effect of pushing neighboring fluid particles outward, an action which is equivalent to adding mass flow to the surrounding fluid; as the sphere shrinks, the action felt by the surrounding fluid is equivalent to mass flow inward toward the center of the sphere. The pulsating sphere is referred to as a *monopole source,* and it is the basis upon which higher-order models can be built. The monopole source is a convenient model for describing sound generated from the open end of an organ pipe or other woodwind instrument, a baffled speaker, or a gunshot.

Consider now a source made up of a doublet of pulsating spheres, as shown in Fig. 3.5. Since the motions of the two spheres are 180° out of phase, the net mass flow across a larger spherical surface enclosing the two spheres will be zero. However, there will be a pulsating momentum flux within the enclosing surface due to the opposing motion of the two spheres, which results in a

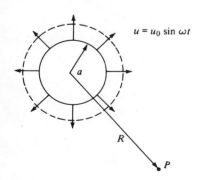

Figure 3.4 Monopole source.

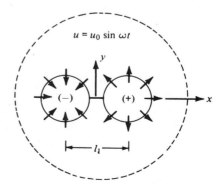

Figure 3.5 Dipole source.

pulsating force directed along the x axis. This doublet of monopoles is called a *dipole source*. The dipole source is a convenient model for describing sound generated by a solid surface imparting force to a fluid, such as the tonal sound of a fan blade or sound from an unbaffled speaker.

We now consider two dipole sources which are 180° out of phase and displaced laterally. The dipole forces are equal in magnitude but always opposite in direction, so that the resulting force on the fluid is zero. However, since the two parallel forces are laterally displaced, they will exert a couple on the fluid. This combination of dipoles is referred to as a *lateral quadrupole source*. On the other hand, if the two dipoles are displaced longitudinally on the axis, as shown in Fig. 3.7, the two opposing forces are collinear. Consequently, the net effect of this combination of sources on the fluid will be a "squeezing" action. This combination is referred to as a *longitudinal quadrupole source*. The lateral quadrupole source is a convenient model for describing jet mixing noise, which is caused by the shearing action (distributed couples) as the high-velocity jet mixes with ambient fluid. The longitudinal quadrupole can be used to describe sound generated by the surface acceleration of two impacting bodies. Consider the cylinders shown in Fig. 3.8 immediately after impact. Surfaces B and C receive negative acceleration pulses at impact, which causes rarefaction (negative monopoles) in the fluid medium, while surfaces A and D undergo positive acceleration at impact. Consequently, the four radiating surfaces cause a disturbance in the medium at impact which is like a longitudinal quadrupole, provided the duration of impact is much longer than it takes for the sound to travel in the medium the length of the cylinders. This provision assures us that the relative phases of the impact pulses generated by the four surfaces will be maintained as they combine to form the far-field acoustic-pressure field.

In general, the fundamental sources developed above can be used to describe sound fields generated by disturbances which are imparted to a fluid medium over an extended surface—such as equivalent mass flow caused by a

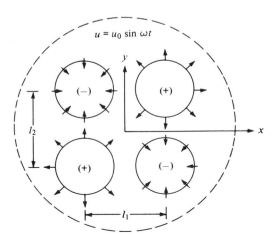

Figure 3.6 Lateral quadrupole source.

$u = u_0 \sin \omega t$

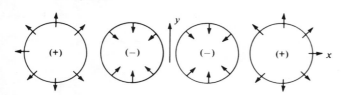

Figure 3.7 Longitudinal quadrupole.

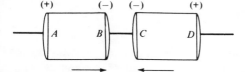

Figure 3.8 Two-body impact.

fluctuating panel, force acting on a fluid by reaction from a solid surface (fan blade), or a turbulent region within a quiescent fluid. In theory, an equation giving the sound pressure at any point in the medium can be obtained by considering appropriate sources spread over the surface causing the disturbance and integrating this expression over the generating surface. However, in practice the mathematical difficulties encountered in carrying out this integration limit its application.

Interference and directionality Two important features of a sound field which are characterized by the models described above are sound interference and directionality. Consider the monopole source shown in Fig. 3.9, where P is an observation point at distance R from the source. The observer at point P will feel the acoustic pressure propagating from point A as well as from point B. Since sound propagates in a fluid at finite speed c_0 and there are differences in distances of travel from the two points to the observer at P, at some locations the disturbances may arrive out of phase and cancel each other. The phenomenon of sound cancellation due to sounds arriving at a point from two different locations on a source is called *interference*. For the case of a monopole source, whenever the wavelength of sound is much greater than the dimensions of the radiator, $\lambda \gg a$, and the acoustic pressure is measured at large distances from the source, $R \gg a$, the interference will be negligible. Hence, under these conditions contours of equal sound-pressure levels would form spheres around the source, and we say that the monopole source is nondirectional.*

On the other hand, if we consider a plane through the origin and perpendicular to the axis of a dipole source (plane yz in Fig. 3.5), the acoustic pressure

---

* The concept of a *point source* (or simple source) is often used in describing sound radiation. With this idealization the source is considered concentrated at a point (namely, $a = 0$) so that there are no near-field effects. Hence, a point (simple) source is equivalent to a monopole source of "zero" radius which radiates sound uniformly in all directions.

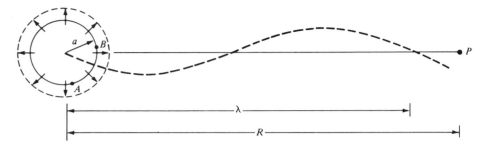

Figure 3.9 Parameters which relate to sound interference.

received from any two points symmetric with respect to that plane will always be 180° out of phase for any point on the plane, regardless of source and wavelength dimensions. However, interference will be negligible along the axis of the dipole under the conditions specified above for a monopole source. Hence, contours of equal sound-pressure levels plotted in a plane containing the axis of a dipole source will take the form of figures of eight. Directional patterns also exist for quadrupole sources and can be described in the same way as the pattern for the dipole (see Table 3.1).

In general the sound field of any extended source will display directional patterns resulting from interference. If sound-pressure levels were measured in a free field, one would expect a 0- to 6-dB decrease in level with doubling of distance from the source, depending on whether the sound field is plane, cylindrical, or spherical. Moreover, any compact source will appear as a point source if we move far enough away from it. Hence, in the absence of reflections we would expect a 6-dB drop per doubling of distance at sufficient distances from the source. (What can be considered a sufficient distance will be discussed in Sec. 3.3.) Additional decreases in sound level can occur at large distances as a result of atmospheric effects on the sound propagation.

One method of locating major noise sources in a region of multiple sound sources is systematically to measure sound levels and then construct equal-level contours to describe the field. These sound-pressure contours are similar to elevation contours on a map. As we move away from a source, a characteristic drop in level will occur. Consequently, the major sources will stand out like hilltops on a map with elevation contours. A typical pattern of equal-sound-level contours is shown in Fig. 3.10.

Equivalent-piston model Another physical model which can be used to build the basic sources discussed above is a rigid circular piston. Consider the case of a piston mounted in an infinite baffle and vibrating with simple harmonic motion. The pressure amplitudes in the medium will be symmetrical about the center of the piston if the wavelength of radiated sound is much longer than the piston dimensions. Hence, the sound field produced is equivalent to that produced by a hemispherically radiating monopole source. If the baffle is removed, the outward flow of mass on one side of the piston is canceled by an equal inward flow

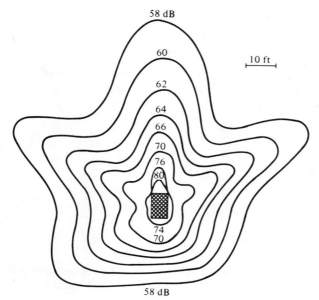

Figure 3.10 Equal-level contours.

on the other side. Hence, there will be no net flow of mass. However, there will be a momentum flux imparted by the piston to the medium and, hence, a force. Thus, the unbaffled piston is equivalent to a dipole source. Quadrupole sources can also be constructed from piston sources by considering combinations of dipole sources, as was done earlier with pulsating spheres (see Table 3.1).

Source strength—radiation efficiency Consider the basic monopole source represented by a pulsating sphere with surface velocity $u = u_0 \sin \omega t$, shown in Fig. 3.4. This motion creates a mass flow in the surrounding medium that is proportional to the maximum rate of volume flow. In general, the strength of *any* source whose elements vibrate in phase is equal to the maximum rate of volume flow (or volume velocity) given by the integral over the source surface S,

$$Q = \iint_S u_n \, dS \tag{3.20}$$

where u_n is the velocity component at the surface element normal to dS. The quantity Q, known as the "source strength," becomes the product of surface area and velocity amplitude for a monopole source,

$$Q = 4\pi a^2 u_0 \tag{3.21}$$

The general expression for acoustic pressure radiated by a pulsating sphere is given by Eq. (3.15); for the monopole source this becomes

$$p(r, t) = \frac{A}{r} \sin(\omega t - kr + \phi) \tag{3.22}$$

The far-field velocity field as given by Eq. (3.16) then becomes

$$u(r, t) = \frac{p(r, t)}{\rho_0 c_0} = \frac{A}{\rho_0 c_0 r} \sin(\omega t - kr + \phi) \tag{3.23}$$

Writing the acoustic pressure in terms of the monopole-source strength and using Eqs. (3.1) and (3.2) yields the following expressions for the average sound intensity and total sound-power output for a monopole source:

$$I_m = \frac{\rho_0 c_0 k^2 Q^2}{32\pi^2 r^2} \tag{3.24}$$

and

$$W_m = \frac{\rho_0 c_0 k^2 Q^2}{8\pi} \tag{3.25}$$

where k is the wave number given by Eq. (1.6):

$$k = \frac{2\pi}{\lambda} = \frac{\omega}{c_0} = \frac{2\pi f}{c_0}$$

We see from Eq. (3.24) that the far-field sound intensity of a monopole source is nondirectional and obeys the inverse-square law (-6 dB per doubling of distance from the source).

The dipole source is considered next. The distance l_1 (see Fig. 3.5) is assumed very small, but the dipole-source strength Ql_1 remains finite as $l_1 \rightarrow 0$. Expressions for the far-field sound intensity and sound power of the dipole source are [1]:

$$I_d = \frac{\rho c k^4 (Ql_1)^2 \cos^2\theta}{32\pi^2 r^2} \tag{3.26}$$

and

$$W_d = \frac{\rho c k^4 (Ql_1)^2}{24\pi} \tag{3.27}$$

The directional properties of the dipole sound field are determined by the $\cos^2\theta$ term appearing in Eq. (3.26). Comparing the sound power of the monopole and dipole sources, we find that

$$\frac{W_d}{W_m} = \frac{k^2 l_1^2}{3} \tag{3.28}$$

At low frequencies (long wavelengths) the dipole is much less efficient than the monopole source. This explains why a baffled loudspeaker is much more effective in producing low-frequency sound than an unbaffled speaker.

Finally, the acoustic power of a quadrupole source is

$$W_{\text{lat}} = \frac{\rho c k^6 (Ql_1 l_2)^2}{480\pi} \tag{3.29}$$

and

$$W_{\text{long}} = \frac{\rho c k^6 (Ql_1 l_2)^2}{40\pi} \tag{3.30}$$

where Ql_1l_2 is the quadrupole-source strength and the subscripts "lat" and "long" refer to lateral and longitudinal quadrupole sources respectively [1]. Comparing the sound power of the quadrupole sources with that of the monopole gives [1]

$$\frac{W_{\text{lat}}}{W_m} = \frac{k^4 l_1^2 l_2^2}{60} \tag{3.31}$$

$$\frac{W_{\text{long}}}{W_m} = \frac{k^4 l_1^2 l_2^2}{5} \tag{3.32}$$

Hence, we see that quadrupole sources are much less efficient sound radiators than monopole at low frequencies.

The results of the discussions on fundamental source mechanisms and models are summarized in Table 3.1. The pulsating-sphere and vibrating-piston representations of the four basic sound sources are shown and the sound pattern of each source indicated. The net effect of each source on the medium is stated, the expression for sound power is given, and the relative efficiency of each source is indicated. Finally, examples where these models can be used to describe practical sources of sound are suggested.

3.3 NEAR- AND FAR-FIELD CHARACTERISTICS

Most practical sound sources radiate nonplanar sound waves. Consequently, the acoustic pressure and particle velocity at points in a region near most sources of sound radiation (even monopole sources) will not be in phase, so that the intensity at a point cannot be expressed as a simple relationship involving the mean square pressure and characteristic impedance of the medium [such as Eq. (3.8)]. For this reason, sound levels measured in this region generally cannot be used to estimate the sound power of the source. Moreover, values of sound levels measured close to a source may show appreciable fluctuations with position. Because of these fluctuations it is not possible to use near-field data to predict sound-pressure levels far away from the source.

The extent of the near field is a function of the sound frequency of interest, the dimensions of the source, and the relative phasing of radiating surfaces of the source. As a rule of thumb, the near field usually extends outward from the source origin (the "acoustic center") for a distance equal to one or two characteristic source lengths. In addition, the measurement location should be at least one wavelength away from the source, based on the frequency of interest ($\lambda = c/f$), in order for near-field effects to be unimportant.

As we move away from the source in a free (nonreflecting) sound field, particle velocity and acoustic pressure become simply related, as in a plane wave. This region is known as the *far field* of the source, and it has the following characteristics:

Table 3.1 Source models

Source	Monopole	Dipole	Lateral quadrupole	Longitudinal quadrupole
Pulsating sphere model				
Fluctuating piston model				
Directional pattern				
Net effect	Mass flow	Force	Couple	Squeeze
Radiation efficiency	$\dfrac{W_m}{W_m} = 1$	$\dfrac{W_d}{W_m} = \dfrac{k^2 l_1^2}{3}$	$\dfrac{W_{\text{lat}}}{W_m} = \dfrac{k^4 l_1^2 l_2^2}{60}$	$\dfrac{W_{\text{long}}}{W_m} = \dfrac{k^4 l_1^2 l_2^2}{5}$
Examples where models are used	• Baffled speaker • Gun shot • Auto exhaust • Vibrating panel • Pulsating balloon	• Unbaffled speaker • Propeller blade • Vibrating beam or panel edges • Tuning fork	• Jet mixing • Turbulence	• Impacting bodies

72

1. The sound pressure changes with radial distance R relative to the acoustic center of the source region according to (a) $1/R$, for spherical waves, (b) $1/\sqrt{R}$, for cylindrical waves, and (c) constant, for plane waves.
2. The acoustic intensity and pressure are related (as in a plane wave traveling away from the origin) by the equation

$$I = \frac{p^2}{\rho c}$$

The theoretical conditions under which the characteristics outlined above will exist are:

1. *For a compact or point source* ($L_{max} \ll \lambda$),

$$R \gg \lambda \tag{3.33}$$

   where L_{max} is the maximum source dimension.
2. *For an extended finite source* ($L_{max} > \lambda$),

$$R \gg \lambda \tag{3.34}$$

$$\frac{R}{\lambda} \gg \left(\frac{L}{\lambda}\right)^2 \tag{3.35}$$

   where L is a major or characteristic dimension of the source and R is the distance from the source center.

Condition (3.35) must be satisfied when the characteristic length L of the source is greater than the sound wavelength. Conditions (3.33) through (3.35) specify the region where we would expect to find far-field characteristics in a sound field. In this region, the sound levels decrease by 6 dB per doubling of distance from the source, and the measured levels can be used to estimate sound power of the source or to predict sound levels at other locations in the far field.

In practice, the far-field limits specified by Eqs. (3.33) through (3.35) can often be reduced without appreciable error. A widely used guideline (equivalent to that described earlier for the near field) states that the far field is established when:

1. R is at least one wavelength of the frequency of interest from the nearest surface of the source.
2. R is at least one major source dimension from the nearest surface of the source.

Figure 3.11 shows the sound-pressure levels as a function of distance from the source under steady-state conditions. The shaded areas indicate variations in sound-pressure level with position in the sound field. A vertical dashed line is used to separate the near and far fields of the source. This line can be determined for any particular noise source by taking a sequence of sound-level measurements on a radius leading from the assumed acoustic center of the source. A 6-dB decrease in level per doubling of distance along the radius would indicate the beginning of the far field. The position of the line separating the near and far fields is a *function of the source alone*.

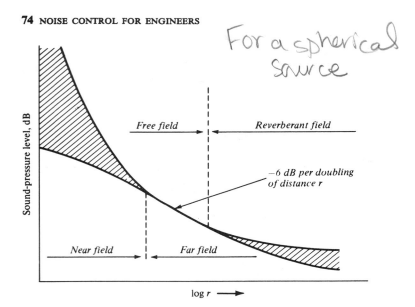

For a spherical source

Figure 3.11 Variation in sound-pressure level with distance from source.

3.4 FREE-FIELD AND REVERBERANT-FIELD CHARACTERISTICS

It should be kept in mind that the discussion of near and far fields assumes that the effect of reflected sounds is negligible. In reality, as sound radiates outward from a source, some of the acoustical energy will eventually reach an obstacle or wall which will reflect some of it back toward the source. This is particularly true for noise sources located in a building or other enclosure. In regions near the source, where the sound field is predominantly caused by the source, we say we are in the *free field* or *direct field* of the source. In regions where the reflected sound has a dominant effect on the sound levels, we say we are in the *reverberant field*.

Variations in sound-pressure levels can occur as a function of position in the reverberant field due to standing waves, if the source radiates one or more dominant pure tones. If the generated sound is broadband and reflecting surfaces are present, the reverberant sound field will be quite uniform, as can be observed from sound-level measurements in the room. However, as we approach the source with a sound-level meter, the direct-sound component increases above the reverberant component, and we move into the direct field. A second dashed line is constructed in Fig. 3.11 showing separation of the free and reverberant sound fields. The location of this line is a *function of the source environment* (i.e., room walls and other reflecting objects) rather than of the source itself. Just as it is impossible to use near-field data to predict sound-pressure levels accurately in the far field, it is also impossible to predict sound-pressure levels in a reverberant field based on free-field sound levels alone.

3.5 ANECHOIC AND REVERBERANT CHAMBERS

A reverberant sound field in which the reflected sounds approach and leave each point in the field uniformly from all directions is called a *diffuse field*. A diffuse field is an idealized concept which is very difficult to achieve in practice. Nevertheless, the concept has many practical applications, which will be developed in the chapters which follow.

An *anechoic sound field* is one that is "without echoes" or reflections. Again, a truly anechoic field is difficult to achieve in practice. However, anechoic (free-field) conditions can be approached if the background levels resulting from reflected sound are sufficiently low.

A noise control engineer may encounter many test procedures which must be carried out under free-field or diffuse-field conditions. These idealized conditions are achieved to a degree in specially designed rooms called anechoic and reverberation chambers. In an *anechoic chamber* the walls of the room are designed to be almost 100 percent absorptive for a specified range of frequencies, and free-field conditions exist nearly to the boundaries of the room. Thus, it is possible to determine the directional properties and the sound power of a noise source in an anechoic room by taking a number of sound-level measurements in the far field surrounding the source. If the source is large, it may take a very large anechoic chamber to satisfy the far-field criteria outlined earlier.

A *reverberation chamber* is constructed with hard rigid walls designed to reflect nearly 100 percent of the incident sound. Hence, the sound field produced by a source is nearly diffuse except in the vicinity of the source. The opposite walls of a reverberation chamber are sometimes nonparallel, and the room may be equipped with a large rotating reflective vane to minimize standing waves and make the sound field more diffuse. If diffuse field conditions can be approximated, it is possible to obtain the sound power of a source placed in the reverberant room from a single measurement (or at most a few measurements) of the sound-pressure level. This capability is important for evaluating noise control treatments applied to a source, or for determining sound-power ratings for a product. Reverberation chambers are also used to measure the absorption properties of acoustical materials. These measurements are described in Chaps. 4 and 6.

REFERENCE

1. Crocker, M. J., A. J. Price, *Noise and Noise Control*, CRC Press, Cleveland, 1975.

IMPORTANT TERMS AND FORMULAS

Point source: $\quad I = \dfrac{W}{4\pi r^2}$

Line source: $\quad I = \dfrac{W}{2\pi r}$

Plane source: $\quad I = \text{constant} = \dfrac{W}{S}$

Sound-pressure-level contours

Near field

Far field

Direct field

Reverberant field

Diffuse field

Anechoic chamber (room)

Reverberation chamber (room)

Source models: Monopole, dipole, quadrupole

Radiation efficiency

PROBLEMS

3.1 What power output is required to produce an SPL of 60 dB at a distance of 100 m if both source and hearer are at ground level? Assume that the ground is flat, unobstructed, and nonabsorbing.
  Answer: 108 dB.

3.2 Two sound sources with sound power of 4 W and 10 W are placed at a distance from a listener of 10 m and 20 m respectively. What will the SPL be at the listener's position if the ground is flat, unobstructed, and assumed nonabsorbing?
  Answer: 97.5 dB.

3.3 The following terms are used to describe the characteristics of sound fields. Give a brief definition of each: (*a*) free field, (*b*) far field, (*c*) reverberant field, (*d*) near field, (*e*) diffuse field.

3.4 A noise study has been performed on a pneumatic drill in an underground hard-rock mining site. It is determined that:
  (*a*) Overall SPL at operator's position is 110 dBA.
  (*b*) Overall SPL is relatively independent of position within a 10-ft radius of the operator, that is, it is nearly uniform at 110 dBA.
  (*c*) Most of the acoustic energy produced by the drill lies in the 2000- to 8000-Hz frequency range.
  (*d*) The primary noise source is the air exhaust. Which, if any, of the terms in Prob. 3.3 apply to the sound field in the region 2 to 10 ft from the drill?

3.5 A long, continuous line of traffic is being monitored for noise. At 100 ft from the center line of the roadway a sound-pressure-level reading of 72 dB is obtained. What will be the SPL at 200 ft? Assume that the ground is flat, unobstructed, and nonabsorbent.

3.6 A pulsating spherical balloon has a diameter of 6 in. For what range of frequencies would you expect the balloon to act as a nondirectional sound source? What would be the extent of the near field for this range of frequencies?

3.7 Five types of sound fields are listed in Prob. 3.3.
  (*a*) In which of these types of sound fields is it possible to use sound levels measured at one location to predict levels at another location in the field?
  Answer: Far field, diffuse field.
  (*b*) Give a brief outline of measurements and other observations you would make to establish the existence of each of the types of sound fields listed.

3.8 Tire noise becomes one of the major sources of automobile noise during high-speed freeway driving. Consider the interaction of a rolling tire with the roadway, and try to relate each of the basic models for noise sources (monopole, dipole, quadrupole) to a particular part of the tire motion.

ACOUSTICS OF ROOMS AND ENCLOSURES

The noise control engineer often encounters situations which require an understanding of the behavior of sound in rooms or large enclosures. It may be necessary to estimate the sound level which will result when a noisy piece of machinery is placed in a room, or in a room adjacent to it. Alternatively, given a situation where a noise source is already present in a room, the engineer may be required to specify an acoustical treatment for the room and/or to design an enclosure for the noise source and to estimate the expected reduction in noise levels in the room brought about by the treatment. In this chapter we will develop the underlying concepts and identify the particular quantities and characteristics of rooms and sound sources which must be specified in order to deal with the situations listed above.

Although we will be dealing with the behavior of sound in rooms, the concepts developed will be applicable to large enclosures used in noise control as well. An enclosure is considered large if its shortest dimension is at least one wavelength (preferably two wavelengths) longer than that of the lowest-frequency component of the sound of interest. Thus, if the lowest frequency of concern is 2000 Hz, an enclosure with 1 ft sides would be considered large, [Eq. (1.4)]. However, for a lower frequency of 250 Hz, the dimensions of the enclosure would have to be on the order of 10 ft in order to be considered large.

4.1 ABSORPTION AND TRANSMISSION COEFFICIENTS, ROOM ABSORPTION

In general, when sound impinges on a wall, some of the acoustical energy will be reflected, some will be absorbed, and some will be transmitted by the wall, as explained in Chap. 1. Let the sound intensity* associated with the incident, reflected, absorbed, and transmitted portions of the sound be denoted by I_i, I_r, I_a, and I_t respectively, as shown in Fig. 4.1. Then the absorption and transmission coefficients, which are quantities representing the fraction of incident energy absorbed or transmitted by a wall, are defined as follows:

Absorption coefficient:
$$\alpha = \frac{I_i - I_r}{I_i} \tag{4.1}$$

Transmission coefficient:
$$\tau = \frac{I_t}{I_i} \tag{4.2}$$

Careful consideration of Eq. (4.1) reveals that the absorption coefficient is a measure of acoustical energy which is *not reflected*, and only in that sense is it a measure of the energy taken up (absorbed) by a material. Thus, if sound intensity I is incident on a surface area S with absorption coefficient α, the acoustical energy absorbed (not reflected) by that surface is $I\alpha S$. If 100 percent of the incident acoustic energy flows through a surface (such as an open window), none of the energy is reflected, and the absorption coefficient is unity, $\alpha = 1$. On the other hand, if sound impinges on a "hard" wall which reflects 100 percent of the acoustic energy, then $\alpha = 0$.

As might be expected, the fraction of energy absorbed or transmitted by a wall depends not only upon the frequency of the sound and the material of which the wall is made, but also on the angle of incidence of the sound wave striking the wall. In practice, published values for absorption coefficients of various materials are usually obtained from experiments carried out under conditions of either normal incidence, α_n, or random incidence, α_{SAB} (after Sabine). The issue is complicated further by the use of a third quantity called the statistical (energy) sound absorption coefficient, α_{ST}. The need for three types of absorption coefficient and the basis for each is discussed next in an attempt to clarify this issue.

The statistical (energy) absorption coefficient α_{ST} [1] is an idealized quantity defined as the ratio of sound energy absorbed by a surface of infinite extent to

---

* The sound intensity was defined in Sec. 1.6 as $I =$ acoustic energy flow per unit of area per unit of time.

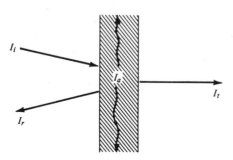

Figure 4.1 Sound impinging on a wall.

the sound energy incident upon the surface when the incident sound field is diffuse (see Sec. 3.5.) This concept is used in the theoretical analysis of sound buildup in enclosures or of flow between adjacent rooms (see Sec. 4.2). From such analyses one is able to derive basic design equations relating the sound level in a room to the power of the sound source and the transmission and absorption properties of the surfaces of the enclosure. Hence, the statistical absorption coefficient is an essential part of the conceptual framework needed (1) to provide the engineer with a basic understanding of the acoustical energy flow in enclosures and (2) to develop the necessary design equations used in control of sound in rooms and enclosures. Absorption coefficients of acoustical materials measured under laboratory conditions are then related to the statistical absorption coefficients to provide the engineer with the information needed to deal with practical noise problems.

The normal-incidence sound absorption coefficient α_n is a quantity easily obtained in the laboratory using a standing-wave tube (sometimes called an acoustic impedance tube). A loudspeaker is used to transmit plane waves longitudinally along the tube which impinge normally on a test specimen placed at the other end of the closed tube. (The measurement of α_n is described in Sec. 6.2.) The statistical absorption coefficient can also be calculated from the standing-wave-tube data [2]. However, the validity of these coefficients is limited because of the small size of material samples used in the test. Moreover, the normal-incidence sound absorption coefficient is inappropriate for most applications since, in general, sound waves striking the surface of a room or enclosure arrive from many different angles. Nevertheless, this information—which is easily and quickly obtainable—can be very useful in comparing the relative merits of similar sound-absorbing materials.

The Sabine absorption coefficients α_{SAB} are obtained using standardized test conditions in which a patch of material is placed in a large, highly reverberant room having a sound field which is approximately diffuse [3]. Values for the absorption coefficients are calculated from data obtained by measuring the rate of decay of sound in the room both with and without a sample of the material placed in the test chamber (see Sec. 6.2). Most sound absorption coefficients that are published are determined in this manner.

Although the Sabine absorption coefficients are obtained under near-diffuse sound-field conditions, the material test samples are of finite size. Consequently, due to edge effects and the fact that the sample may be placed away from a room surface, values of sound absorption coefficients obtained by the reverberation room technique exceed the statistical absorption coefficients by as much as 50 percent for frequencies near 500 Hz, and by as much as 20 percent at higher frequencies up to 4 kHz. In fact, for highly absorbent materials computed values of α_{SAB} may exceed unity by as much as 20 or 30 percent, which implies that *more than 100 percent of* the sound falling on the material is absorbed [4]! In spite of these shortcomings, the Sabine absorption coefficients provide a consistent measure for evaluating the acoustical properties of materials and are used extensively for the acoustical design of rooms and enclosures.

The symbols α_n, α_{ST}, and α_{SAB} have been introduced to distinguish between three types of sound absorption coefficients encountered in the literature. Throughout the remainder of this book the symbol α will be used without subscripts, except where we feel it is important to distinguish which type of coefficient is being implied. The Sabine sound absorption coefficient is the quantity most often used in practical noise control applications, and it is the type implied by α in the design equations to be developed in the sections which follow. The Acoustical and Insulating Materials Association publishes a compendium of sound absorption coefficients (α_{SAB}), obtained under carefully controlled standardized conditions, for a large variety of structural materials. The reader is referred to Chap. 8 for a listing of absorption coefficients for common building materials.

Finally, it must be kept in mind when evaluating materials for noise control applications that sound absorption coefficients depend also on material thickness and methods of mounting, the latter effect providing a means of substantially improving the absorption characteristics of a given material (see Sec. 8.2).

A fourth quantity, the *room-averaged sound absorption coefficient* $\bar{\alpha}$, is defined as follows:

$$\bar{\alpha} = \frac{\sum\limits_{i}^{n} \alpha_i S_i}{S} \tag{4.3}$$

where S_i = area of ith surface
$\quad \alpha_i$ = absorption coefficient of ith surface
$\quad S$ = total surface area of room = ΣS_i
$\quad n$ = total number of absorptive surfaces in room

The room-averaged sound absorption coefficient is a measure of the acoustical absorption of the total enclosure and is the quantity most often used in predicting average sound-pressure levels in rooms under steady-state near-diffuse conditions.

The quantity in the numerator of Eq. (4.3) is called the *room absorption*, denoted by the symbol A:

$$A = \sum\limits_{i}^{n} \alpha_i S_i = \bar{\alpha} S \tag{4.4}$$

If a diffuse sound field of intensity I exists in a room, the acoustical energy absorbed per unit of time by the room is given by

$$I \sum\limits_{i}^{n} \alpha_i S_i = I\bar{\alpha}S = IA \tag{4.5}$$

The quantity $\alpha_i S_i$ appearing in Eqs. (4.3) through (4.5) has units of area called sabins,* and is equivalent in absorption to a similar area of open window.

---

* The term *sabins* is used if measured in square feet, and *metric sabins* if measured in square meters.

However, absorbing objects contained in a room must be accounted for when computing the total room absorption in these equations. Since such objects (for example, chairs, tables, podiums, and even people) have ill-defined areas, it is common practice to assign a value of sabin absorption units A_i (equivalent to $\alpha_i S_i$) to each object, and to sum the total absorption due to objects

$$A_0 = \sum A_i \qquad (4.6)$$

This absorption is then added to the numerator in Eq. (4.3), or to the room absorption in Eq. (4.4), with *no change in the total area S.*

4.2 BUILDUP AND DECAY OF SOUND IN A ROOM, REVERBERATION TIME

If a sound source of power W is suddenly turned on in a quiet room, there will be a flow of acoustic energy into the room, with the maximum sound intensity occurring near the source. Sound waves will travel outward from the source and eventually impinge on a surface or boundary of the room; some of the sound energy will be absorbed by the surface, and the remainder willl be reflected back into the room. After several reflections in a reverberant room with scattering objects, the flow of energy will approach diffuseness. Since there is a continuous flow of energy into the room, the energy density in the reverberant sound field will build up until an equilibrium, or steady-state, condition persists. During buildup the rate at which energy flows into the room, W, must be balanced by the rate of energy flow into the reverberant field, W_R, and the rate of energy being absorbed by the room, W_A; that is,

$$W = W_R + W_A \qquad (4.7)$$

If the sound source is now suddenly turned off, terminating the flow of energy into the room, the sound in the room will continue to reverberate, with some acoustic energy absorbed on each reflection. The resulting decay in sound intensity level will continue until a value equal to the ambient intensity level of the room is reached. The sound-level buildup of the reverberant sound field and the time required for the sound to decay are both important properties of room acoustics which must be understood by the noise control engineer.

Sound Buildup in a Room

Let $\bar{\varepsilon}$ be the average energy density in the reverberant sound field of a room resulting from a sound source placed in the room. In general, the energy density will vary with time as the sound builds up or decays. Assuming a diffuse sound field, $\bar{\varepsilon}$ will be uniform throughout the room, and the flow of energy will be equally likely in every direction. Hence, if we look at an element of volume dV in the room, the energy contained within the element $\bar{\varepsilon}dV$ can be considered to flow spherically outward from dV, causing an intensity $\bar{\varepsilon}dV/4\pi r^2$ at radial distance r. Consider now the normal component of this intensity as it impinges on an element of area dS on the bounding surface of the room (see Fig. 4.2). The intensity of sound on dS caused by the flow from dV will be $(\bar{\varepsilon}dV/4\pi r^2)\cos\theta$. In order to consider the total sound intensity on dS, we must integrate the contribution from all volume elements on the hemisphere enclosing dS, that is,

$$I = \int_{\text{Hemisphere}} \frac{\bar{\varepsilon}dV}{4\pi r^2}\cos\theta = \int_{r=0}^{c}\int_{\theta=0}^{\pi/2}\int_{\phi=0}^{2\pi} \frac{\bar{\varepsilon}\cos\theta}{4\pi r^2}r^2\sin\theta\,dr\,d\theta\,d\phi$$

where the limit $r = c$ is the distance the energy will flow from dV in unit time. Evaluating this equation, we obtain the instantaneous intensity at the surface of the room during sound buildup:

$$I = \frac{\bar{\varepsilon}c}{4} \tag{4.8}$$

where c is the sound propagation velocity. Note that the intensity in the diffuse field is only one-fourth of that obtained for a plane wave falling normally on a surface [see Eq. (1.20)].

We are now in a position to derive an expression for sound-energy buildup in the room. The rate of energy absorbed by the room is given by Eq. (4.5):

$$W_A = S\bar{\alpha}I = AI = \bar{\varepsilon}\frac{cA}{4} \tag{4.9}$$

where A is the room absorption. But the rate of energy buildup in the room, $(d/dt)\bar{\varepsilon}V$, is by definition the rate of energy flow into the diffuse reverberant

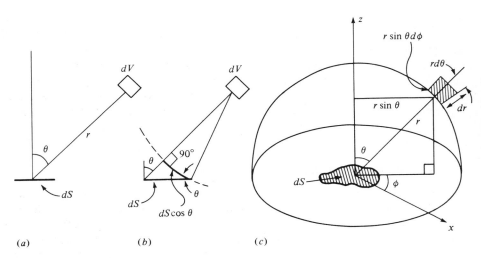

(a)   (b)   (c)

Figure 4.2 Acoustic intensity in a diffuse field (Ref. 6, with permission).

field, W_R. Hence, the energy balance equation, Eq. (4.7), becomes

$$V\frac{d\bar{\varepsilon}}{dt} + \frac{cA}{4}\bar{\varepsilon} = W$$

Solving this elementary differential equation for initial conditions $\bar{\varepsilon} = 0$ at time $t = 0$, one obtains

$$\bar{\varepsilon} = \frac{4W}{Ac}\left(1 - e^{-\frac{Ac}{4V}t}\right) \tag{4.10}$$

After sufficient time has elapsed, equilibrium will be reached. The resulting steady-state energy density of the diffuse sound field in the room is obtained by letting $t \to \infty$ in Eq. (4.10), to yield

$$\bar{\varepsilon}_{max} = \frac{4W}{Ac} \tag{4.11}$$

The sound intensity in the room under steady-state conditions is obtained from Eq. (4.8):

$$I_{max} = \frac{\bar{\varepsilon}_{max}c}{4} = \frac{W}{A}$$

Alternately, this equation may be written in the form

$$W = I_{max}A = W_A \qquad \text{steady state} \tag{4.12}$$

Equation (4.12) is an energy-balance equation stating that under steady-state conditions the rate at which energy flows into the room is balanced by the rate at which energy is being absorbed by the room, while the net flow of energy into the reverberant field is zero.

Decay of Sound in a Room, Reverberation Time

If the sound source in the room is now suddenly shut off, the sound in the room will continue to reverberate, with some of the acoustical energy absorbed with each reflection, until the level of sound intensity decays to a value equal to the ambient intensity level of the room. The time required for the sound intensity level to decay 60 dB is called the reverberation time T_{60} of the room.

The reverberation time is the single most important parameter used in judging the acoustical properties of a room. If T_{60} is large (i.e., it takes many reflections to absorb the acoustical energy), there will be a large buildup of sound in the room. A certain amount of buildup is desirable in a lecture room so that the speaker's voice can be more easily heard. On the other hand, in a large room the reflected syllables may be sufficiently retarded that they interfere with the direct speech, making the speaker unintelligible. Reverberation is desirable in a music room for aesthetic value. The reflected sound causes a "blending" of sound from different instruments which is pleasing to most listeners. Recommended reverberation times for various spaces, ranging from broadcast studios to churches, are given in Fig. 6.2.

Two factors influence the reverberation time of a room: the total room absorption $\bar{a}S$ and the room volume V. If $\bar{a}S$ is *increased*, more sound is absorbed with each reflection, resulting in a *shorter time* for sound decay and *less sound buildup*. Similarly, if the volume of a room is *decreased*, the sound does not have to travel as far between absorptive reflections, resulting in a *shorter reverberation time* and *less sound buildup*. Thus we see that the reverberation time T is inversely proportional to room absorption but directly proportional to room volume. That is,

$$T_{60} = K\frac{V}{A} \tag{4.13}$$

where K is a constant of proportionality. If the room is very large, the absorption of sound by air must also be taken into account.

A simple derivation of the equation for reverberation time follows which will give the constant of proportionality K. Consider the case of a sound source in a room being shut off at time t when the sound-energy density in the room has reached a value $\bar{\varepsilon} = \bar{\varepsilon}_0$. The rate of decay of the energy density will depend entirely on the absorption of sound by the room, that is,

$$-\frac{d}{dt}(\bar{\varepsilon}V) = W_A = IA = \frac{\bar{\varepsilon}c}{4}A \tag{4.14}$$

Integrating this equation yields the following expression for decay of the sound-energy density in the room:

$$\bar{\varepsilon} = \bar{\varepsilon}_0 e^{-\frac{Ac}{4V}t} \tag{4.15}$$

The *reverberation time* T_{60} was defined as the time required for the sound intensity level in the room to decay 60 dB after the sound source has been shut off. If we let I_0 and I_{60} be the initial and final intensities during this decay, the change in intensity level can be written as

$$\Delta L_I = 10 \log I_{60} - 10 \log I_0 = 10 \log \frac{I_{60}}{I_0} = 60 \text{ dB}$$

or

$$\frac{I_{60}}{I_0} = 10^{-6} \tag{4.16}$$

Substitution of Eq. (4.8), relating intensity to energy density in a diffuse field, and the relation $T_{60} = t_{60} - t_0$ into Eq. (4.16) gives

$$\frac{I_{60}}{I_0} = e^{-\frac{Ac}{4V}T_{60}} = 10^{-6}$$

Solving this equation for the reverberation time yields

$$T_{60} = \frac{0.161 V}{A} \qquad \text{mks units}$$

$$T_{60} = \frac{0.049 V}{A} \qquad \text{English units} \tag{4.17}$$

Equations (4.17) are valid for the decay of a diffuse sound field in a rather "live" room, say, $\bar{\alpha} < 0.20$. However, we see that difficulties arise when we try to apply them to rooms with large absorption. For example, if $\bar{\alpha} = 1$, all of the sound would be absorbed on the first reflection, implying a reverberation time of zero. However, Eq. (4.17) would give a finite value of T_{60} under these conditions. These difficulties are overcome in the simplified analysis which follows.

Again we assume that a diffuse sound field has been built up in a room and that its initial intensity is I_0 at the time the source is shut off. The intensity of the sound energy absorbed by the first reflection on all surfaces of the room would be $I_0\bar{\alpha}$. Hence, after the first reflection the intensity of the sound energy remaining in the room would be $I_1 = I_0(1 - \bar{\alpha})$. Similarly, after two reflections the intensity is $I_2 = I_0(1 - \bar{\alpha})^2$, and after n reflections, $I_n = I_0(1 - \bar{\alpha})^n$. What we would like to determine is the number of reflections required for the intensity level to decay 60 dB. Then, if we knew the mean free path of the sound between reflections, and the speed of sound, this information could be used to determine the reverberation time. Using Eq. (4.16), we obtain

$$\frac{I_{60}}{I_0} = \frac{I_n}{I_0} = (1 - \bar{\alpha})^n = 10^{-6}$$

This equation can be solved to give the number of reflections for a 60-dB decay in intensity level,

$$n = \frac{-6 \ln 10}{\ln(1 - \bar{\alpha})} \tag{4.18}$$

We now define the mean free path d which a sound wave will travel in the room between successive reflections. The total energy absorbed by the room per second will then be $(\bar{\varepsilon}V)\bar{\alpha}c/d$. But from Eq. (4.9) the total rate of energy absorbed by the room is $(\bar{\varepsilon}c/4)S\bar{\alpha}$. Equating these two results and solving for the mean free path between reflections gives

$$d = \frac{4V}{S} \tag{4.19}$$

The time required for n reflections will be

$$T_{60} = \frac{nd}{c} = \frac{4Vn}{Sc} = \frac{24 \ln 10 V}{-S \ln(1 - \bar{\alpha})}$$

Finally,

$$T_{60} = \frac{0.161 V}{-S \ln(1 - \bar{\alpha})} \qquad \text{mks units}$$

$$T_{60} = \frac{0.049 V}{-S \ln(1 - \bar{\alpha})} \qquad \text{English units} \tag{4.20}$$

Equations (4.20) give a reverberation of zero for a room-averaged sound absorption coefficient of unity, which is consistent with the physical interpretation of total absorption at the first reflection. Moreover, for small values of $\bar{\alpha}$, say $\bar{\alpha} < 0.20$, the quantity $-S \ln(1 - \bar{\alpha})$ is approximately equal to $S\bar{\alpha}$, in which case Eqs. (4.20) reduce to those given by (4.17).

If the room is very large, so that it is necessary to take into account the sound energy absorbed by air, the reverberation-time equations must be modified as follows:

$$T_{60} = \frac{0.161 V}{A + 4mV} \qquad \text{mks units}$$

$$T_{60} = \frac{0.049 V}{A + 4mV} \qquad \text{English units} \qquad (4.22)$$

where m is called the energy attenuation constant for air [5]. Values of m are given in Fig. 6.5 as a function of sound frequency and relative humidity of air at 68°F. At frequencies below 1000 Hz for large rooms, and for all frequencies in smaller rooms, the effect of air on reverberation time can almost always be ignored. However, in large rooms at high frequencies the absorption of sound by air will be a major factor in determining reverberation times.

4.3 NORMAL MODES OF VIBRATION OF AN ENCLOSURE

The path which sound travels as it propagates can be visualized using the concepts of ray theory, in which the normal at any point on the wave front of sound represents the direction of wave motion. As the wave front moves, the normal traces out a ray which corresponds to the path of sound propagation. Since sound radiates spherically outward from a small source placed in a room, initially there will be infinitely many rays directed outward from the source, not unlike the bursting of fireworks in a dark sky. When the rays encounter room boundaries, they will be reflected back into the room, with angles of reflection equal to angles of incidence. If we were to trace all possible paths which the sound can take as it travels in the room, we would find that there are certain paths which repeat themselves—e.g., the path of sound reflecting back and forth between two parallel walls. There will be a periodicity associated with each of these closed paths which is determined by the length of the path l and the speed of sound. If the frequency of the sound being radiated is such that at the completion of a circuit the sound being radiated is in phase with the reflected wave, the two will reinforce each other. Consequently, with each circuit more sound energy is pumped into that path, and there will be a buildup of energy in that mode of sound travel resulting in resonant standing waves. These standing waves are referred to as *normal modes of vibration* of an enclosure.

The radiated sound will be in phase with the reflected sound if its wavelength, or any integer multiple thereof, is equal to the path length l, i.e.,

$$n\lambda = l \qquad (4.23)$$

Using the relationship between sound wavelength and frequency, $f = c/\lambda$, one obtains an expression for the frequency f_n associated with the normal mode of vibration:

$$f_n = \frac{nc}{l} \qquad (4.24)$$

Consider, for example, the case of sound reflecting back and forth, say in the x direction, between two walls separated by a distance l_x. The length of the path which is repeated by the sound is $2l_x$, and the *resonance frequency* associated with this mode of vibration will be

$$f_n = \frac{nc}{2l_x} \qquad (4.25)$$

Sound radiating from a source will in general have many different frequencies. Consequently, any particular sound source may excite many of the different normal modes of vibration associated with an enclosure. The normal modes and associated natural frequencies of an enclosure will depend on its shape, as can be seen by tracing possible closed sound paths. It can be shown using wave theory that the normal modes of vibration of a rectangular hard-walled enclosure are given by [6]:

$$f_n = \frac{c}{2}\sqrt{\left(\frac{n_x}{l_x}\right)^2 + \left(\frac{n_y}{l_y}\right)^2 + \left(\frac{n_z}{l_z}\right)^2} \qquad (4.26)$$

where n_x, n_y, and n_z= integers 0, 1, 2, . . . , ∞
    l_x, l_y, and l_z= dimensions of room along axes
    c= speed of sound

The standing-wave patterns associated with normal modes of vibration cause variations in sound-pressure level with respect to position in the room. Consequently, the room superimposes its own acoustic characteristics on the nature of a sound source placed in it. For this reason a loudspeaker system must be adjusted differently for each room, and for each position in the room where it is placed. Similarly, if the sound source has a strong pure-tone component (e.g., the blade passage frequency of a high-speed fan) which corresponds to one of the natural frequencies of the room in which it is placed, most of the sound buildup will be contained in a single normal mode and can result in large variations in sound level. On the other hand, if many modes of the room are excited, the sound field tends to become uniform.

An indication of the way in which the sound levels in a room can vary is obtained by looking at the sound-pressure distribution in the normal modes of vibration of a rectangular enclosure, given by [4]:

$$p \sim \sum_{n_x=0}^{\infty} \sum_{n_y=0}^{\infty} \sum_{n_z=0}^{\infty} A_{lmn}\cos\left(\frac{n_x\pi x}{l_x}\right)\cos\left(\frac{n_y\pi y}{l_y}\right)\cos\left(\frac{n_z\pi z}{l_z}\right) \qquad (4.27)$$

where the origin of the coordinate system has been chosen to coincide with a corner of the room. We see that for each of the normal modes of vibration the maximum pressure will occur when all the cosine terms are simultaneously equal to unity, i.e., at the eight corners of the enclosure. Consequently, a sound source placed at a corner of the room will excite the maximum number of room modes. On the other hand, if the sound source is placed at the center of a rectangular room where all the odd modes have minimum pressure amplitude, only the even modes (one-eighth of the total number of possible modes) can be effectively excited. Hence, we see that even the location of the sound source in a room will have an effect on the resulting sound field.

The decay of sound in a room will also depend upon which normal modes of the room have been excited. Consequently, the reverberation times obtained for a room will be influenced by the location of the source in the room (which determines which normal modes will be excited) and by the measuring point in the sound field (which determines which normal modes are being sampled for decay).

The response of a room to a transient or time-varying sound source will depend upon the reverberation time of the normal modes of vibration. The standing waves associated with the natural frequencies of a rectangular room or enclosure can be separated into three types: *axial modes*, which move parallel to one of the major axes of the room and are one-dimensional [i.e., two of the integers in Eq. (4.26) are zero]; *tangential waves*, which move in one of the major planes of the room and are two-dimensional [i.e., only one of the integers in Eq. (4.26) is zero]; and *oblique waves*, which are oblique to all pairs of walls (none of the integers is zero). While modes of different types usually have different reverberation times, modes of the same type have essentially the same reverberation times when losses in the medium are negligible.

It is often of interest to know how many modes of each type can exist below a given frequency, or within a specified frequency band. The number of normal modes of vibration of a hard-walled rectangular enclosure is closely approximated (usually within one or two modes) by this equation [1]:

$$N = \frac{4\pi f^3 V}{3c^3} + \frac{\pi f^2 A}{4c^2} + \frac{fL}{8c} \qquad (4.28)$$

where $A = 2(l_x l_y + l_y l_z + l_z l_x) = $ total surface area
$L = 4(l_x + l_y + l_z) = $ sum of all edges
$V = $ volume of room

It should be noted that the first term in this equation predominates for high frequencies.

The number of normal modes within a given band of frequencies (modal density) is determined by differentiating Eq. (4.28), to get

$$\Delta N = \left(\frac{4\pi f^2 V}{c^3} + \frac{\pi f A}{2c^2} + \frac{L}{8c} \right) \Delta f \qquad (4.29)$$

Again, the first term in this equation predominates at high frequencies. In fact, it can be shown that

$$\Delta N \cong \frac{4\pi f^2 V}{c^3} \Delta f \qquad (4.30)$$

for high frequencies, regardless of the shape of the room.

Now, suppose a sound source sends out a pulse of sound frequency f_0 and duration Δt. This pulse will be transmitted in the room without serious distortion of shape provided a sufficient number (10 or more) of normal modes are present within the frequency band $f_0 \pm (\Delta f/2)$, where $\Delta f = 1/\Delta t$[1]. For example, if the pulse length is 10^{-1} s, the range of natural frequencies of interest will be $f_0 \pm 5$ Hz. Hence, if the number of normal modes of the room within that frequency band is larger than about 10, and if in addition the reverberation time of each of the standing waves involved is less than about a second, the pulse will be transmitted with reasonable accuracy in the room.

4.4 STEADY-STATE SOUND-PRESSURE LEVELS

The topics of sound buildup and decay and of normal modes in a room all deal with the reverberant sound field in a room. In any practical situation the sound field will be a mix of both direct and reverberant sound. The particular mix to which the receiver is exposed will depend upon his or her proximity to the source; close to the source most of the sound energy will be that radiating outward, and its intensity will vary with the inverse square of the distance, as with a simple source in a free field (see Sec. 3.2). However, at larger distances from the source the outward radiation is submerged in the randomly scattered reflected sound, which will have a more or less uniform intensity everywhere. Sound-pressure-level equations will be developed in this section which take into account both room and source effects on the sound field and the proximity of the receiver to the source.

Directivity Factor

The sound-pressure level of the direct sound field is produced by sound reaching the receiver in the absence of any reflected sound. A *point source*, for which the sound energy flows radially outward and uniformly across any spherical surface having the source as its center, will produce sound which has intensity at a distance r from the source equal to the total sound power W divided by the surface area over which it is spread:

$$I = \frac{W}{4\pi r^2} \qquad (4.31)$$

On the other hand, most sound sources have directional properties and will not radiate uniformly outward from the source. Consider such a directional source with sound power W (in watts). Let $\vec{\theta}$ represent the orientation with respect to a reference axis passing through the source, I_θ be the intensity of the sound emitted in free space at a distance r from the source in the direction θ, and I_s be the intensity of the sound at the same location with the source replaced by a point source of the same power W. We define the *directivity factor* Q_θ as

$$Q_\theta \equiv \frac{I_\theta}{I_s} = \frac{\text{intensity of directional source of power } W}{\text{intensity of point source of power } W} \qquad (4.32)$$

Rearranging Eq. (4.32) we obtain

$$I_\theta = I_s Q_\theta$$

Combining Eqs. (4.31) and (4.32) yields an expression for the sound intensity at an angle θ and distance r from a directional source of sound power W, in the absence of any reverberant sound:

$$I_\theta = \frac{W Q_\theta}{4\pi r^2} \qquad (4.33)$$

Methods of measuring the directivity factor will be discussed in Chap. 6. However, it is important to recognize that values obtained for Q_θ are dependent not only on the source but also on the way the source is located and oriented in a given space. For example, a uniformly radiating (point) source in free space would have a directivity factor of 1. But, placed in a room, the value of Q_θ may change in certain directions as a result of reflections from surfaces in the room. If the room is large and the source is placed near the geometric center of the room, there would be no change in directivity factor. However, if the source were placed near the center of a highly reflecting wall or floor, the power would now be radiating into a hemisphere, and the value of Q would be about 2, provided the power output is the same. Similarly, if the source were moved to a location near an edge of the room, the power would radiate into a quarter sphere, and the value of Q_θ would be about 4; for the source placed in the corner at three hard walls, the value of Q_θ would increase to 8, providing the power output of the source is the same.

Near and Far Fields—Direct and Reverberant Fields

The total sound pressure perceived in a room can be separated into two parts—the direct field, which is sound coming directly from the source to the receiver, and the reverberant field, which is composed of all sound which has undergone one or more reflections by surfaces in the room. The intensity of the direct sound at a distance r from a source of power W has been determined [Eq. (4.33)] as

$$I_\theta = \frac{W Q_\theta}{4\pi r^2}$$

The intensity of the reverberant sound field can be related to the sound power of the reverberant field if we make the following assumptions. We assume that the reverberant field is diffuse,* so that $I_r S \bar{\alpha}_{ST}$ represents the rate of reverberant sound energy absorbed by the walls of the room, where I_r is the intensity of the reverberant field, $\bar{\alpha}_{ST}$ is the average statistical absorption coefficient of the room, and S is its total surface area [see Eq. 4.9)]. Further, if we assume steady-state conditions, the rate at which reverberant sound energy is absorbed must be equal to the reverberant sound power supplied. This latter quantity will be the sound power of the source minus the sound power absorbed with the first reflection, i.e., $W(1 - \bar{\alpha}_{ST})$. Hence, we have $I_r(S\bar{\alpha}_{ST}) = W(1 - \bar{\alpha}_{ST})$, or

$$I_r = \frac{W(1 - \bar{\alpha}_{ST})}{S \bar{\alpha}_{ST}} = \frac{W}{R} \tag{4.34}$$

where the quantity $R = S\bar{\alpha}_{ST}/(1 - \bar{\alpha}_{ST})$ is called the *room constant*. For most practical situations the room constant R can be replaced by the room absorption $S\bar{\alpha}_{SAB}$, so that Eq. (4.34) becomes

$$I_r = \frac{W}{S\bar{\alpha}_{SAB}} \tag{4.35}$$

In practice the mean square pressure, rather than sound intensity, is measured in a room. This quantity is related to the average energy density in the far field of a sound source by the equation

$$p_{rms}^2 = \rho c^2 \bar{\varepsilon} \tag{4.36}$$

but is not simply related to the sound intensity[1]. For the direct field the relation between mean square pressure and sound intensity is $p_{rms}^2 = \rho c I_\theta$, but for a diffuse field it becomes $p_{rms}^2 = 4\rho c I_r$ [see Eq. (4.9)]. Consequently, the total sound pressure in a room will be the sum of the mean square pressures, as given by Eq. (1.15), $p_{rms}^2 = \rho c I_\theta + 4\rho c I_r$, or

$$p_{rms}^2 = W\rho c \left(\frac{Q_\theta}{4\pi r^2} + \frac{4}{\bar{\alpha}S} \right) \tag{4.37}$$

Dividing both sides of this equation by p_{ref}^2 and taking 10 times the $\log_{10}$ of each side reduces the equation to

$$L_p = L_w + 10 \log \left(\frac{Q_\theta}{4\pi r^2} + \frac{4}{\bar{\alpha}S} \right) \qquad \text{mks units}$$

or $\qquad L_p = L_w + 10 \log \left(\frac{Q_\theta}{4\pi r^2} + \frac{4}{\bar{\alpha}S} \right) + 10 \text{ dB} \qquad \text{English units} \tag{4.38}$

Equation (4.38) relates the sound-pressure level L_p to the sound-power level L_w of the source, its directivity Q_θ, and the total absorption of the room $S\bar{\alpha}$. If the receiver is close to the source, r is small and the first term in the parentheses is dominant. Consequently, the direct sound field is the main contributor to the

---

* This is a good assumption in many practical situations where many irregular surfaces exist in a room.

sound level at that location, and changing the room absorption will have a negligible effect on the level. On the other hand, as we move away from the source r becomes large, so that the last term in the parentheses dominates. In this case we are in the reverberant field, and increasing the room absorption can be an effective method of reducing the sound-pressure level. For example, if we let L_{p_1} be the sound level corresponding to room absorption $(\bar{\alpha}S)_1$ and L_{p_2} be the new sound level at the same location for a new room absorption $(\bar{\alpha}S)_2$, it can be shown that (see Prob. 4.3)

$$L_{p_1} - L_{p_2} = NR = 10 \log\left(\frac{(\bar{\alpha}S)_2}{(\bar{\alpha}S)_1} \right) \qquad (4.39)$$

Equation (4.39) indicates that if the total room absorption is doubled, the sound-pressure level in the reverberant sound field can be reduced by as much as 3 dB. Similarly, for a quadrupling of room absorption a 6-dB reduction in the reverberant field may be achieved. However, a tenfold increase in room absorp-

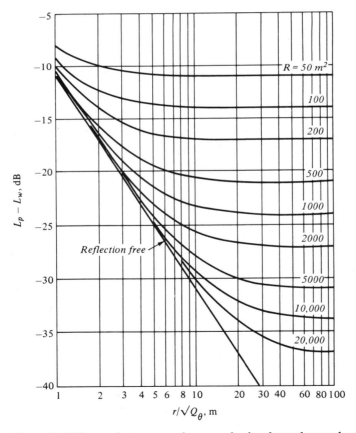

Figure 4.3 Difference between sound-pressure level and sound-power level in a room as a function of the room constant R_T, the distance from the source r, and the directivity factor Q_0 (*Source: Edward Magrab*, Environmental Noise Control, *1975. Reprinted by permission of John Wiley & Sons,*

tion is needed for a 10-dB reduction. Hence, we see that for most applications adding sound-absorptive material to a room as a means of noise control can provide moderate changes in overall sound-pressure levels provided we are not in the direct sound field.

Equation (4.39) shows the importance of knowing how much absorption is already contained in a room before prescribing additional absorption material as a method of noise control. If a substantial amount of absorption is already present, it may be uneconomical or even impossible to obtain as much as a 3-dB reduction in the reverberant sound field. On the other hand, for a very "live" room as much as a 10-dB reduction can be achieved.

The relative importance of contributions of the direct and reverberant sound fields to the sound-pressure level in a large irregular enclosure is shown in Fig. 4.3, which plots $L_p - L_w$ versus the distance $r/\sqrt{Q_\theta}$ from the source. The curve for the direct-field contribution, having a 6-dB decrease per doubling of distance from the source, represents the maximum reduction we can expect to get by increasing the amount of absorption in a room.

4.5 ENCLOSURES FOR ACOUSTICAL MEASUREMENTS

Examination of Eq. (4.37) reveals that the mean square pressure of the sound field in a room is dependent upon the sound power of the source, its directivity, and the room absorption of the enclosure. A more precise relationship is obtained by replacing the room absorption with the room constant R and by including air absorption if the room is very large and one is interested in high frequencies. If the term $4/\bar{a}S$ is much larger than the first term of the equation, i.e., if the room absorption is small and the sound-pressure level is measured sufficiently far from the source, the mean square pressure is proportional to the sound power. This provides the basis for determining the sound power radiated from a source in a reverberation room. On the other hand, if the room is highly absorbent, the first term dominates and the mean square pressure is proportional to the directivity factor Q_θ. Consequently, anechoic rooms with highly absorbent walls can be used to determine the directional properties of a sound source.

The acoustic properties of a sound source are completely defined once its sound power and directivity factor have been determined. Methods of measuring these properties under laboratory and field conditions are given in Chap. 6. In this section we indicate important factors which must be considered in the design, qualification, and use of reverberant and anechoic rooms for purposes of determining the characteristics of a sound source. References and standards which deal with these factors in detail are also given.

Reverberation Rooms—Evaluation of Diffusivity

A test chamber designed to have nearly perfectly acoustically reflecting surfaces is referred to as a *reverberation room*. The reverberation room can be used to determine the sound power of a source, transmission loss and impact isolation of panels, and Sabine absorption coefficients of acoustical materials. One of the most important properties of a reverberation room needed in order to perform the functions listed above is that the sound field produced in the room should be diffuse. The diffuseness of the field is primarily governed by the modal response of the room. Schroeder [7] has developed an equation for the "cutoff frequency":

$$f_c = 2000\left(\frac{T_{60}}{V}\right)^{1/2} \qquad \text{mks units}$$

$$f_c = 11,885\left(\frac{T_{60}}{V}\right)^{1/2} \qquad \text{English units} \qquad (4.40)$$

which is the lowest frequency at which the reverberant field can be considered to be statistically reliable. As the frequency of sound increases above the cutoff frequency, the number of normal modes in a frequency band rapidly increases, resulting in a more diffuse sound field.

Another important property of a reverberation room is the spatial variation of the reverberant sound field. The *variance* $V_n{}^2$ and *standard deviation* V_n are statistical quantities which give a measure of the spatial variation in sound-pressure level measured throughout the reverberation chamber. The variance is defined by the relation $V_n{}^2 = \Sigma(L_i - \overline{L})^2/n(n-1)$, where $\overline{L} = \Sigma L_i/n$ is the sample mean of n measured levels. As the spatial variance of the sound-pressure level increases, a larger number of measurements must be taken at different locations in the room in order to estimate the true space-averaged sound-pressure level. Lubman [8, 9] shows that the variance for a specified reverberation room and frequency band of sound can be approximated by the expression

$$V_n{}^2 = \left(1 + \frac{BT_{60}}{6.9}\right)^{-1} \qquad (4.41)$$

where B is the bandwidth of the signal and T_{60} is the reverberation time of the room. Equation (4.41) gives values of $V_n{}^2$ within ± 10 percent if $BT_{60} > 10$ and within $\pm 2\frac{1}{2}$ percent if $BT_{60} > 20$ [6].

Equations (4.40) and (4.41) show that in order to achieve a lower cutoff frequency in a reverberation room it is necessary to increase the volume of the room or to decrease its reverberation time. However, both of these changes cause an increase in the spatial variance of the sound-pressure levels in the room. Consequently, the design of reverberation chambers demands the optimization of several conflicting requirements. A good set of design rules has been produced by Towson [10] to deal with these problems.

Once an estimate of variance is obtained, we can determine the number of spatial samples of sound-pressure level needed for a reverberation room in order to estimate the space-averaged sound-pressure level within a specified degree of confidence. The number of samples needed is given by the equation [9]:

$$N > \left(\frac{2.5 V_n}{e}\right)^2 \qquad (4.42)$$

where e is the allowable sampling error and 2.5 is a constant chosen for 98.75 percent certainty that the sample mean will differ from the true mean by less than e. For example, suppose we wish to estimate the space-averaged sound-pressure level which would differ from the true average by less than ± 1 dB. Since a 1-dB difference in sound-pressure level corresponds to a 25.9 percent change in sound power [see Eq. (4.38)], we would substitute $e = 0.259$ in Eq. (4.42), along with our estimated value of V_n^2 from Eq. (4.41), to obtain the number of samples required to have 98.75 percent confidence that the calculated space-averaged sound-pressure level would be within ± 1 dB of the true space-averaged level.

In general, we should have satisfactory diffusion in a reverberation room provided we are above the Schroeder cutoff frequency given by Eq. (4.40) and have obtained an acceptable value of variance estimated by Eq. (4.41). Moreover, examination of Eqs. (4.41) and (4.42) shows that the number of measurements required to determine the space-averaged sound-pressure level to a given degree of precision can be reduced by half if the reverberation time of the room or the bandwidth of the signal is doubled. One commonly accepted guideline for satisfactory diffusion of steady-state sound in a reverberation room is that there should be at least 20 distinct room-resonant modes in the frequency band of interest, as determined by Eq. (4.29). References 10 to 22 give other methods of improving the diffusivity of reverberation rooms and the reliability of determining space-averaged sound levels.

Anechoic Rooms—Free-Field Evaluation

One is often interested in determining the directional properties of a sound source which would occur if the source were placed in free space. Controlled environments which simulate free space can be achieved with properly designed rooms having walls which absorb nearly 100 percent of the sound reaching them from the inside, while at the same time providing a barrier against sound reaching the room from the outside. Test chambers so constructed are called anechoic (without echo) rooms. Two types of anechoic test chambers are commonly used; the *fully anechoic* room has highly absorbent material on all of its interior surfaces, including the floor, while the *semi-anechoic* chamber has a hard floor so that the test environment simulates an open space over a hard surface, as commonly found outdoors on a paved surface.

A well-designed anechoic room will have 99 percent sound absorption at its walls for all frequencies of interest. This high degree of absorption is achieved through the use of large porous wedges at the walls of the room. As a rule of thumb, the wedge must protrude from the wall for a depth of at least 1/4 wavelength of the lowest frequency to be used in the chamber. This requirement is based on the concept that the particle velocity of the air is zero at the wall and has maximum velocity at 1/4 wavelength, hence the tip of each wedge will reach into the portion of the sound field having the highest particle velocity, where it will be most effective. Because of the limiting size of the wedges and the room, there will be a lower cutoff frequency for the anechoic chamber below which 99 percent of the sound energy cannot be absorbed by the walls.

The most common way to evaluate an anechoic room is to use the inverse distance test, in which the sound-pressure level should decrease at a rate of 6 dB per doubling of distance from the source in its far field. The test procedure is to use a pure-tone (from 31.5 to 20,000 Hz) omnidirectional source placed at one corner of the chamber and to record sound-pressure level versus distance as a microphone is moved in a straight line away from the source. The 6-dB (± 1 dB) rule is then used to determine (1) the lower cutoff frequency of the chamber and (2) the region within the chamber for which the free-field conditions are met.

In addition to providing free-field conditions within the chamber, the anechoic room must also provide a very low level of background sound. A well-designed room will provide ambient levels in the chamber below those corresponding to a noise-criterion curve of NC = 15 to 20. A minimum requirement for any anechoic room is that the combined source plus ambient sound level be 10 dB above the ambient level alone. (See References 23 to 27 for more details on the design of anechoic rooms.)

REFERENCES

1. Morse, P. M., and K. U. Ingard, *Theoretical Acoustics*, McGraw-Hill, New York, 1968.
2. Dupont, P., and W. Davern, "Calculations of the Statistical Absorption Coefficient from Acoustic Impedance Tube Measurements," *Acoustica* 9:15–16 (1959).
3. American Society for Testing Materials, "Sound Absorption of Acoustical Materials in Reverberation Rooms," ASTM C423-66, Philadelphia, rev. June 1970.
4. Magrab, E. B., *Environmental Noise Control*, Wiley, New York, 1975.
5. Beranek, L. (ed.), *Noise and Vibration Control*, McGraw-Hill, New York, 1971.
6. Crocker, M. J., and A. J. Price, *Noise and Noise Control*, vol. I, CRC Press, Cleveland, Ohio, 1975.
7. Schroeder, M. K., "Effects of Frequency and Space Averaging on the Transmission Response of Multimode Media," *J. Acoust. Soc. Amer.* 46:2 (1969), pp.277–283.
8. Lubman, D., "Precision of Reverberant Sound Power Measurements," 52:2 (1974), pp. 523–533.
9. Lubman, D., "Spatial Averaging in Sound Power Measurements," *J. Sound Vibr.* 16:43 (1971).
10. Towson, P. G., "A Study of the Criteria for the Design of Reverberation Chambers," *J. Acoust. Soc. Amer.*, December 1966.
11. Scharton, T. D., P. E. Rentz, D. Lubman, and P. H. White, *Techniques for Improving the Low-Frequency Performance of Small Reverberation Chambers*, Bolt, Beranek & Newman, Report No. 1867 (1970), Bolt, Berands and Newman Inc., Cambridge, Mass.
12. Ingalls, D. J., "The Use of Stationary Near-Field Diffusers for Improving Low-Frequency Measurements in a Reverberant Room," *J. Acoust. Soc. Amer.* 49:89(A) (1971).
13. Ingalls, D. J., "The Effects of Large Panels on the Eigenvalues of Rectangular Rooms," paper presented to the Acoustical Society of America, San Diego, 1969.
14. Schultz, T. J., "Sound Power Measurements in a Reverberant Room," paper presented to the Acoustical Society of America, Houston, Tex., 1970.
15. Ebbing, C. E., "Experimental Evaluation of Moving Sound Diffusers for Reverberant Rooms," *J. Sound Vibr.* 16:99 (1971).
16. Ebbing, C. E., and D. T. Ingalls, "Experimental Evaluation of Microphone Traverses in a Reverberant Room, *J. Acoust. Soc. Amer.* 47:116(A) (1970).

17. Tichy, J., "The Effect of Rotating Vanes on the Sound Field in Reverberation Chambers," *J. Acoust. Soc. Amer.* **49**:89(A) (1971).
18. Tichy, J., "The Effect of Boundary Conditions on the Statistical Properties of the Sound Field in Enclosures," *J. Acoust. Soc. Amer.* **50**:98(A) (1971).
19. Tichy, J., and P. K. Baade, "Effect of Rotating Diffusers and Sampling Techniques on Sound-Pressure Averaging in Reverberant Rooms," *J. Acoust. Soc. Amer.* **56**:1 (1974), pp. 137–143.
20. Sepmeyer, L. W., "Computed Frequency and Angular Distribution of Normal Modes of Vibration in Rectangular Rooms," *J. Acoust. Soc. Amer.* **37**:3 (1965), pp. 413–423.
21. Friberg, R., "The Acoustic Laboratory of Rockwool AB, Skovde, Sweden," paper presented at the 6th International Congress on Acoustics, Tokyo, 1968.
22. Beranek, L. L., and J. P. Sleeper, Jr., "The Design and Construction of Anechoic Sound Chambers," *J. Acoust. Soc. Amer.* **18**:1 (1946), pp. 140–150.
23. Koidan, W., G. R. Hruska, and M. A. Pickett, "Wedge Design for the National Bureau of Standards' Anechoic Chamber," *J. Acoust. Soc. Amer.* **52**:1 (1972), pp. 1071–1076.
24. Velizhanina, K. A., and S. H. Rzhevkin, "The Investigation of Sound-Absorbent Structures for the Anechoic Chamber of the Physics Department of the Moscow State University," *Sov. Phys. Acoust.* **3**:21 (1957). [Eng. trans., *Akust. Zh.* **3**:28 (1957).]
25. Myneke, H., "The New Acoustics Laboratory of the Catholic University at Leuven," paper presented at the 6th International Congress on Acoustics, Tokyo, 1968.
26. Diestel, H. G., "Zur Schallausbreitung in reflexionsarmen Räumen," *Acustica* **12**:113 (1962).
27. Ingerslev, F., O. J. Pedersen, M. J. Moller, and S. Kristensen, "New Rooms for Acoustic Measurements at the Danish Technical University," *Acoustica* **19**:185–199 (1967/68).

IMPORTANT TERMS AND FORMULAS

Absorption coefficient: $\quad \alpha = \dfrac{I_i - I_r}{I_i}$

Transmission coefficient: $\quad \tau = \dfrac{I_t}{I_i}$

Room-averaged sound absorption coefficient: $\quad \bar{\alpha} = \displaystyle\sum_{i=1}^{n} \left(\dfrac{\alpha_i S_i}{S} \right)$

Room absorption: $\quad A = \displaystyle\sum_{i=1}^{n} \alpha_i S_i = \bar{\alpha} S$

Reverberation time: $\quad T_{60} = \dfrac{0.161\,V}{A} \qquad$ mks units

$$T_{60} = \dfrac{0.161\,V}{-S\,\ln(1 - \bar{\alpha})} \qquad \text{mks units}$$

Energy attenuation constant for air: $\quad m$

Resonant modes of a room

Resonant frequencies of a room: $\quad f_n = \dfrac{c}{2} \sqrt{\left(\dfrac{n_x}{l_x} \right)^2 + \left(\dfrac{n_y}{l_y} \right)^2 + \left(\dfrac{n_z}{l_z} \right)^2}$

Modal density: $\quad \Delta N = \left(\dfrac{4\pi f^2 V}{c^3} + \dfrac{\pi f A}{2c^2} + \dfrac{L}{8c} \right) \Delta f$

$$\simeq \dfrac{4\pi f^2 V}{c^3} \Delta f \qquad \text{for high frequencies}$$

Directivity factor: Q_θ

Room constant: $R = \dfrac{S\bar\alpha}{1 - \bar\alpha}$

Sound level in reverberant room:

$$L_p = L_w + 10 \log\left(\frac{Q_\theta}{4\pi r^2} + \frac{4}{\bar\alpha S}\right) \qquad \text{mks units}$$

Reverberation room

Anechoic room

Schroeder cutoff frequency: $f_c = 2000\left(\dfrac{T_{60}}{V}\right)^{1/2}$ mks units

Standard deviation of sound levels: $V_n{}^2 = \dfrac{\Sigma\left(L_i - \bar L\right)^2}{n(n - 1)}$

PROBLEMS

4.1 Three different types of sound absorption coefficients were defined in the text: α_n, α_{ST}, α_{SAB}. What is the practical importance of each of these quantities?

4.2 What physical phenomena are involved in extracting energy from a sound field by absorptive material?

4.3 Derive an expression for the change in sound-pressure level $L_{p2} - L_{p1}$ in terms of the ratio of room absorption A_2/A_1 [see Eq. (4.39)]. Plot the level difference, $\Delta p = L_{p2} - L_{p1}$ for $1 < A_2/A_1 < 8$.

Answer: Semireverberant field,

$$L_{p1} - L_{p2} = 10 \log\left[\left(1 + \frac{16\pi r^2}{A_1}\right)\bigg/\left(1 + \frac{16\pi r^2}{A_2}\right)\right]$$

Reverberant field,

$$L_{p1} - L_{p2} = 10 \log (A_2/A_1)$$

4.4 In what way does a "diffuse" sound field differ from a "reverberant" sound field? What measurements would you make to determine whether the sound field in a room was diffuse or reverberant?

4.5 What factors affect the reverberation time of a large room?

4.6

Octave center frequency, Hz	Room absorption, ft²	Sound-power level of source, dB
125	20	81
250	25	91
500	40	91
1000	50	101
2000	60	101
4000	80	89
8000	100	78

A small source, with known sound-power characteristics given in the accompanying table, is placed in a 12 × 16 × 8-ft room which has room absorption properties as indicated. Predict the A-weighted sound level at position B if (a) the source is placed in the corner of the room at position 1, (b) the source is placed on the floor at the center of the room in position 2. (c) Would you expect the reverberation time of the room measured at position B to be different for the two source positions? Explain.

Answer: (a) 100.3 dBA, (b) 96.4 dBA

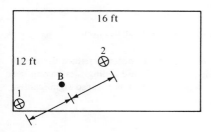

4.7 A Wankel engine is operating on a test stand in a large room.

(a) Indicate how you would locate the following zones of the sound field produced by the engine: (i) the near field, (ii) the free field, (iii) the far field, (iv) the reverberant field.

(b) In which of these zones can the directivity of the source be determined?

4.8 An engine develops 0.01 W acoustic power. The manufacturer quotes a directivity factor (linear weighting) of 3.16 directly in front of the engine. What is the sound-pressure level (unweighted) at a point 18 m in front of the engine, when the engine is mounted outdoors on a concrete pad?

Answer: 84.5 dB

4.9 A small turbine is located in a large 10 × 30 × 50-ft room as shown. The ear location R of a worker stationed in the room is indicated in the diagram. The 2000-Hz octave-band sound level measured at location A is 110 dB Re 2×10^{-5} N/m². The material acoustical properties of the

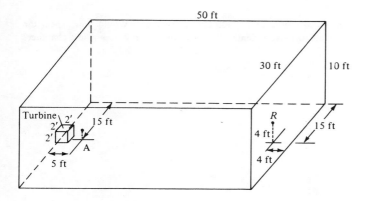

room are shown in the table below:

	Material	Absorption coefficient
Floor	Concrete	0.02
Walls	Concrete block	0.29
Ceiling	Concrete	0.02

Estimate the sound-pressure level in the 2000-Hz band at the operator's ear position.

Answer: 94 dB

4.10 Two identical rooms enclose noise sources A and B respectively. In order to reduce the sound levels in the rooms, they are treated in an identical manner, using wall and ceiling tiles having the absorption characteristics shown. After the treatment, the level in room A is reduced significantly, while in room B the level is affected only imperceptibly. Explain.

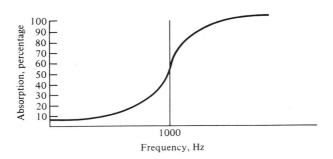

4.11 A reverberation room is built of concrete-block walls and is 10 ft high by 20 ft wide by 30 ft long. After construction the reverberation time at 1000 Hz is found to be 25 s.

(*a*) What is the approximate average room absorption? Average absorption coefficient?

Answer: $\bar{a} \simeq 0.054$

(*b*) What will be the sound-power level L_w of a source that produces a sound level of 76 dB at 1000 Hz?

Answer: $L_w \simeq 80.5$ dB

(*c*) Estimate the number of room modes in the 125-Hz octave band. Would you expect the steady-state sound field in this band to be sufficiently diffuse to use the room as a test chamber? Explain.

PART
TWO

PRACTICAL ASPECTS
OF NOISE CONTROL

INSTRUMENTATION FOR MEASUREMENT AND ANALYSIS OF NOISE

In this chapter we will discuss the major types of acoustical instrumentation and their important characteristics. Understanding the operation and use of acoustical instrumentation is essential for obtaining accurate and reliable measurements. These measurements, coupled with engineering judgment and skill, form the basis for virtually all noise control programs. We will begin by reviewing the terminology and fundamental concepts that underlie acoustical measurements. Before proceeding further, the reader should review Secs. 1.8 and 1.9.

5.1 TERMINOLOGY AND FUNDAMENTAL CONCEPTS

Intensity, Energy Density, Sound Power

All instrumentation for field acoustical measurements responds to acoustic pressure. Other related quantities—such as intensity, energy density, and sound power—must be calculated from pressure measurements. The root-mean-square value of the acoustic pressure is normally calculated because it is related to the response of the human ear as well as to intensity, energy density, and sound power. Recall from Chap. 1:

$$p_{rms} = \sqrt{\frac{1}{T} \int_0^T p^2(t)\, dt} \qquad (1.12)$$

where T is the time interval over which the mean square pressure is averaged and $p(t)$ is the instantaneous value of acoustic pressure.

Intensity is the average energy per unit time passing through a unit area of the medium. For a free progressive wave, the far field intensity is related to rms pressure by:

$$I = \frac{p_{rms}^2}{\rho_o c} \tag{1.13}$$

where $\rho_o c$ = characteristic impedance of the medium. For a combination of uncorrelated free progressive waves impinging on the surfaces of a reverberation room at all angles of incidence (i.e., for a diffuse sound field), the intensity *within* the room is

$$I = \frac{p_{rms}^2}{4\rho_o c} \tag{5.1}$$

The term "uncorrelated" means that no two free progressive waves are of exactly the same frequency. Recall that when sound waves of the same frequency are combined, the mean square acoustic pressure of the combination is not proportional to intensity, and p_{rms}^2 depends not only upon the mean square pressure of each wave, but also upon the phase relationship between the waves [Eq. (1.16)]. In practice, sound waves of identical frequency are usually present at a given measurement location. However, these effects tend to average out, provided that p_{rms}^2:

- · is determined over a band of frequencies, and
- · is more or less uniform over the frequency band

To minimize these effects, p_{rms}^2 is frequently averaged on an energy basis over at least 1/2 wavelength of the center frequency of the band. A traversing microphone mounted on a cable or boom is used for this purpose. A second method for averaging p_{rms}^2 employs up to six microphones placed at random locations in the sound field. The sound pressures measured by the microphones are averaged on an energy basis to provide an equivalent sound-pressure level.

The term "energy density" refers to the average acoustic energy present within a volume element of the medium. This energy is both kinetic (resulting from motion of the medium) and potential (resulting from compression-rarefaction of the medium). In a free progressive wave, the energy density ε is related to p_{rms} by

$$\varepsilon = \frac{p_{rms}^2}{\rho_o c^2} \tag{1.21}$$

In a reverberant space, where sound waves arrive and depart from all angles with equal probability, it was shown in Chap. 4 that

$$\varepsilon = \frac{p_{rms}^2}{4\rho_o c^2} \tag{5.2}$$

This relationship assumes uncorrelated sound waves, or, in practice, it assumes that p_{rms}^2 is distributed over a band of frequencies, none of which is dominant.

The term "sound power" refers to the portion of total power produced by a source (such as an engine, fan, or punch press) that results in radiated sound waves. For virtually all noise sources the sound power is a tiny fraction of the total power produced or consumed. Therefore, sound power is *independent of surroundings*, whereas sound pressure is dependent on both sound power and the influence of surroundings. If the surroundings produce a reverberant sound field, a free field, or a free field above a reflecting plane, this dependence is known. As a result, sound power can be calculated from measurements of energy density or acoustic intensity. For uncorrelated sound waves, these quantities are proportional to p_{rms}^2, as we have just seen.

Performance Characteristics of Acoustical Instrumentation

The four most important performance characteristics of acoustical instrumentation are frequency response, dynamic range, crest factor capability, and response time. In every case, one must ascertain that the specifications of the instrumentation system being used are adequate in each of these areas. Keep in mind that:

• Measured values are determined by the variable being measured (in this case acoustic pressure) *and* the characteristics of the measuring system.
• A good measuring system has a negligible (or predictable) influence on the variable being measured.

Frequency response defines that range of frequencies over which an instrument or measuring system reproduces (within acceptable limits) the correct relative amplitudes of the variable being measured. The limits of acceptability vary with the type of instrumentation and the manufacturer. Typical limits for microphones are ± 2 dB; for tape recorders, ± 1 dB or ± 3 dB; and for loudspeakers, ± 5 dB.*

Requirements for frequency response vary widely with the application; the gain should be constant (flat) within acceptable limits over a range of frequencies that encompasses all of the significant information present in the variable being measured. The uses for measured values also influence frequency-response requirements. For example, an inexpensive reel-to-reel (or even cassette) recorder can be used to provide an A-weighted time history of a noise source having no dominant frequencies below 100 or above 5000 Hz. On the other hand, the measurement of jet-aircraft flyover noise may require a "flat" frequency response from 50 to 15,000 Hz. For this application, an instrumentation tape recorder would be needed. An FM tape recorder capable of reproducing dc levels (0 Hz) is required for accurate measurement of structural vibrations and impulses.

---

* Recall that a change of ± 3 dB in a mean square quantity represents a doubling or halving of that quantity.

Dynamic range describes the amplitude ratio between the maximum input level and the self-noise (or "noise floor") of an instrument or system. Dynamic-range requirements also depend upon the application. In general, the minimum input level of interest should be at least 10 dB greater than the noise floor: in other words, the minimum signal/noise ratio should be 10 dB. If the noise level is nearly constant (as in a manufacturing plant), a dynamic range of 20 or 30 dB may be adequate. However, if the noise level varies widely (community noise is an example), a dynamic range of 50 or 60 dB may be required. A dynamic range of 60 to 80 dB is typical of many sound level meters, frequency analyzers, and instrumentation tape recorders.

The *crest factor* of an input signal is the ratio of its peak value to its rms value. Since sound waves are random in nature, crest factors of 3 or 4 are not uncommon; in fact, crest factors up to 40 may be encountered in the measurement of impulsive sounds. The measuring system should be able to accommodate crest factors of this magnitude without overloading. For example, an rms reading instrument should be able to display the rms level on a readable scale without overloading when the signal reaches its peak values.

Response time is that time interval required for an instrument to respond to a full-scale step input. The response time of microphones, electronic circuits, and tape recorders is more than adequate for most acoustical inputs; system response is usually limited by output devices such as meters and graphic level recorders. For this reason, measurement of impulsive sounds is achieved by storing the peak level (which may be reached within a few milliseconds) in a capacitor, followed by display on the output meter. (The peak level of an impulsive noise indicated on a conventional sound level meter may be as much as 30 dB less than the true peak level.)

On a conventional sound level meter a "fast" or "slow" meter response can be selected. This setting controls the response time to provide either an "instantaneous" (200-ms response time) or an "average" (1-s response time) sound-pressure level. However, the voltage available at the "ac output" terminal varies with the input sound pressure and is unaffected by the meter response.

5.2 FREQUENCY ANALYSIS

Frequency analysis refers to the resolution of a voltage signal (which is proportional to a quantity such as mean square pressure) into a series of contiguous (adjoining) frequency bands. The result is a "frequency spectrum," as illustrated in Figs. 1.9 and 5.4.

The principal uses for frequency analysis in noise control are

- to identify dominant sources of noise;
- to optimize the selection of methods, materials, and structures for controlling noise;

· to evaluate the effects of noise control measures; and
· to determine compliance with noise criteria such as NC (or PNC) and speech-interference level

A frequency analysis can be performed in a number of different ways: The bandwidth can be either constant or a constant percentage of center frequency; the center frequency can be tuned either continuously or in discrete steps; and the analysis can be performed in either "real time" or "extended time." We will now define the terms just used and discuss each of these methods.

An ideal filter response characteristic is shown in Fig. 5.1. All frequencies within the passband (bandwidth) of the filter are accepted fully, and all frequencies outside the passband are rejected fully. An actual response characteristic is also shown. The "skirts" of the actual characteristic are steep but not infinitely so; therefore, information outside the passband (defined by the −3-dB or "half-power" points) is also accepted by the filter. However, this information is attenuated to such an extent that its contribution to the energy within the passband is usually negligible. The reader should understand clearly that no matter what the bandwidth of the filter, a frequency analysis provides a measure of the total acoustical energy *within* the bandwidth to which the analyzer is tuned. There is one reading obtained for each bandwidth; its value is *decibels per bandwidth.*

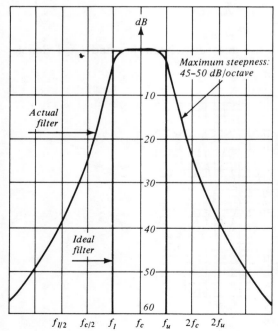

Figure 5.1 Filter response characteristics.

Constant-percentage bandwidth analysis is currently the most widely used. In this type, the bandwidth is a constant *percentage* of the center frequency. The center frequency is the geometric mean of the bandwidth, defined by

$$f_c = \sqrt{f_l f_u} \tag{5.3}$$

where f_c = center frequency of band, Hz
f_l = lower cutoff (-3 dB) frequency of filter response, Hz
f_u = upper cutoff (-3 dB) frequency of filter response, Hz
$f_u - f_l$ = bandwidth of filter

The use of constant-percentage bandwidth analysis is based on the observed response of the human ear to bands of noise: as the center frequency of the band increases, the band of frequencies judged to be equally wide increases in proportion. Thus a family of constant-percentage filter response characteristics is identical when plotted on a log-frequency scale (Fig. 5.2).

The most common constant-percentage bandwidth analyzers are full-octave (70.7 percent), 1/3-octave (23.6 percent), 1/10-octave (7 percent), and 1 percent. Center frequencies of the first two are standardized by international agreement (Table 5.1). Typical filter response characteristics are shown in Fig. 5.2. For the full-octave set,

$$
\begin{aligned}
f_{c,\,i+1} &= 2f_{c,\,i} \\
f_{u,\,i} &= 2f_{l,\,i} \\
f_{l,\,i} &= f_{u,\,i-1} \\
f_{u,\,i} &= f_{l,\,i+1}
\end{aligned}
\tag{5.4}
$$

where subscript i denotes the ith filter and subscripts $i + 1$ and $i - 1$ denote

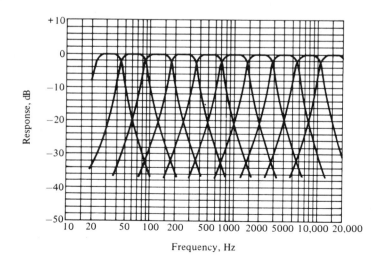

Figure 5.2 "Preferred series" octave-band-filter characteristics. *(From B & K Instruments, Inc.)*

Table 5.1 Center frequencies for octave and 1/3-octave bands in the preferred series

Octave band	1/3-octave band	Octave band	1/3-octave band
	25		800
31.5	31.5	1000	1000
	40		1250
	50		1600
63	63	2000	2000
	80		2500
	100		3150
125	125	4000	4000
	160		5000
	200		6300
250	250	8000	8000
	315		10,000
	400		12,500
500	500	16,000	16,000
	630		20,000

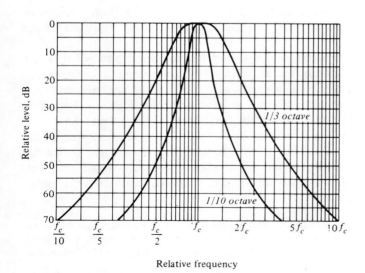

Figure 5.3 One-third-octave and 1/10-octave filter response characteristics. *(From GenRad.)*

filters continguous to the *i*th filter. Each octave filter in the preferred series is spanned by three 1/3-octave filters, which subdivide the octave band geometrically into three continguous bands. Relationships involving upper and lower cutoff frequencies are developed in Prob. 5.5.

For the 1/3-octave set,

$$f_{c, i+1} = 2^{1/3}f_{c, i} = 1.26f_{c, i} \qquad (5.5)$$

For the 1/10-octave set, each octave bandwidth is subdivided geometrically into 10 contiguous bands, so that

$$f_{c, i+1} = 2^{1/10}f_{c, i} = 1.07f_{c, i}$$

Virtually all full-octave frequency analyses are "stepped"; that is, the analyzer can be tuned only to the center frequencies of the preferred series (Fig. 5.4). One-third-octave frequency analyses can be either stepped or "continuously tunable"; in the latter case, any center frequency within the range of the analyzer can be selected. With this type of analysis, it is especially important to recognize that the amplitude scale is in decibels *per bandwidth* (see Prob. 5.8). Almost all constant-percentage analyzers narrower than 1/3 octave are continuously tunable.

Selection of filter bandwidth is dependent upon the nature of the noise spectrum and the purpose of the analysis. If the source spectrum is "broadband" (with acoustic energy distributed more or less uniformly over a wide range of frequencies), or if a criterion value (such as NC or PNC) is being calculated, a full- or 1/3-octave analysis is adequate. However, if the source contains one or more dominant pure tones, their identification usually requires a 1/10-octave or narrower analysis.[*] Identifying dominant pure tones is important because of their annoyance potential and because effective noise control requires that the source be pinpointed.[†]

In general, the analysis bandwidth should be the widest possible that will provide needed information. This is particularly true when a conventional stepped or continuously tunable analyzer is used, because the analysis time for a given precision is inversely proportional to bandwidth. Examples of frequency spectra obtained with different bandwidths are shown in Figs. 1.9 and 5.4.

Fixed-bandwidth frequency analysis can employ bandwidths as wide as 100 Hz or as narrow as 2 Hz. The narrow bandwidth has the capability for identifying clustered pure tones; the bandwidth of a narrow-band constant-percentage analyzer may be too wide for this purpose, particularly at higher frequencies.

---

[*] Noise regulations of the State of Illinois identify a "prominent discrete tone" when the level in a given 1/3-octave filter exceeds the arithmetic average of the two adjacent filters by 5 dB (160 to 10,000 Hz) or 15 dB (25 to 125 Hz)—provided that the band level of the given filter exceeds the band level of *each* adjacent filter.

[†] Generation of pure tones frequently results from phenomena such as movement of a rotating blade past a stationary object, meshing of gear teeth, or valve operation in engines and compressors.

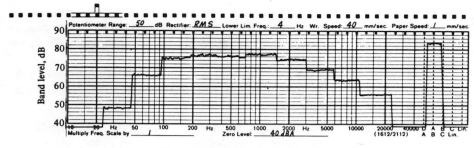

(*a*) A-weighted octave band analysis (stepped).

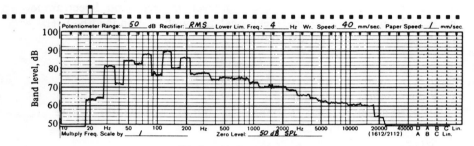

(*b*) One-third octave analysis (stepped).

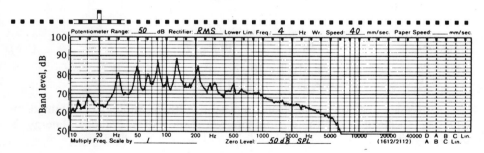

(*c*) 3 percent bandwidth analysis (continuously tuneable).

Figure 5.4 Frequency spectrograms of noise from a 10-kW portable generator. *(From B & K Instruments, Inc.)*

"Real-time" frequency analysis refers to frequency spectra that are calculated and presented with virtually no delay—essentially in real time. This type of analysis is performed in a variety of ways by both constant-percentage-bandwidth and constant-bandwidth filtering. The averaging times (and in some cases the averaging methods) for incoming data are open to choice. One or more spectra can be stored and recalled for comparison or averaging with subsequent spectra; band levels are available as a visual display and as analog or digital input data to plotters or computers. Advances in the capability and versatility of real-time analysis are occurring rapidly. The initial cost of these analyzers is often justified by savings in time and processing costs when large-scale or continuing projects involving research, development, monitoring, or enforcement are undertaken.

Conversion from one analysis bandwidth to another is often necessary for quantitative comparison of data obtained with different bandwidths. The conversion procedure assumes that:

- Acoustic energy is uniformly distributed over the initial bandwidth.
- Sound levels can be combined or decomposed on an energy basis.

If the desired bandwidth is narrower than the initial bandwidth, the conversion relation is based upon the "spectrum level" in each band. Spectrum level is the sound level read by an ideal analyzer with a bandwidth 1 Hz wide. Assuming uniform energy distribution:

$$p_{SL}^2 \Delta f_1 = p_1^2$$

where p_{SL} = mean square pressure in each 1-Hz band
$\quad \Delta f_1$ = initial bandwidth
$\quad p_1^2$ = mean square pressure in initial bandwidth, where $L_{p_1} = 10 \log_{10}(p_1^2/p_{ref}^2)$

Therefore,

$$10 \log_{10} \frac{p_{SL}^2}{p_{ref}^2} \Delta f_1 = 10 \log_{10} \frac{p_1^2}{p_{ref}^2}$$

$$L_{SL} + 10 \log_{10} \Delta f_1 = L_1$$

from which
$$L_{SL} = L_1 - 10 \log_{10} \Delta f_1 \qquad (5.6)$$

where L_{SL} = spectrum level, dB Re 20 μN/m^2
$\quad L_1$ = sound-pressure level in initial bandwidth

The expression for converting from one bandwidth to another is obtained by equating spectrum-level values for the two bandwidths (valid if energy is uniformly distributed over both the initial and desired bandwidths):

$$L_2 = L_1 + 10 \log_{10} \frac{\Delta f_2}{\Delta f_1} \qquad (5.7)$$

where subscripts 1 and 2 denote initial and desired bandwidths, respectively.

Combination of two or more bandwidths into a single wider bandwidth (as, for example, combining three 1/3-octave sound levels into the corresponding octave sound level) is performed on an energy basis as follows:

$$\frac{p_{ob}^2}{\rho_o c} = \frac{p_1^2}{\rho_o c} + \frac{p_2^2}{\rho_o c} + \frac{p_3^2}{\rho_o c}$$

where p_{ob} denotes octave-band mean square pressure and p_1, p_2, p_3 denote 1/3-octave-band mean square pressures. Thus,

$$L_{ob} = 10 \log_{10} \frac{p_{ob}^2}{p_{ref}^2} = 10 \log_{10} \frac{p_1^2 + p_2^2 + p_3^2}{p_{ref}^2} \qquad (5.8)$$

where L_{ob} = octave-band sound level, dB Re 20 μN/m². This result can also be obtained by combining the three 1/3-octave sound levels two at a time, using Fig. 1.6.

5.3 ACOUSTICAL INSTRUMENTATION

In this section we will describe briefly the major components, operation, and use of the principal types of acoustical instrumentation. Additional information is available from manufacturers' technical brochures.

Sound Level Meter

This instrument is described in Sec. 1.9. It consists of a sensitive pressure transducer (or microphone), a 10-dB step-attenuator, a battery-powered amplifier, weighting networks, and a meter which responds to the rms pressure with "slow" and "fast" averaging. In addition, some sound level meters have impulse sound measurement capability (peak and rms), a "flat" (20 to 20,000 Hz) response setting, and an output terminal which provides a time-varying voltage that is proportional to the overall or weighted sound pressure. The amplifier frequency response is typically flat within 2 dB from 2 to 15,000 Hz; overall frequency response is usually determined by the microphone characteristic. In some cases the microphone and preamplifier can be removed from the instrument case in order to take remote sound measurements through an extension cable. Usually, an accelerometer can be substituted for the microphone when measurement of structural vibrations is desired. Typical sound level meters are shown in Fig. 5.5.

Specifications for sound level meters are published by the American National Standards Institute (ANSI). The specifications prescribe limits on microphone and weighting-network frequency-response characteristics, the influence of instrument geometry on measured sound levels, and temperature and humidity effects. One standard applies to "Precision Sound Level Meters" (Type 1); a second, less rigorous standard applies to Type 2 or "General-Purpose Sound Level Meters." Either type is acceptable for enforcement of regulations, but some noise control applications require the greater precision of the Type 1 sound level meter.

Sound Level Meter–Octave-Band Analyzer

This is the basic instrument for noise control work. It consists of a Type 1 or Type 2 sound level meter, combined (often in a single case) with an octave-band analyzer. All the features of sound level meters enumerated above are also available. A schematic diagram of this instrument is shown in Fig. 5.6. When two step-attenuators are provided, the input attenuator should be adjusted (with the weighting selector on "linear" and the output attenuator at its maximum

Calibrator

Precision (Type I)
sound level meter

Survey (Type II)
sound level meter

Figure 5.5 Representative sound level meters. *(From B & K Instruments, Inc.; from GenRad.)*

value) for an on-scale reading. To avoid overloading the input amplifier, all further adjustments must be made by adjusting the output attenuator. On some instruments the input attenuator adjusts automatically, and only the output attenuator requires manual adjustment. A dc as well as an ac output may also be provided; the former is proportional to meter deflection (L_p), while the latter is a time-varying voltage proportional to acoustic pressure.

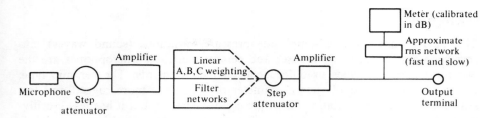

INTERNAL COMPONENTS OF SOUND LEVEL METER/OCTAVE BAND ANALYZER

Figure 5.6 Representative sound level meter–octave band analyzer. *(Photograph from GenRad.)*

Microphone

This device converts small-amplitude pressure variations (sound waves) into corresponding voltages. Condenser and ceramic-cartridge microphones are the two most common types used for acoustic measurements. The ceramic type, shown in Fig. 5.7, usually has a diameter of 1 in. It is more rugged and less sensitive to humidity variations than the condenser type, but it has less sensitivity and a narrower range of frequency response. A piezoelectric crystal is deformed slightly by arriving sound waves and generates a charge proportional to the acoustic presssure.

Condenser microphones consist of two plates separated by a small distance, as shown in Fig. 5.8. One of the plates is very thin and deflects slightly when sound waves impinge upon it; a corresponding change in capacitance results. Opposite charges on the plates are established by a polarization voltage (on the order of 200 V), or by permanently embedding the charges on each surface during manufacture (electret microphone). Microphones of these types are usually $\frac{1}{2}$ in or 1 in in diameter. The $\frac{1}{2}$-in-diameter size is becoming widely used because it combines high sensitivity and good dynamic range (typically 20 to 140 dB) with good frequency response (flat within 2 dB from 20 to 15 kHz). The lower limit is determined by a small bleed hole located behind the diaphragm to provide static-pressure equalization; the upper limit is determined by microphone diameter. (When microphone dimensions approach the wavelength of impinging sound, the presence of the microphone interferes with the sound field

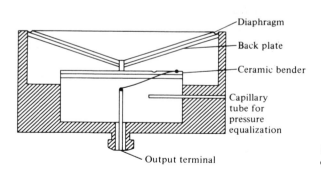

Figure 5.7 Schematic diagram of ceramic microphone [9].

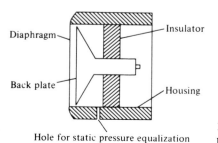

Figure 5.8 Schematic diagram of condenser microphone [9].

and affects the frequency response.) All precision sound level meters use a condenser-type (conventional or electret) microphone; most Type 2 sound level meters use ceramic microphones.

All microphones, regardless of type, are designed for optimum frequency response in specific sound fields. The two designations in widest use are "normal incidence"* and "random incidence." The first term means that the microphone has its best frequency response for sound waves arriving at normal incidence; in other words, the microphone should be pointed toward the source of sound. Random-incidence microphones have optimum frequency response when sound waves arrive simultaneously from all angles of incidence, as in a reverberant sound field.

Frequency-response curves for various types and sizes of microphones are shown in Figs. 5.9 and 5.10. Table 5.2 lists typical applications for these microphones. Note that measurement errors are 3 dB or less at all frequencies below 4000 Hz, regardless of sound field or microphone type and size. Furthermore, these errors have even less significance in cases where only comparative (before and after) measurements are desired.

When making noise measurements, always hold the sound level meter away from the body, and do not stand in the path of direct sound waves. In cases where reverberant sound dominates, location of the observer is not important.

---

* This type is also referred to as a "free-field" microphone.

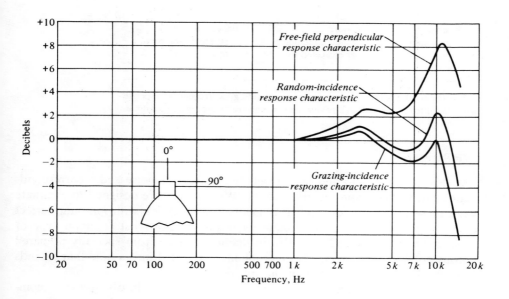

Figure 5.9 Frequency-response characteristics of 1-in-diameter ceramic microphone [9].

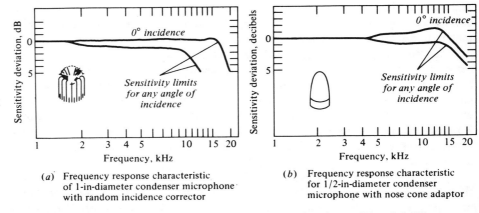

(a) Frequency response characteristic of 1-in-diameter condenser microphone with random incidence corrector

(b) Frequency response characteristic for 1/2-in-diameter condenser microphone with nose cone adaptor

Figure 5.10 Frequency-response characteristics of condenser microphones. *(From B & K Instruments, Inc.)*

Table 5.2 Types of microphones for various applications

Measurement condition	Class of microphone	Typical applications
Perpendicular incidence	Free-field	Product noise
Grazing incidence	Pressure,* random-incidence, or corrected free-field	Moving sound source
Random incidence	Pressure, random-incidence, or corrected free-field	Factory noise; reverberation room measurements

* Pressure microphones are designed to provide good frequency response when mounted in the wall of a cavity; an earphone calibrator is one example.

Windscreen

The flow of air around and over a microphone creates noise and a corresponding output voltage from the microphone. Windscreens are designed to eliminate wind noise (during outdoor measurements, for example), with minimum effect on microphone sensitivity or frequency response. The most common type of windscreen is a sphere, 2.5 to 4 in in diameter, made from specially prepared porous polyurethane foam. The microphone is inserted into a hole that extends from the surface to the center of the sphere.

Windscreens attenuate low-velocity wind noise about 10 dB, and are recommended for wind velocities less than 15 mi/h. Somewhat higher velocities are acceptable during measurement of A-weighted sound levels, because the wind noise is concentrated at low frequencies (below 125 Hz). The effect of a windscreen on microphone sensitivity is negligible at frequencies below 12 kHz; the effect on microphone frequency response is less than 1 dB below 1 kHz and less than 2 dB between 1 and 12 kHz.

A windscreen should be used for all outdoor noise measurements. It is important to verify that wind noise is at least 10 dB below the combined source and wind noise levels; otherwise, sound levels attributed to the source may be in error. A windscreen is also recommended to protect the microphone in applications where physical damage may occur.

Recording Analyzer

This instrument consists of a stepped or continuously tunable frequency analyzer and a graphic level recorder (Fig. 5.11). The level recorder drives the frequency analyzer to provide a synchronized plot of sound-pressure level versus frequency (called a *frequency spectrogram*). The electrical output from the analyzer is converted to an equivalent sound-pressure level by a logarithmic potentiometer in the graphic level recorder. The user can adjust the response of the pen movement and the chart speed to provide an optimum combination of signal averaging and analysis time. Both portable (battery-operated) and mains-powered graphic level recorders are available.

Real-Time Analyzer

This instrument provides an almost instantaneous spectrum of incoming data that have been averaged for a selected time interval. One type, shown in Fig. 5.12, consists of a series of contiguous 1/3-octave filters (typically 25 to 20 kHz)

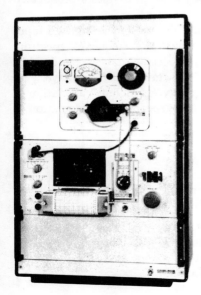

Figure 5.11 Recording spectrum analyzer. *(From GenRad.)*

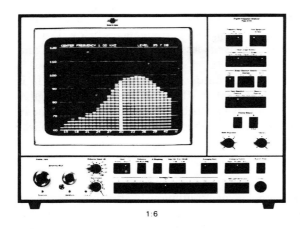

1:6

Figure 5.12 Digital real-time frequency analyzer. *(From B & K Instruments.)*

which continuously monitor the output signal from a sound-level meter or tape recorder. Averaging times, typically from 1/8 up to 128 s, are open to choice. In some cases these types of averaging can also be selected: (1) linear; (2) exponential, in which recent data are weighted more heavily than earlier data; and (3) statistical, in which averaging times are adjusted to a specified confidence level.

A second type of real-time analyzer is called a *time-compression analyzer.* The input is first digitized and stored in a memory, where it is sampled and converted back to an analog signal that is increased in frequency by several orders of magnitude. Thus, a corresponding reduction in scanning time by a narrow-band filter is possible. A typical frequency analysis divides a preselected total bandwidth into 200 or 400 equal subbands (or lines).

A third type of analyzer employs numerical processing of a digitized input signal to calculate its Fourier transform. The result is a frequency spectrum obtained by an FFT (fast Fourier transform) process. Analysis bandwidths include 200-line or 400-line, and in some cases full-octave and 1/3-octave.

Additional features found in some real-time analyzers include calculation of peak spectra, storage and comparison of two or more spectra, and calculation of transfer functions.

Tape Recorder

An adequate tape recorder is an essential component of an acoustical instrumentation system, for the following reasons:

- Sound levels can be recorded in the field for later analysis.
- Capture of transient and intermittent sounds is possible.
- By making a tape loop of representative sound levels, a frequency analysis can be obtained from a few seconds of data.
- A permanent record is available for later use.

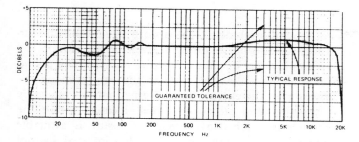

Figure 5.13 Frequency-response characteristics of data recorder. *(From GenRad.)*

Of course, the frequency response (Fig. 5.13) and dynamic range of the tape recorder must be suitable to capture the important characteristics of the incoming sound, as discussed in Sec. 5.1.

Calibrator

This instrument, shown in Fig. 5.14, presents a sound field of known intensity, at one or more frequencies, to a microphone inserted into a cavity at one end. Either a sound level meter or an entire measurement system can be calibrated in this way. A calibrator is indispensable for ensuring accurate measurements and for establishing reference levels on tape recordings or frequency spectrograms. Calibration is discussed in greater detail in Sec. 5.4.

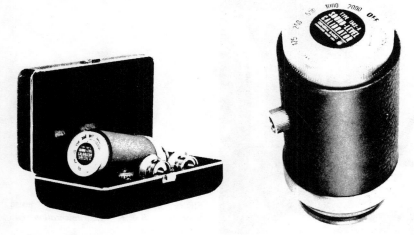

Figure 5.14 Acoustic calibrator. *(From GenRad.)*

Noise Dosimeter

This instrument is a compact sound level meter that is worn by an individual to determine his or her total exposure to noise during a given period (Fig. 5.15). Usually the individual is an employee of an industrial firm, and the time period is an 8-hr workshift. A microphone is located close to the ear receiving the greater noise exposure; arriving acoustic energy is transformed into a voltage by the microphone, then A-weighted and stored in a cell located within the instrument case. The stored-energy equivalent of noise exposure is available either on the instrument or from a module into which the cell is inserted. Output is expressed as a percentage of daily noise exposure permitted by OSHA regulations. An indication of exposure to 115 dBA (15 min or less daily exposure) is also provided. Under present regulations, dosimeters can be used for *monitoring* of employee noise exposures, but not for *enforcement*. Although several brands of dosimeters have been approved by OSHA and MSHA (Mine Safety and Health Administration) for this purpose, no performance standard for dosimeters presently exists (1979).

Noise-Level Analyzer

This type of instrument is usually battery-operated. Several varieties, some with specialized uses, are available. Each type continuously samples an input signal (from a microphone, for example) and calculates quantities such as L_x, L_{eq}, and L_{dn}. The last two are defined in Sec. ; L_x is that A-weighted noise level exceeded x percent of the time. For example, L_{10} is that dBA level exceeded 10

Figure 5.15 Employee wearing noise dosimeter *B & K Instrumentation for Noise Surveys.*

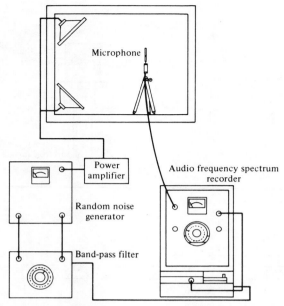

(a) Measurement of absorption coefficient in reverberation room

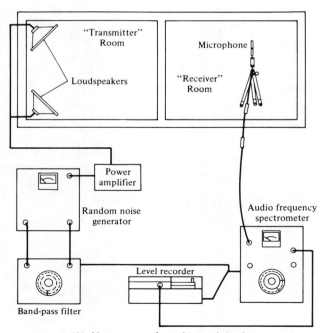

(b) Measurement of sound transmission loss

Figure 5.16 Instrumentation systems for acoustical measurements. [(*a*), (*b*), (*d*) *from B & K Instruments, Inc.*]

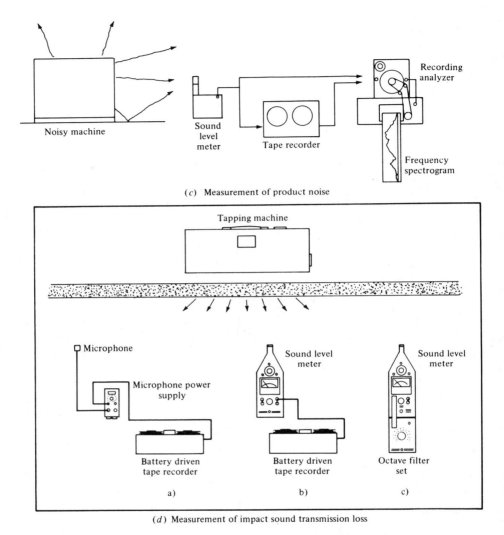

(c) Measurement of product noise

(d) Measurement of impact sound transmission loss

Figure 5.16 (continued) Instrumentation systems for acoustical measurements.

percent of the time during a specified period. A principal use for L_x is to assess the impact of existing or proposed highways and mass transit arteries on residential areas. One type of analyzer calculates L_1 to L_{99} and L_{eq} by dividing the input signal into 256 level classes spanning a selectable dynamic range of 64 dB.

5.4 TYPICAL APPLICATIONS

Several representative acoustical measurement systems are illustrated in Fig. 5.16 (see pp. 123–124). The output quantity of interest is usually

- a frequency analysis of a noise event; or
- an analysis of acoustic energy accumulated during a given time period

To assure display of output data at correct levels, a calibration signal must be used as input to the *entire* measuring system. If a tape recorder is used, the following procedure, or its equivalent, should be followed:

1. Record the calibration signal on tape. Adjust the input level of the tape recorder so that it is well below full scale (this allows the recorder to accept a relatively high crest factor without distortion). Be certain to announce the attenuator setting (range) of the sound level meter directly onto the tape.
2. Record the noise events of interest. Adjust the sound level meter range so the input is within the dynamic ranges of the sound level meter and the tape recorder. Again, be certain to announce the range used for recording. *Do not* change the input recording level.
3. During playback, set the level (using the calibration signal) so that the scale on the output device has a maximum value identical to that of the sound level meter when the calibration signal was recorded. Make no further changes in playback level.
4. To establish the correct output level for the noise event of interest, the maximum scale value on the output device must be the same as used during recording. For example, if the attenuator was set at 110 dB during calibration (corresponding to 0 dB on the meter), the output scale maximum value is 120 dB. If the noise event of interest was recorded with an attenuator setting of 80 dB, then the corresponding maximum value on the output scale is 90 dB.

REFERENCES

1. B & K Instruments, Inc., *Architectural Acoustics*, Cleveland, Ohio, 1968.
2. B & K Instruments, Inc., *Measuring Microphones*, Cleveland, Ohio, 1971.
3. Beranek, L. L. (ed.), *Noise and Vibration Control*, McGraw-Hill, New York, 1971.

4. Broch, J. T., *Acoustic Noise Measurements*, 2d ed., B & K Instruments, Inc., Cleveland, Ohio, 1971.
5. Hyzer, William G., "Choosing Basic Instruments to Analyze Noise Problems," *Research / Development*, October 1975.
6. Hyzer, William G., "Using Real-Time Acoustic Analyzers," *Research / Development*, June 1976.
7. Instrumentation Reference Issue, *Sound and Vibration*, March 1977.
8. Noise Measurements and Instrumentation Issue, *Noise Control Eng.* November-December 1977.
9. Peterson, A., and E. Gross, *Handbook of Noise Measurement*, 7th ed., General Radio Company, Concord, Mass., 1974.
10. Schneider, A. J., "Microphone Orientation in the Sound Field," *Sound and Vibration*, February 1970.

IMPORTANT TERMS AND FORMULAS

Root-mean-square pressure: $p_{\text{rms}} = \sqrt{\dfrac{1}{T} \int_0^T p^2(t)\, dt}$

Intensity

Energy density

Frequency response

Dynamic range

Crest factor

Response time

Frequency analysis

Filter bandwidth

Constant-percentage bandwidth, constant bandwidth

Conversion from one bandwidth to another: $L_2 = L_1 + 10 \log_{10} \dfrac{\Delta f_2}{\Delta f_1}$

Sound level meter

Octave-band analyzer

Microphone

Windscreen

Recording analyzer

Real-time analyzer

Tape recorder

Calibrator

Noise dosimeter

Noise-level analyzer

PROBLEMS

5.1 The frequency response of a tape recorder is shown in the accompanying figure, along with a 1/3-octave spectrum of a noise source as measured by a frequency analyzer.

(a) Calculate and plot the 1/3-octave frequency spectra of the noise source and the output from the tape recorder.

(b) Calculate the dBA and SIL values of the spectra plotted in (a).

(c) Discuss the significance of results obtained in (a) and (b) for assessing compliance with dBA and SIL criterion values.

(d) What results would you expect in (a) if the source of noise was human speech?

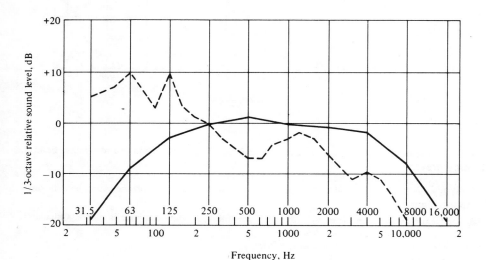

5.2 How do "broadband" and "dominant-pure-tone" sources differ from one another? Draw a typical octave-band spectrum for each. Identify several examples of each type of spectrum.

5.3 Assume that the acoustic power in the octave band centered at 125 Hz consists of a uniform noise with an octave-band sound-pressure level of 75 dB and a pure-tone component with an octave-band sound-pressure level of (a) 77 dB; (b) 80 dB; (c) 85 dB. What is the combined octave-band sound-pressure level of the broadband noise and the pure tone?

5.4 Draw an octave-band spectrum of a noise source that produces two discrete pure tones, one at 1000 Hz with an L_p of 90 dB, and one at 353 Hz with an L_p of 100 dB. Let the SPL scale on the spectrogram range from 40 to 100 dB. Explain the results, and discuss their significance for frequency analysis of equipment noise. Calculate the corresponding overall, A-weighted, and C-weighted sound-pressure levels.

5.5 (a) Using material presented in this chapter, obtain expressions for the upper and lower cutoff frequencies of a 1/3-octave filter characteristic, in terms of its center frequency f_c.

(b) Calculate the center, lower cutoff, and upper cutoff frequencies for the three 1/3-octave filters that span the octave band centered at 500 Hz. Sketch typical response characteristics for the octave filter and for each 1/3-octave filter.

5.6 An octave-band spectrum of a hydraulic pump is shown. Calculate the overall and A-weighted levels, and plot both unweighted and A-weighted octave-band spectra. Discuss the relative merits of these two types of spectra.

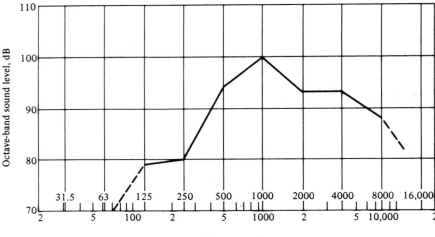

Frequency, Hz

5.7 The octave-band level of a noise source with uniform energy distribution over the octave band is L_p dB.

    (*a*) Calculate the average band level of each 1/3-octave band within the octave band.

    (*b*) If each 1/3-octave band had the same acoustic energy, what would the sound level in each band be?

5.8 The frequency spectrum from a continuously tunable 1/3-octave analyzer is shown. Calculate:

    (*a*) The overall sound-pressure level.

    (*b*) The corresponding octave-band spectrum.

    (*c*) The A-weighted level, dBA.

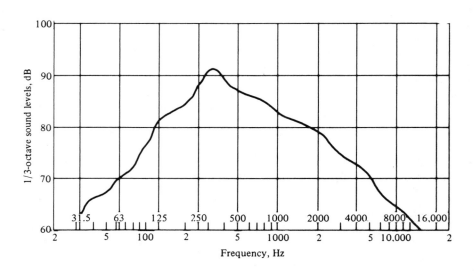

Frequency, Hz

5.9 Construct octave-band spectra for:

(a) Two broadband noise sources, each with an overall L_p of 100 dB (one has a spectrum that increases with frequency and the other has a spectrum that decreases with frequency).

(b) Two broadband noise sources, each with a sound level of 90 dBA (one has an increasing spectrum, the other a decreasing spectrum).

(The term "broadband" means that the octave-band sound level in a given band does not differ by more than 10 dB from the sound levels in the two adjacent bands.)

5.10 A random noise source and a "pink" noise source each have an overall level of 100 dB and a frequency range of 20 to 20,000 Hz. (A pink noise source produces sound with equal energy per *octave* bandwidth. The source is called "random noise" if the average energy per cycle is uniform from 20 to 20,000 Hz.)

(a) Obtain expressions for the spectrum level of each source.

(b) Plot the spectrum of each source as measured by (i) an octave-band analyzer (31.5 to 8000 Hz) and (ii) an analyzer with a fixed bandwidth of 1000 Hz (analysis band: 20 to 10,000 Hz).

ACOUSTICAL MEASUREMENTS

In this chapter we will discuss some common acoustical measurements. All of these measurements are obtained from sound-pressure levels recorded under controlled environmental conditions. Important properties of noise sources (such as sound power and directivity) or of acoustical materials and structures (such as absorption coefficient, transmission loss, and insertion loss) are determined in this way.

6.1 REVERBERATION TIME

Reverberation time T_{60} was defined in Chap. 4 as the time in seconds for a reverberant sound field to decay by 60 dB after a noise source has been shut off. Calculation of reverberation time is based upon the initial slope of the sound level decay, which is usually obtained for each octave band of interest. A typical situation for measuring reverberation time is shown in Fig. 6.1. Random noise* is broadcast into the space and shut off; the decay of the sound field is filtered before it is displayed on a graphic level recorder. (This arrangement usually provides a greater dynamic range for the decay curve than the alternative method, in which the frequency analyzer is used to filter the output from the random noise generator.) If desired, decay of the sound field can be tape recorded (either overall or in various frequency bands) for later display on a graphic level recorder. Of course, the overall sound-field decay must be filtered to obtain a decay curve for each frequency band of interest. Accurate measurement of reverberation time requires that the decay rates (in decibels per second) of the frequency analyzer and graphic level recorder be at least twice that corresponding to the shortest reverberation time. The response of the instrumentation system can be measured by connecting a constant-level input from the random noise generator directly to the measurement instrumentation system, and then disconnecting the input and observing the decay rate on the graphic level recorder.

---

* An impulsive sound source, such as a starter's pistol or large balloon, can also be used.

It is not unusual for reverberation times to vary significantly within a given space, unless the sound field is diffuse. For this reason several measurements at each of several representative locations should be obtained and averaged. From Fig. 6.1, note that:

- The available decay curve (25 dB) is less than the 60 dB upon which T_{60} is based. (A minimum decay of 15 dB is recommended.)
- The slope used for calculation of T_{60} is determined at a point on the decay curve located just below the range of values present before the source is shut off.
- The amount of variation in the decay curve is a function of the width of the frequency band whose decay is being measured and of the differing decay rates of oblique, tangential, and axial room modes. The narrower the frequency band, the more randomness is present both before and during decay. Axial modes persist longer than tangential or oblique modes because losses in the medium (usually air) are less, and because losses at room surfaces are usually less. The relatively long persistence of strong axial modes can give rise to an annoying characteristic called *flutter echo*. This effect can be reduced by altering the shapes of opposite walls to make them nonparallel, or by adding acoustical absorption to one or both of the surfaces.

Reverberation time is used primarily:

- As a guide or criterion for assessing the acceptability of spaces such as broadcast studios, classrooms, auditoriums, and concert halls (Fig. 6.2).

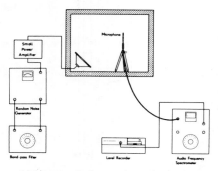

(a) Instrumentation for measuring reverberation time

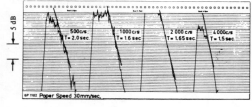

(b) Representative sound decay curves

Figure 6.1 Measurement of reverberation time. (*From B & K Instruments, Inc.*)

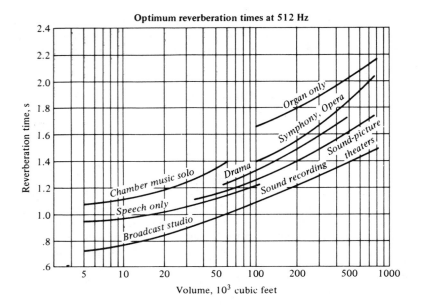

Optimum reverberation times at 512 Hz

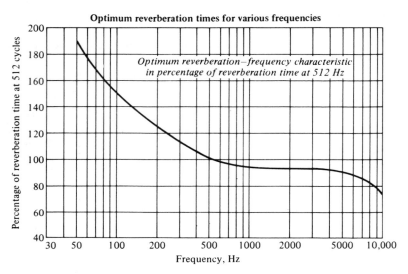

Optimum reverberation times for various frequencies

Figure 6.2 Recommended reverberation times for various uses. *(From Don Davis*, Acoustic Tests and Measurements, *H. W. Sams & Co., New York, 1965.)*

• As a measurement from which room absorption can be calculated, to assess practicability of controlling reverberant sound in a room.

• As a measurement, obtained in a reverberation room, from which the random-incidence (Sabine) absorption coefficient of acoustical materials can be calculated.

6.2 ABSORPTION COEFFICIENT AND ACOUSTIC IMPEDANCE

The absorption coefficient was defined earlier as the fraction of sound energy, incident upon an acoustical material or structure, that is "absorbed." In most instances the sound waves are confined within a room or other space, so that the energy absorbed is converted to minute amounts of heat within the absorbing material. However, when the material is part of a wall, for example, some of the energy is simply radiated away from the space through small vibrations of the material surface.

Absorption coefficients are usually measured in the presence of plane waves at normal incidence (in a standing-wave tube), or in the presence of randomly incident sound waves (in a reverberation room). Normal-incidence measurements are easier to obtain and are useful for rank-ordering materials; random-incidence measurements usually approximate more nearly the conditions of actual use.* Each of these measurement methods is described in the following paragraphs.

Normal-Incidence Absorption Coefficient

A standing-wave (or impedance) tube consists of a tube (usually circular) with a loudspeaker at one end and a probe tube or small microphone capable of traveling along the tube axis (Fig. 6.3). The other end terminates with a sample of acoustical material, or an element such as a silencer or tailpipe. The tube

---

* The value of the normal-incidence absorption coefficient is usually less than the corresponding value for random incidence. A method for converting normal-incidence measurements to random incidence, suitable for many building materials, is described in Refs. 4 and 6.

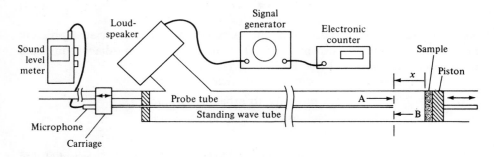

Figure 6.3 Equipment for measuring normal-incidence absorption coefficient.

diameter d and length L are selected such that

$$d < \lambda < L$$

where λ = wavelength of the pure tone produced by the loudspeaker. If $\lambda \leqslant d$, sound waves within the tube become nonplane; if $\lambda \geqslant L$, a pressure minimum may not be present within the tube. The microphone or probe-tube diameter should be less than 5 percent of the cross-sectional area to avoid interference with the sound field.*

The acoustic pressure at any point within the tube is the sum of incident- and reflected-wave pressures. Referring to Fig. 6.4a, the incident wave at a particular location is given by $p_i = A \sin \omega t$, and the reflected wave is given by

$$p_R = B \sin\left(\omega t - 2\frac{\omega}{c}x - \theta\right) \tag{6.1}$$

The expressions $2(\omega/c)x$ and θ represent relative phase shifts introduced into p_R by the distance $2x$ which the wave travels and by θ, the phase angle between incident and reflected waves at the termination. (The reflected wave p_R is an earlier incident wave, with an amplitude determined by reflection at the termination and a phase angle determined by $2x$ and θ.) Note that the amplitudes A and B are constant within the tube, if losses at the tube walls are negligible. The mean square pressure amplitude at any location, obtained by summation of incident and reflected waves (see Prob. 6.3), is

$$|p_i + p_r|^2_{rms} = \frac{A^2}{2} + \frac{B^2}{2} + AB \cos\left(2\frac{\omega}{c}x + \theta\right) \tag{6.2}$$

Thus, two traveling waves with exactly the same frequency combine to produce, at a given location, a harmonic wave with a fixed amplitude. In other words, a "standing wave" is created. As the measurement location changes, only the phase angle $2(\omega/c)x$ changes: the minimum amplitude is $A - B$, and the maximum amplitude is $A + B$. A pressure minimum occurs whenever

$$2\frac{\omega}{c}x + \theta = N\pi, \quad N = 1, 3, 5, \ldots \tag{6.3}$$

A pressure maximum occurs whenever

$$2\frac{\omega}{c}x + \theta = N\pi, \quad N = 0, 2, 4, \ldots \tag{6.4}$$

As N increases, the distance from the termination to the associated pressure minimum or maximum also increases. The distance between adjacent pressure maxima or minima is $\lambda/2$ (see Prob. 6.2).

The normal-incidence absorption coefficient α_n is given by

$$\alpha_n = \frac{\text{intensity absorbed by sample}}{\text{intensity incident upon sample}}$$

---

* Impedance-tube specifications are described in ASTM Standard C.384-58, "Standard Method of Test for Impedance and Absorption of Acoustical Materials by the Tube Method."

Absorption Coefficient

- Incident and reflected waves in
  standing wave tube

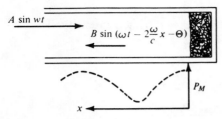

- Vector representation of incident and
  reflected waves at surface of sample

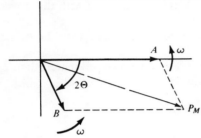

Absorption coefficient $\alpha_n = 1 - \dfrac{B^2}{A^2}$

Pressure amplitude $P_M = A + B \angle \Theta$

Reflection factor $= \dfrac{B}{A} \angle \Theta$

$\qquad\qquad\quad = R_0 \angle \Theta$

(a) Normal incidence

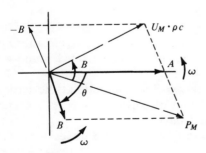

Pressure amplitude $P_M = A + B \angle \Theta$ at termination $(x = 0)$

Particle velocity amplitude $U_M = \dfrac{A - B \angle \Theta}{\rho c}$ at termination $(x = 0)$

Acoustic impedance $Z = \dfrac{P_M}{U_M} \angle \beta$

(b) Acoustic impedance

Figure 6.4 Standing-wave-tube
measurements.

Since no energy is lost from the tube, the numerator is equal to

$$\frac{A^2 - B^2}{\rho c}$$

where $A^2/\rho c$ = incident intensity and $B^2/\rho c$ = reflected intensity. Thus

$$\alpha_n = 1 - \frac{B^2}{A^2} \tag{6.5}$$

An equivalent expression, in terms of p_{max} and p_{min}, is

$$\alpha_n = \frac{4 p_{max}/p_{min}}{(1 + p_{max}/p_{min})^2} \tag{6.6}$$

where $p_{max} = A + B$, the maximum sound pressure measured with the traversing microphone

$p_{min} = A - B$, the minimum sound pressure measured with the traversing microphone

If the traversing microphone is connected to a sound-level meter, then Lp_{max} and Lp_{min} will be measured. It can be shown (see Prob. 6.5) that

$$\frac{p_{max}}{p_{min}} = 10^{(L_{p\,max} - L_{p\,min})/20}$$

by use of this relationship a convenient graph of α_n versus $L_{p\,max} - L_{p\,min}$ can be plotted.

Acoustic Impedance

The impedance Z of acoustical materials and structures can also be calculated from measurements in an impedance tube. The definition of acoustic impedance is

$$Z = \frac{p}{u}$$

where $p = A + B \angle \theta$, the acoustic-pressure amplitude at the termination, obtained by vector combination of incident and reflected sound-wave amplitudes

$u = (A - B \angle \theta)/\rho c$, the net particle-velocity amplitude at the termination, obtained by vector summation of particle velocities associated with incident and reflected sound waves

$\angle \theta$ = phase angle between incident and reflected sound waves

Figure 6.4b shows a vector representation of pressure and particle velocity from which Z can be calculated. An expression for the magnitude of the acoustic impedance is given in Prob. 6.9b. Expressions for the variables θ and R_0 are given in Probs. 6.7 and 6.9a, respectively. The phase angle β between the pressure and particle velocity can be determined by referring to Fig. 6.4. Acoustic impedance is usually calculated for a range of pure-tone frequencies; it is a useful property for predicting the performance of dissipative materials and silencer elements.

Random-Incidence (Sabine) Absorption Coefficient

The Sabine absorption coefficient α_{SAB} for randomly incident sound is calculated from reverberation time measurements obtained in a reverberation room. Usually the decay of sound is recorded in octave bands of random noise, first with the room empty and then with a test sample of the acoustical material in place. The sample of material is installed exactly as it would be in actual use; the minimum area for acceptable accuracy is about 4 ft^2.

Because the test space is normally a reverberation room with a small amount of absorption, Eqs. (4.17) apply. The appropriate equation is written for each test condition, in each octave band of interest; thus*

$$T_e = \frac{0.049\,V}{A_e}$$

and

$$T_s = \frac{0.049\,V}{A_s}$$

where T_e = reverberation time for empty room
T_s = reverberation time with sample in place
A_e = total absorption in empty room, sabins
A_s = total absorption with sample in place, sabins

Combining these equations:

$$0.049\,V\left(\frac{1}{T_s} - \frac{1}{T_e}\right) + A_e = A_s$$

If the test object has a definable surface area,

$$A_e = \bar{\alpha}_{\text{SAB}}\,S \qquad \bar{\alpha}_{\text{SAB}} \leqslant 0.2$$

and $\qquad\qquad\qquad\qquad\qquad\qquad\qquad\qquad\qquad\qquad\qquad\qquad$ (6.7)

$$A_s = \bar{\alpha}_{\text{SAB}}\,S + S_s(\alpha_s - \alpha_i)_{\text{SAB}}$$

where $\bar{\alpha}_{\text{SAB}}$ = average absorption coefficient in empty room
α_s = absorption coefficient of test sample
α_i = absorption coefficient of surface covered by test sample
S = surface area of empty room, ft^2
S_s = surface area of test sample, ft^2

---

*Recall that A is the number of square feet (sabins) or square meters (metric sabins) of "ideal" absorber (with $\alpha = 1.0$) that is equal to the actual absorption in a given space.

After substitution and rearrangement of terms:

$$(\alpha_s)_{\text{SAB}} = \frac{0.049\,V}{S_s}\left(\frac{1}{T_s} - \frac{1}{T_e}\right) + \alpha_i \tag{6.8}$$

In some cases, values for α_{SAB} in excess of 1.0 may be calculated and/or published. This apparent violation of physical laws occurs from diffraction of sound waves by the edges of the sample or from exposure of the rear surface of the sample to impinging sound (when the sample is spaced away from the wall, for example), or both. Current practice adjusts α_{SAB} values of 1.0 or greater to 0.99.

If the reverberant space is large, losses due to propagation of reflected sound waves through the medium can become significant. In this case, the expressions for T_{60} become

$$T_{60} = \frac{0.161\,V}{A + 4mV} \qquad \text{mks units}$$

$$T_{60} = \frac{0.049\,V}{A + 4mV} \qquad \text{English units} \tag{4.22}$$

The attenuation constant m in English units for air at standard temperature and pressure can be obtained from Fig. 6.5.

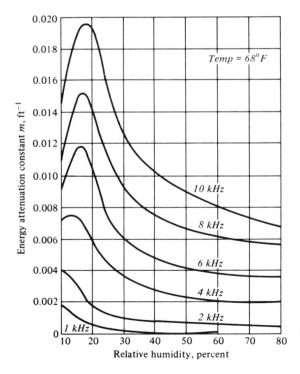

Figure 6.5 Attenuation constant for propagation of sound waves in air. *(From L. L. Beranek, Noise Control, McGraw-Hill, New York, 1960.)*

Sometimes it is necessary to estimate the amount of absorption present in a manufacturing area, classroom, or auditorium where measurement of reverberation time is either impractical or impossible. After the absorption has been estimated, the reverberation time can be calculated, or the amount of additional absorption required to reduce reverberant sound levels can be determined. In these situations, absorption data for the various surfaces and objects present in the room are obtained from published material (see Table 8.4, for example). The total absorption of the various surfaces is then estimated from the following equations: For all $\alpha_i < 0.2$,

$$A = \sum_i S_i \alpha_i \qquad (6.9)$$

where S_i = area of a given surface and α_i = absorption coefficient of the surface. For $\bar{\alpha} > 0.2$ and all α_i approximately equal,

$$A = -S \ln(1 - \bar{\alpha}) \qquad (6.10)$$

For large differences between α_i, and at least one value where $\alpha_i > 0.2$,

$$A = -\sum_i S_i \ln(1 - \alpha_i) \qquad (6.11)$$

When the values for α_i or $\bar{\alpha}$ exceed 0.63 in Eq. (6.10) or (6.11), the apparent absorption exceeds 1 sabin per unit area. In this case, the assumption that the sound field is diffuse has been violated, and the equations are no longer valid.

Values for α_n, α_{SAB}, and α_{ST} are frequency-dependent and are usually listed in tabular form at octave-band center frequencies from 125 to 4000 Hz. In some cases the Noise Reduction Coefficient value is specified; this single number rating is the arithmetic average of Sabine absorption coefficients at the four intermediate octave-band frequencies:

$$\mathrm{NRC} = \frac{\alpha_{250} + \alpha_{500} + \alpha_{1000} + \alpha_{2000}}{4}$$

Care should be exercised when using NRC values for comparison or selection of materials, because their absorption coefficients can vary widely with frequency even though their NRC values may be similar.

6.3 DIRECTIVITY

The directivity factor Q_θ of a given noise source is the ratio (at angle θ) of the acoustic intensity at radius r in a free field to the intensity of an ideal (point) source with the same acoustic power. Thus

$$Q_\theta = \frac{(p_{\mathrm{rms}}^2)_\theta}{(\bar{p}_{\mathrm{rms}}^2)} \qquad (6.12)$$

where $(p_{rms}^2)_\theta$ = mean square acoustic pressure measured at angle θ and radius r from the source

$\bar{p}_{rms}^2$ = mean square acoustic pressure averaged over the surface of an imaginary sphere or radius r centered on the source

An approximation for $\bar{p}_{rms}^2$ can be calculated from

$$\bar{p}_{rms}^2 = \frac{1}{n} \sum_n p_{i\,rms}^2$$

where $p_{i\,rms}^2$ = mean square acoustic pressure at one of n equally spaced locations on the surface of the imaginary sphere. Note that the definition of Q_θ requires that some values be less than 1 if others are greater than 1.

The directivity index DI of a noise source in a free field is defined by

$$\begin{aligned} \mathrm{DI}_\theta &= 10 \log_{10} Q_\theta \\ &= L_{p\theta} - \overline{L_p} \end{aligned} \tag{6.13}$$

where $L_{p\theta}$ = sound level at angle θ and radius r from the source, and $\overline{L_p}$ = average sound level at radius r from the source. The average sound level can be calculated from a series of n measurements on the surface of an imaginary sphere according to

$$\overline{L_p} = \sum_{\log} L_{p_i} - 10 \log_{10} n \tag{6.14}$$

The summation symbol means that the levels L_{pi} must be summed logarithmically, using Fig. 1.6 or the relation

$$\sum_{\log} L_{p_i} = 10 \log_{10} \left[\sum_{i=1}^{n} 10^{L_{p_i}/10} \right] \tag{6.15}$$

Since the directivity of a source is a function of frequency, values of Q_θ and DI_θ should be determined in all frequency bands of interest. A typical directivity pattern for jet noise is given in Fig. 6.6.

The directivity index of an arbitrary sound source radiating nonuniformly into a free field can be determined from Eq. (6.13) by placing the source in an anechoic room and measuring the sound level L_{pi} at n equally spaced locations

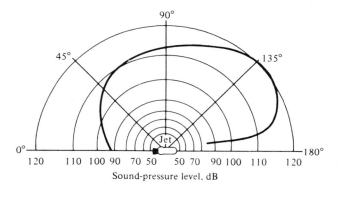

Figure 6.6 Radiation pattern of a noise source with pronounced directivity [3].

at the surface of an imaginary sphere of radius r centered at the source. The radius r of the microphone locations should be chosen so that all locations fall in the far field of the source (-6 dB per doubling of distance from source), but far enough away from the edges of the test room so that free-field conditions prevail. Coordinates for equal spacing of microphones on a unit sphere are given in Table 6.1 for 20-, 12-, and 8-point arrays. These values must be multiplied by r to obtain microphone locations in the anechoic test chamber.

If the source is normally located above a reflecting plane, then corresponding values for Q_θ and DI_θ should be calculated from measurements made in a semi-anechoic room. (Determination of directional properties in a reverberation room is not possible because the sound field is diffuse and, therefore, nondirectional.) Microphone locations for directivity measurements in a semi-anechoic room are given in Fig. 6.7.

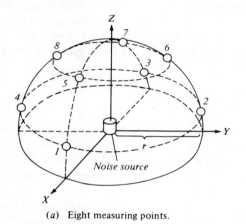

(a) Eight measuring points.

Microphone positions	X	Y	Z
1	0.97r	0	0.25r
2	0	0.97r	0.25r
3	−0.97r	0	0.25r
4	0	−0.97r	0.25r
5	0.63r	0	0.78r
6	0	0.63r	0.78r
7	−0.63r	0	0.78r
8	0	−0.63r	0.78r

r = radius of hemisphere

○ = microphone positions

(b) Six measuring points.

Microphone positions	X	Y	Z
1	0.89r	0	0.45r
2	0.28r	0.85r	0.45r
3	−0.72r	0.53r	0.45r
4	−0.72r	−0.53r	0.45r
5	0.28	−0.85r	0.45r
6	0	0	r

Figure 6.7 Examples of the distribution of measuring points over a hypothetical hemisphere surrounding the source of noise [3].

6.4 SOUND POWER

Sound power usually represents only a tiny fraction of the total power developed by mechanical devices. As a result, sound power is almost always independent of surroundings (the source is "unaware" of its surroundings). By comparison, sound *pressure* is dependent on both sound power and the influence of surroundings.

Sound power is a valuable measure of acoustical performance because it is dependent only on the characteristics of the source. However, the purchaser may have difficulty in converting sound-power data for a machine to corresponding sound-pressure levels after installation. In some cases manufacturers will specify sound levels (usually in dBA) at specified distances and directions; examples are large cooling towers and transformers. In the first case, A-weighted sound levels at a distance of 50 ft with the equipment located above a reflecting plane (asphalt, concrete surface, etc.) may be specified. These surroundings are typical of actual use; since the sound levels are measured in the free field, the corresponding levels at other distances can be estimated from spherical spreading:

$$\text{dBA}_{r_2} = \text{dBA}_{r_1} - 10 \log_{10} \frac{r_2^2}{r_1^2} \tag{6.16}$$

where r_1 is the initial measurement distance and r_2 is the desired measurement distance. In the second case, close-in (near-field) sound levels may be specified at various locations around the transformer, for example. The NEMA (National Electrical Manufacturers Association) Code requires a series of A-weighted measurements at 1 ft from the nearest surface.

The sound-power level L_w of a noise source is calculated from measurements of sound-pressure level in specified environments (sound fields). These environments are a free field, a free field above a reflecting plane, and a reverberant field. Each of these measurement methods is discussed below.

Measurement of Sound Power in a Free Field

A free field, in which sound waves travel outward from the source without reflection, is simulated in an anechoic room. All interior surfaces of the room are covered with acoustical material that absorbs at least 99 percent of the direct sound radiated by the source above a minimum (or cutoff) frequency. The most common types of materials are

- Glass-fiber wedges, 18 to 24 in deep, with a base approximately 10 in square (cutoff frequency approximately 100 Hz)
- Perforated sheet metal covering 4 in of glass fiber (cutoff frequency approximately 250 Hz)

Sound power is calculated from a series of free-field sound-level measurements (in full- or 1/3-octave bands) obtained on the surface of an imaginary sphere centered on the source. The portion of sound power passing through a segment of the spherical surface S_i is given by

$$W_i = I_i S_i$$

$$= p_{i_{rms}}^2 \frac{S_i}{\rho c}$$

where $W_i =$ sound power passing through area S_i, in a given frequency band
$I_i =$ average intensity passing through surface area S_i
$p_{i_{rms}}^2 =$ mean square acoustic pressure at center of surface area S_i

The total acoustic power W generated by the source is, from Sec. 1.6,

$$W = \sum_{i=1}^{n} \frac{p_{i_{rms}}^2 S_i}{\rho_o c} \tag{1.19}$$

If each segment has the same area S,

$$W = \frac{S}{\rho_o c} \sum_i p_{i_{rms}}^2 \tag{6.17}$$

Equation (6.17) can also be written

$$W = \frac{\bar{p}_{rms}^2 4\pi r^2}{\rho_o c} \tag{6.18}$$

where

$$\bar{p}_{rms}^2 = \frac{\sum\limits_{i=1}^{n} p_{i_{rms}}^2}{n} \tag{6.19}$$

the average mean square pressure on the surface of the sphere and

$$nS_1^{\cdot} = 4\pi r^2$$

is the surface area of the sphere

If both sides of Eq. (6.18) are divided by the reference values for L_p and L_w, the value for $\rho_o c$ at standard conditions (415 mks rayls) is substituted, and 10 times the logarithm of both sides is taken, the result is

$$L_w = \overline{L_p} + 20 \log_{10} r + 11 \text{ dB} \tag{6.20}$$

where r is in meters. If r is expressed in feet:

$$L_w = \overline{L_p} + 20 \log_{10} r + 0.5 \text{ dB} \tag{6.21}$$

where $L_w =$ sound-power level of source
$\overline{Lp} =$ sound-pressure level of source in a specific frequency band, averaged over the surface of a sphere of radius r on an energy basis
$r =$ distance from "acoustic center"* of source

* The "acoustic center" is that point from which the sound power can be generated in a given frequency band to establish a sound field identical to that produced by the actual source.

Table 6.1 Coordinates of unit sphere

20-point array			12-point array			8-point array		
x	y	z	x	y	z	x	y	z
0	0.93	0.36	0	0.89	0.45	0	0.82	0.58
0	0.93	−0.36	0.53	0.72	−0.45	0	0.82	−0.58
0.58	0.58	0.58	0.85	0.28	0.45	0.82	0	0.58
0.58	0.58	−0.58	0.85	−0.28	−0.45	0.82	0	−0.58
0.93	0.36	0	0.53	−0.72	0.45	0	−0.82	0.58
0.36	0	0.93	0	−0.89	−0.45	0	−0.82	−0.58
0.36	0	−0.93	−0.53	−0.72	0.45	−0.82	0	0.58
0.93	−0.36	0	−0.85	−0.28	−0.45	−0.82	0	−0.58
0.58	−0.58	0.58	−0.85	0.28	0.45			
0.58	−0.58	−0.58	−0.53	0.72	−0.45			
0	−0.93	0.36	3	0	1			
0	−0.93	−0.36	0	0	−1			
−0.58	−0.58	0.58						
−0.58	−0.58	−0.58						
−0.93	−0.36	0						
−0.36	0	0.93						
−0.36	0	−0.93						
−0.93	0.36	0						
−0.58	0.58	0.58						
−0.58	0.58	−0.58						

Equations (6.20) and (6.21) are valid for measurements obtained in the free field of the source. A guideline for estimating the minimum distance r_{min} for free-field conditions is: r_{min} should be the greater of a major source dimension, or a wavelength of the center frequency of interest, from the nearest surface of the source.* In addition, measurement locations should be at least $\lambda/2$ away from absorbing surfaces. Table 6.1 can be used to determine suitable microphone locations for free-field sound-power measurements.

Measurement of Sound Power in a Free Field above a Reflecting Plane

A free field above a reflecting plane can be simulated by a room with a "hard" (acoustically reflective) floor and absorbing walls and ceiling. This type of facility is popular because the source can be placed directly on the floor (rather than suspended) and because directional properties can be measured in an environment similar to that commonly found in actual use. Sound level measurements are recorded on the surface of an imaginary hemisphere centered

---

* This guideline is useful in many practical situations where, in the frequency band of interest, the noise is more or less uniform and not highly directional. However, the minimum measurement distance should be increased if a dominant pure tone is present or if the source is highly directional, particularly at frequencies above 3000 Hz.

on the source (see Fig. 6.7), and an average mean square pressure is calculated, as described earlier. The resulting equations for W and L_w are identical to Eqs. (6.20) and (6.21), except for a 3-dB correction. This correction occurs because the total sound power of the source passes through a hemisphere rather than a sphere (the floor is assumed to be a perfect reflector). For a free field above a reflecting plane,

$$L_w = \overline{Lp} + 20 \log_{10} r + 8 \text{ dB} \qquad (r \text{ in meters}) \qquad (6.22)$$

$$L_w = \overline{Lp} + 20 \log_{10} r - 2.5 \text{ dB} \qquad (r \text{ in feet}) \qquad (6.23)$$

One potential difficulty with measurements above a reflecting plane may arise when the source generates a dominant pure tone. In this instance, significant standing waves will result from the interaction of direct sound and sound waves reflected from the floor.* As a result, the mean square acoustic pressure and Lp are not directly related to acoustic intensity. Assuming that such a relationship exists [by use of Eq. (6.22) or (6.23)] can introduce an error of 5 to 10 dB into the value of L_w calculated for the frequency band that includes the pure tone. Standing-wave effects can be minimized by locating the source of the pure tone as close as possible to the reflecting plane. This procedure minimizes the difference in path lengths traveled by direct and reflected sound waves, so that the phase difference between the waves approaches zero.

Measurement of Sound Power in a Reverberant Field

Perhaps the most common method for measuring sound power utilizes a reverberation room (or, with some sacrifice in accuracy, a space in which reflected sound is dominant). The source is located in the room, usually in a corner or near a wall, so that maximum room response occurs. Theoretically, only a single measurement of Lp in each frequency band of interest is required, provided that the measurement location is in the diffuse sound field. A sound field is assumed diffuse if the following apply:

• $\overline{\alpha} < 0.2$ in the frequency band of interest ($\overline{\alpha}$ is the average absorption coefficient for the room).
•   At least 20 distinct room modes are present in the frequency band of interest.[†]
•   Direct sound from the source is insignificant as compared with reverberant sound.

---

*As discussed in Sec. 6.2, all reflected waves combine with direct sound to produce standing waves at each frequency in the band of interest. However, if none of these frequencies is dominant, standing-wave effects tend to average out over the band, and the mean square pressure for the band becomes proportional to the acoustic intensity in the vicinity of the measurement location.

[†] This requirement provides an acceptable modal coverage in the lowest frequency band of interest. In a well-designed reverberation room of volume V, the requirement is met if $V > (4/3)\lambda^3$ (λ is center frequency of lowest octave band); or if $V > 4\lambda^3$ (λ is center frequency of lowest 1/3-octave band). The reader should also refer to Sec. 4.5.

In practice, Lp varies somewhat throughout the reverberant space, especially in the lower frequency bands where fewer room modes are present.* In addition, the source may radiate dominant pure tones that produce standing waves in one or more frequency bands. For these reasons, Lp is usually space-averaged on an energy basis over a region having a characteristic dimension of at least 1/2 wavelength of the lowest center frequency of interest.† A microphone is mounted on a boom or traverse for this purpose. The path of the microphone defines a plane if the path is curved, a line if the path is straight. If neither the plane nor the line is parallel to any surface of the room, the accuracy of the space-time-averaged sound pressure will be improved. (A body diagonal of the room is often used when the path is a straight line.) An alternate method employs up to six microphones distributed throughout the reverberant space; the microphone output voltages are averaged on an intensity basis to provide a value of Lp that is representative of room response.

The relationship between mean square acoustic pressure and the sound power in a diffuse sound field, developed in Chap. 4, is

$$W = \frac{\overline{p_{rms}}^2 R}{4\rho c}$$

where $W =$ sound power, W
$\overline{p_{rms}} =$ average rms acoustic pressure, N/m^2
$R =$ room constant, metric sabins
$= S\bar{\alpha}/(1 - \bar{\alpha})$‡
$\rho c =$ characteristic impedance of medium, mks rayls

Introducing the appropriate reference quantities and taking 10 times the logarithm of both sides yields

$$L_W = \overline{Lp} - 10 \log_{10} \frac{4}{R} \text{ dB} \tag{6.24}$$

where $\rho c = 415$ mks rayls. If R is in ft^2, Eq. (6.24) becomes

$$L_W = \overline{Lp} - 10 \log_{10} \frac{4}{R} - 10 \text{ dB} \tag{6.25}$$

It is important to recognize that the sound level at any location in a reverberant space is a combination of direct and reflected sound waves. If direct radiation (which diminishes in intensity as r^2) is negligible, then a reverberant§ (ideally, diffuse) sound field exists at the measurement location. However, direct radiation is significant in cases where r is small and/or the source is highly

---

* In a well-designed reverberation room, variations in Lp should be 2 dB or less. Variations up to 6 dB in lower frequency bands are acceptable in most practical cases.
† The Lp value obtained in this way is termed a *space-time-averaged* sound-pressure level, $\overline{Lp}$.
‡ This expression for R assumes a diffuse sound field, in which $R = S\bar{\alpha}_s/(1 - \bar{\alpha}_s)$. Usually, values for $\bar{\alpha}_{SAB}$, rather than $\bar{\alpha}_s$, are available; in this case a better estimate for R is $R \simeq s\bar{\alpha}_{SAB}$.
§ All measurement locations should be at least $\lambda/2$ of the center frequency of interest away from the nearest surface of the room, for acceptable diffusivity.

directional. In this situation, the direct sound contribution can be calculated from

$$W = \frac{(p_{rms}^2)_\theta}{Q_\theta \rho c} 4\pi r^2 \qquad (6.26)$$

where $p_{rms}^2(\theta)$ = mean square acoustic pressure radiated by source at angle θ and Q_θ = directivity factor at measurement location. The reverberant sound contribution, developed in Chap. 4, is given by $4\rho c W/R$. The mean square acoustic pressure at the measurement location is obtained by combining the direct and reverberant contributions on an energy basis:

$$p_{rms}^2 = (p_{rms}^2)_d + (p_{rms}^2)_r$$

Thus:

$$p_{rms}^2 = \frac{\rho c Q_\theta W}{4\pi r^2} + \frac{4\rho c W}{R}$$

Solving for W:

$$W = \frac{p_{rms}^2}{\rho c} \left(\frac{Q_\theta}{4\pi r^2} + \frac{4}{R} \right)^{-1} \qquad (6.27)$$

A similar expression [Eq. (4.38)] was developed in Chap. 4. Expressing Eq. (6.27) in terms of Lp and L_w, and substituting 415 mks rayls for ρc:

$$L_w = L_p - 10 \log_{10}\left(\frac{Q_\theta}{4\pi r^2} + \frac{4}{R} \right) \qquad \text{dB} \qquad (6.28)$$

where R, a are in metric units. If R, a are in feet and feet squared, respectively,

$$L_w = L_p - 10 \log_{10}\left(\frac{Q_\theta}{4\pi r^2} + \frac{4}{R} \right) - 10 \qquad \text{dB} \qquad (6.29)$$

Measurement of Sound Power Using a Reference Source

A simple method for measuring the sound power of a source, usually in place, employs a reference source whose sound-power output (in octave or 1/3-octave frequency bands) is known. The procedure requires an open space in which reverberant sound dominates. The frequency spectra of the actual and reference sources should also be similar; that is, they should be broadband in nature, without dominant pure tones. Two reference sources in current use are

• An unhoused 6-in-diameter squirrel-cage blower driven by a 1/4-hp electric motor (ILG Industries)
• An 8-in loudspeaker driven by selectable bands of random noise (B & K Instruments)

Each of these sources generates a relatively flat sound-power spectrum from 100 to 10,000 Hz. The measurement procedure is:

1. Select one (or preferably several) representative microphone locations in the reverberant field. Each location should be in view of the noise source.
2. Measure the ambient-noise spectrum with both sources shut off, so that its contribution to sound levels with sources operating can be assessed.
3. Measure the sound levels (overall and in frequency bands) at each location, with each source operating separately. The reference source should be located close to the actual source. Average the sound levels from the measurement locations on an energy basis.

Calculation of the sound power of an actual source proceeds as follows. A reverberant sound field is present, so Eq. (6.24) or (6.25) can be written:

$$L_w = \overline{L_p} + C \tag{6.30}$$

where L_w = sound-power level of source, overall or in a given frequency band
$\overline{L_p}$ = average sound level
C = constant determined by surroundings

The constant C is identical when either source is operating because measurement locations are the same, source locations are similar, and sound-power spectra are similar. Therefore,

$$L_{w,s} = \overline{L_{p,s}} + C$$

$$L_{w,c} = \overline{L_{p,c}} + C$$

where subscript s refers to the actual source and subscript c refers to the reference source. Subtracting yields, after rearrangement of terms,

$$L_{w,s} = L_{w,c} + \overline{L_{p,s}} - \overline{L_{p,c}} \tag{6.31}$$

All of the terms on the right side of Eq. (6.31) are known, so L_{ws} can be calculated.

6.5 ATTENUATION OF SOUND BY STRUCTURES

Four measurements are commonly used to describe the ability of a barrier (such as a wall, floor, door, or enclosure) or other structure (such as a muffler) to *attenuate* the passage of acoustic energy: these are airborne sound transmission loss, noise reduction, insertion loss, and impact sound transmission loss.

Airborne sound transmission loss Airborne STL is defined as follows:

$$\text{STL} = 10 \log_{10} \frac{1}{\tau} \tag{6.32}$$

where τ is the transmission coefficient and is equal to incident intensity/transmitted intensity. Measurement of sound transmission loss (often shortened to "transmission loss") requires mounting the test panel between two reverberation rooms. The rooms are isolated from the surroundings and each other, so that all the acoustic energy in the *receiver* room is transmitted from the *source* room through the test panel. The source of sound is usually random noise, and averaged sound levels in the source and receiver rooms ($\bar{L}_1$ and $\bar{L}_2$, respectively) are measured in the preferred 1/3-octave bands extending from 125 to 4000 Hz.* Test panels usually measure 8 by 8 ft, except for doors and panels of smaller size. Construction and installation of panels are the same as in actual use, but unwanted transmission paths (at the edges of the panel, for example) are eliminated insofar as possible.†

Sound transmission loss is calculated from

$$\text{STL} = \bar{L}_1 - \bar{L}_2 + 10 \log_{10} \frac{S}{a} \qquad \text{dB} \qquad (6.33)$$

This equation is obtained as follows. The sound power impinging on the test specimen from the source side is

$$W_s = \frac{\bar{p}_s^2}{4\rho c} S \qquad \text{W}$$

where W_s = sound power generated in source room, W
$\bar{p}_s^2$ = space-time average mean square pressure in source room, N/m²
S = surface area of test specimen, m²

In the receiver room the rate of energy transmission into the room equals the rate of energy absorption, at steady-state conditions. Thus

$$W_r = IA$$

or

$$W_r = \frac{\bar{p}_r^2 A}{4\rho c} \qquad \text{W}$$

where I = average intensity at room surfaces, W/m²
W_r = sound power delivered to receiver room
$\bar{p}_r^2$ = space-time average mean square pressure in receiver room, N/m²
A = absorption in receiver room, m²

From the definition of transmission coefficient:

$$\tau = \frac{\bar{p}_s^2 S}{\bar{p}_r^2 A}$$

* Sometimes "average transmission loss" or "average attenuation" values are published. These values are usually an arithmetic average of 1/3-octave STL data from 125 to 4000 Hz. Average STL is of relatively little value for design purposes, particularly at low and high frequencies.

† For further information, refer to ASTM Standard E90-70, "Standard Recommended Practice for Laboratory Measurement of Airborne Sound Transmission Loss of Buildings."

where ρc is identical in both the source and receiver rooms. Therefore,

$$\text{STL} = 10 \log_{10} \frac{\bar{p}_s^2}{\bar{p}_r^2} \frac{S}{A}$$

$$= 10 \log_{10} \frac{\bar{p}_s^2 / p_{\text{ref}}^2}{\bar{p}_r^2 / p_{\text{ref}}^2} + 10 \log_{10} \frac{S}{A}$$

$$= 10 \log_{10} \frac{\bar{p}_s^2}{p_{\text{ref}}^2} - 10 \log_{10} \frac{\bar{p}_r^2}{p_{\text{ref}}^2} + 10 \log_{10} \frac{S}{A}$$

$$= \bar{L}_1 - \bar{L}_2 + 10 \log_{10} \frac{S}{A}$$

In actual installations, the transmission loss is less than that measured in a laboratory test, often by 5 or more dB. The principal reason for this difference is the presence of alternate transmission paths (flanking paths) introduced during fabrication or construction. When field STL is measured, the absorption in the receiver room is usually estimated, as is the contribution from flanking paths.

Frequently, a structure will present several transmission paths to arriving sound waves; an example is a partition or wall with glass panels and one or more doors with leaks around the edges. Each of these paths has a specific transmission coefficient in each frequency band of interest (the coefficient of airborne paths such as cracks around doors is approximately 1). Let the transmission coefficients in a given frequency band be designated by τ_i. The acoustic power transmitted by all elements is proportional to $\Sigma_i \tau_i S_i$, where S_i is the surface area of element i. An equivalent transmission coefficient τ_{eq} is obtained from

$$\tau_{\text{eq}} S = \sum \tau_i S_i$$

$$\tau_{\text{eq}} = \frac{\sum \tau_i S_i}{S} \tag{6.34}$$

where S is the surface area of the composite structure. The corresponding sound transmission loss is given by

$$\text{STL} = 10 \log_{10} \frac{1}{\tau_{\text{eq}}} \tag{6.35}$$

Sound transmission class STC is a single-number rating used primarily to rate the speech privacy of a barrier or other structure. It is determined from a plot of STL data measured in 1/3-octave bands from 125 to 4000 Hz. An "STC contour," shown in Fig. 6.8, is fitted to the data subject to the following conditions:

1. The STL value at any frequency cannot be more than 8 dB below the STC contour.

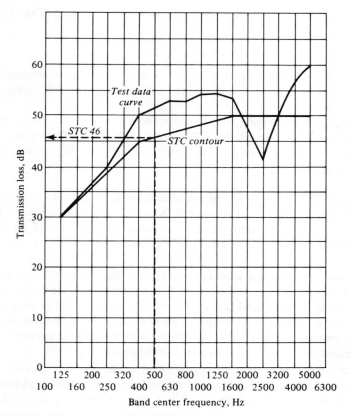

Figure 6.8 Representative transmission loss data and corresponding STC contour. *(From Owens-Corning Fiberglass Corp.)*

2. The sum of all "deficiencies" (STL less than contour value) at all frequencies cannot exceed 32 dB.

The STC value is obtained from the STL value of the highest-valued contour at 500 Hz.

The sound transmission class number is used to rate the acoustic performance of walls, floors, ceilings, doors, folding partitions, panels, and other architectural structures. It is frequently specified as a performance criterion by architects and engineers for places where speech privacy is of primary interest. However, the STC rating is of limited value for other applications, such as the design of enclosures for attenuating low-frequency sound (below 250 Hz). In these cases STL data in 1/3-octave bands are preferable.

Noise reduction NR is a field measurement which includes the effect of flanking paths, without correction for the barrier area or the absorption in the receiver room. It is simply the difference between space-time-averaged sound levels (usually measured in 1/3-octave bands from 125 to 4000 Hz) in the receiver and source rooms. Thus

$$\text{NR} = \overline{L}_1 - \overline{L}_2 \tag{6.36}$$

Noise reduction is a useful measurement in many practical situations because it is a measure of the attenuation of a given structure as installed, under conditions of actual service.

A single-number rating for barriers, based on noise reduction data, is termed the *noise isolation class* (NIC) rating. The NIC rating is determined in exactly the same manner as the STC rating, except that NR values, rather than STL values, are plotted.

Insertion loss This is the difference in sound levels measured at a given location before and after a barrier or silencer is installed. This measurement provides a direct indication of the improvement provided by insertion of an attenuating structure between the noise source and the listener.

Impact sound transmission loss This measures the ability of a given structure (usually a floor-ceiling construction) to attenuate mechanical impacts from sources such as footfalls and falling objects. The loading in this case is mechanical contact over a small area, rather than uniform loading from airborne sound. Since the loading is different, a structure with good STL properties may not perform equally well when the source is mechanical impact.

A standard reference source, or tapping machine, is used to obtain impact STL measurements. The source is a motor-driven camshaft that picks up and releases six weights in succession. When the weights are released, they fall through a specified distance before contacting the surface below (usually a floor). The result is a series of impacts, each of a known amplitude, occurring at a specified rate. A typical arrangement is shown in Fig. 6.9.*

Because the tapping machine is a calibrated reference source, only the space-time average L_p in the receiver room† (beneath the tapping machine) need be measured. The relationship between $\overline{L}_p$ and impact STL (ISTL) is obtained as follows.

At steady state, the rate at which acoustic energy is supplied to the receiver room is proportional to $(\bar{p}_{rms}^2)_r A$, where $(p_{rms})_r$ = space-time-averaged acoustic pressure (overall or in a given frequency band) and A = absorption in receiver room. Dividing by p_{ref}^2, introducing a "standard" or "reference" absorption A_0, and taking $10 \log_{10}$ of the resulting expression gives

$$\text{ISTL} = \overline{L}_p + 10 \log_{10} \frac{A}{A_0} \tag{6.37}$$

where $A_0 = 10 \text{ m}^2$.

---

* For further information, refer to ASTM Standard E492-73T, "Impact Sound Transmission through Floor-Ceiling Assemblies Using the Tapping Machine."
† A reverberant sound field in the receiver room is assumed.

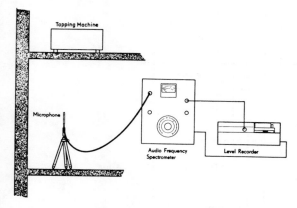

(*a*) Equipment for measuring impact sound transmission loss.

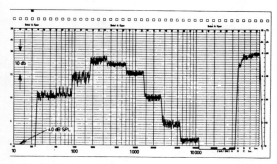

(*b*) Typical octave band spectrum in receiver room.

Figure 6.9 Measurement of impact sound transmission loss. *(From B & K Instruments, Inc.)*

Impact insulation class IIC is a single-number rating that describes the ability of a structure to attenuate impact sounds in the frequency range from 100 to 3200 Hz. The determination of IIC proceeds in the same manner as described for STC, except that a different contour is used (Fig. 6.10). The contour is fitted to the L_{p_r} values, measured in 1/3-octave bands, according to the following criteria:

-   The deficiency at any frequency must be 8 dB or less.
-   The sum of deficiencies at all frequencies must not exceed 32 dB.

(These are the same criteria used to determine STC.) The IIC rating is the contour value at 500 Hz. Recommended IIC and STC values for multifamily dwellings are listed in Table 8.14.

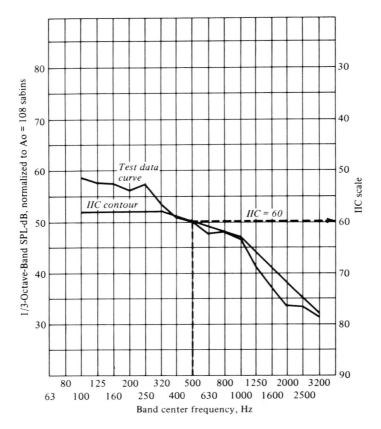

Figure 6.10 Representative impact noise levels and corresponding IIC contour. *(From Owens-Corning Fiberglass Corp.)*

REFERENCES*

1. B & K Instruments, Inc., *Architectural Acoustics*, Cleveland, Ohio, 1968.
2. Beranek, L. L. (ed.), *Noise and Vibration Control*, McGraw-Hill, New York, 1971.
3. Broach, J. T., *Acoustic Noise Measurements*, 2d ed., B & K Instruments, Inc., Cleveland, Ohio, 1971.
4. Davern, W., "Impedance Chart for Designing Sound Absorber Systems," *J. Sound Vibr.*, November 1967.
5. Diehl, George, *Machinery Acoustics*, Wiley-Interscience, New York, 1973.
6. Dubout, P., and W. Davern, "Calculation of the Statistical Absorption Coefficient from Impedance Tube Measurements," *Acustica* **9**:53 (1959).
7. Holmer, C., and D. Lubman, "Comparison of Microphone Traverse and Microphone Array for Determining Space Average Sound Pressure Level in a Reverberation Room," *Noise Control Eng.*, September-October 1976.
8. Peterson, A. P., and Ervin E. Gross, *Handbook of Noise Measurement*, 7th ed., General Radio Company, Concord, Mass., 1974.

* Standards for acoustical measurements are listed in Chap. 7.

IMPORTANT TERMS AND FORMULAS

Reverberation time: T

Normal-incidence absorption coefficient: $\alpha_n = \dfrac{4 p_{max} p_{min}}{(1 + p_{max}/p_{min})^2}$

Standing wave

Acoustical impedance

Sabine absorption coefficient: $\bar{\alpha}_{SAB} = \dfrac{0.161 V}{S_s}\left(\dfrac{1}{T_s} - \dfrac{1}{T_e}\right) + \alpha_i$ mks units

Absorption: $A = \sum_i S_i \alpha_i$

    or $A = -S \ln(1 - \bar{\alpha})$

    or $A = -\sum_i S_i \ln(1 - \alpha_i)$

Directivity index: $DI = 10 \log_{10} Q_\theta$

Sound-power measurement in a free field:

$$L_w = \overline{L_p} + 20 \log_{10} r + 11 \text{ dB} \qquad \text{mks units}$$

Sound-power measurement in a free field above a reflecting plane:

$$L_w = \overline{L_p} + 20 \log_{10} r + 8 \text{ dB} \qquad \text{mks units}$$

Sound-power measurement in a reverberant field:

$$L_w = \overline{L_p} - 10 \log_{10} \dfrac{4}{R} \qquad \text{mks units}$$

Modal coverage

Space-time-averaged sound level: $\overline{L_p}$

Sound-power measurement in a combined sound field:

$$L_w = L_p - 10 \log_{10}\left(\dfrac{Q_\theta}{4\pi r^2} + \dfrac{4}{R}\right) \qquad \text{mks units}$$

Sound-power measurement using a reference source:

$$L_{w,s} = L_{w,c} + \overline{L_{p,s}} - \overline{L_{p,c}}$$

Sound transmission loss: $STL = 10 \log_{10}\dfrac{1}{\tau}$

$$= \overline{L_1} - \overline{L_2} + 10 \log_{10}\dfrac{S}{A}$$

Equivalent transmission coefficient: $\tau_{eq} = \dfrac{\sum \tau_i S_i}{S}$

Sound transmission class, STC

Noise reduction, NR

Impact sound transmission loss, ISTL

$$\text{ISTL} = \overline{L_p} + 10 \log_{10} \frac{A}{A_0}$$

Impact insulation class, IIC

PROBLEMS

6.1 (a) Using Fig. 6.2 as a guide, calculate the amount of absorption required in octave bands from 125 to 4000 Hz in a multipurpose auditorium/gymnasium with length, width, and height of 80 ft, 40 ft, and 25 ft, respectively.

(b) If the gymnasium floor is wood, the walls are painted concrete block, and the ceiling is a steel deck, how much absorption must be added in each octave band to achieve the recommended reverberation time?

6.2 Show that (a) the phase shift $2(\omega/c)x$ in Eq. (6.1) is equivalent to the number of wavelengths represented by $2x$, where each wavelength represents a phase shift of 2π rad, (b) the distance between adjacent pressure minima in an impedance tube is λ-2.

6.3 Derive Eq. (6.2) by treating p_i and p_r as vectors rotating at angular velocity ω (refer to Fig. 6.4).

6.4 (a) Using Eq. (6.2), show that the pressure maximum in an impedance tube is $A + B$ and that the pressure minimum is $A - B$.

(b) Derive the expression for α_n Eq. (6.5), beginning with [Eq. (6.4)].

6.5 Standing-wave measurements are often obtained in decibels by using a sound level meter as the output device.

(a) Show that the "standing-wave ratio" $L_{p,\,max} - L_{p,\,min} = 10 \log_{10} (p_{max}/p_{min})^2$.

(b) Plot a graph of α_n versus the standing-wave ratio, for values of α_n ranging from 1.0 to 0.1.

6.6 The following values were obtained in a standing-wave tube for a sample of acoustical material:

Octave-band center frequency, Hz	$L_{p,\,max}$	$L_{p,\,min}$
125	105	85
250	110	92
500	108	98
1000	110	105
2000	98	89
4000	95	82

Calculate α_n at each frequency and plot α_n versus frequency (connect plotted values with straight lines).

6.7 The phase angle θ at the termination of a standing-wave tube can be calculated if the distances of two adjacent pressure minima from the termination are known. Make use of the fact that adjacent minima are separated by $\lambda/2$ and that $\lambda = c/f$ to obtain

$$\theta = \frac{2\pi L_{min_1}}{L_{min_2} - L_{min_1}} \quad \text{rad}$$

where L_{min_1} = location of minimum nearer to termination.

6.8 A rigid termination to a standing-wave tube results in $B = A$ and $\theta = 0$ rad.

(*a*) Calculate the pressure and particle velocity at the termination. (The particle velocity is the vector summation of the individual particle velocities of the incident and reflected waves.)

(*b*) Plot $|p|$ versus x, the distance from the termination, if $L_{p_{max}} = 100$ dB at a frequency of 500 Hz. Let x range from 0 to λ. On the same graph, plot $|p|$ versus x if $L_{p_{max}} = 100$ dB, $L_{p_{min}} = 95$ dB at a frequency of 500 Hz, and $\theta = 0$ rad.

6.9 The quantity $(B/A) \angle \theta$ is called the *reflection factor*.

(*a*) Show that $R_0 = B/A$, the magnitude of the reflection factor, is given by

$$R_0 = \frac{p_{max} - p_{min}}{p_{max} + p_{min}}$$

(*b*) Use the vector representation of incident and reflected waves shown in Fig. 6.4 to obtain the following expression for acoustical impedance at the termination of a standing-wave tube:

$$Z_0 = \left| \frac{P}{u} \right| = \left(\frac{1 + 2R_0 \cos \theta + R_0^2}{1 - 2R_0 \cos \theta + R_0^2} \right)^{1/2} \rho c$$

6.10 Beginning with $I_t = I_0 e^{-act/4V}$, the equation for decay of a diffuse sound field, obtain the expression for the change in intensity level, $\Delta IL = -1.087(act/V)$.

6.11 A reverberation room measures 8 m by 6.25 m by 5 m high. Sound-level-decay curves are shown for the 500-Hz octave band, with the room empty and with a 4- by 8-ft sample of acoustical material placed in the room. Calculate the random-incidence absorption coefficient.

500-Hz octave band

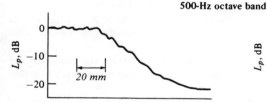 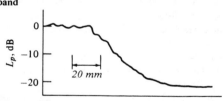

Paper speed, 30 mm/s

6.12 A multipurpose room measures 40 ft by 25 ft by 10 ft high. The ceiling consists of suspended acoustical panels 5/8 in thick, the walls are painted concrete block, and the floor is asphalt tile over poured concrete. Calculate the reverberation times at 500, 1000, and 2000 Hz using Eqs. (4.17), (6.9), (6.11), and (6.12). Which equation is more accurate? Why?

6.13 Beginning with the equation for reverberation time in a diffuse sound field [Eq. (6.15)], derive the equation for the random-incidence absorption coefficient [Eq. (6.18)].

6.14 Plot a curve of sound level $L_{p, r}$ versus distance r from a source in a free field. Use coordinates $L_{p, r} - L_{p, 0}$ and r/r_0, where $L_{p, 0} = $ reference sound level at distance r_0. Let $L_{p, r} - L_{p, 0}$ range from 0 to -24 dB.

6.15 A hydraulic motor generates the following sound levels, in the 1000-Hz octave band, at six positions on the surface of an imaginary hemisphere of 2 m radius centered on the pump and located in a free field above a reflecting plane.

(*a*) If all locations are centered on surface elements of equal area, calculate the sound power and sound-power level of the pump in the 2000-Hz octave band.

(*b*) Calculate the directivity factor and directivity index at each location.

Position	L_p, dB
1	93–95
2	89–90
3	94–95
4	97–98
5	98–99
6	91–92

6.16 The sound reflected into the free field above a reflecting plane can be represented by free-field radiation from an "image source" located the same distance below the plane as the actual source is located above it. Using this concept, construct a constant-value L_p contour for an ideal pure-tone source located 1/2 wavelength above a reflecting plane. Plot the contour in a vertical plane passing through the actual and image sources, for angles from 0 to 90°.

6.17 Solve Prob. 6.16 for source-to-plane distances of a full wavelength, 1/4 wavelength, and 1/8 wavelength.

6.18 Beginning with the equation relating average mean square acoustic pressure and sound power in a free field, obtain the equivalent relationships between $\overline{L_p}$ and L_w, for r in feet and in meters.

6.19 Beginning with the expression for sound power in a reverberant field, obtain Eqs. (6.24) and (6.25).

6.20 A nondirectional sound source is placed in a corner of an 8- by 7- by 5-m reverberation room. In the 1000-Hz octave band, the reverberation time for the room is 5.5 s. Calculate and plot the ratio of direct to reflected sound level at distances of 1 to 6 m from the source. At what distance will the reflected sound level be 10 dB greater than the direct sound level?

6.21 Solve Prob. 6.20 for a nondirectional source located in the middle of the room.

6.22 A source generates a 100-dB sound-power level in the 250-Hz octave band. At a radius of 12 ft in a free field the sound level is 85 dB. Calculate the directivity factor and directivity index at the measurement location.

6.23 Beginning with the definition of directivity factor [Eq. (6.12)], obtain the expression for directivity index [Eq. (6.13)]. Show also that the expression for the space-averaged sound level [Eq. (6.14)] is valid.

6.24 Sound levels measured in the source and receiver rooms of a transmission-loss facility are shown below. The test panel is 8 ft square; the receiver room measures 15 by 18 by 23 ft. All surfaces are poured concrete.

  (a) Calculate the number of room modes in the receiver room, in the 1/3-octave bands centered at 100 and 125 Hz.

  (b) Calculate the transmission loss of the test panel at each frequency, and determine the STC value.

1/3-octave-band center frequency, Hz	$L_{p,s}$, dB	$L_{p,r}$, dB	1/3-octave band center frequency, Hz	$L_{p,s}$, dB	$L_{p,r}$, dB
125	90	67	800	97	65
160	92	68	1000	99	68
200	92	65	1250	100	67
250	93	66	1600	102	67
315	94	67	2000	103	67
400	96	67	2500	103	66
500	97	68	3150	100	62
630	97	66	4000	98	61

6.25 Sound levels measured in an apartment building are shown below. The receiver room measures 20 by 12 by 8 ft; its surfaces are deep-pile carpeting and gypsum board. Determine the IIC value of the floor-ceiling construction.

1/3-octave-band center frequency, Hz	$L_{p,r}$, dB	1/3-octave-band center frequency, Hz	$L_{p,r}$, dB
100	70	630	74
125	72	800	72
160	71	1000	70
200	74	1250	67
250	76	1600	65
315	76	2000	60
400	75	2500	55
500	74	3150	49

6.26 Given two sound levels that differ by values from 1 to 6 dB, construct a graph of the arithmetic average of the sound levels versus the corresponding energy average. What is the maximum difference in sound level for which an arithmetic average is acceptable?

NOISE CRITERIA, STANDARDS, AND REGULATIONS

7.1 INTRODUCTION

Regulations for control of noise date back to early Roman times, when chariot racing was prohibited on village streets at night because of adverse effects on the community. The technology needed to deal with noise was put on a firm basis in 1877 with the publication of Lord Rayleigh's classic work *The Theory of Sound*. However, it was not until passage of the Occupational Safety and Health Act of 1970 and the subsequent Noise Control Act of 1972 that Congress established the policy of the United States to promote an environment for all Americans free from noise that jeopardizes their health and welfare. The passage of these two acts has had a profound impact on how we view our environment and has stimulated much activity at all levels of government in the preparation and promulgation of regulations which are concerned with noise and its control. While the primary responsibility for control of noise rests with state and local governments, federal action is essential to deal with major noise sources in commerce, or noise sources affecting employee health and safety in the workplace, where nationwide uniformity of treatment is required.

In this chapter we will discuss various facets of the regulatory process relevant to noise control engineering, with emphasis on understanding those aspects needed to initiate, design, and evaluate noise control programs. In an attempt to clarify the discussion which follows, the meaning of commonly used and misused terminology is defined below in the language of the noise control engineering profession:

Noise regulation: An authoritative rule dealing with details of procedure for noise control (a regulating principle or law). Implicit with the meaning of regulation is the concept of enforcement of a rule by a constituted authority.

Noise ordinance (United States): A local law or noise regulation enacted at the community, township, or country level of government.

Noise standard: A documented method, procedure, or specification related to some aspect of noise (measurement, its effect on people, permissible levels, etc.). In general a noise standard stands on its own as an authoritative procedure or specification generated by a group of particularly competent individuals.

Federal noise standard: A standard which has been adopted as part of a federal noise regulation. When used in this sense the standard becomes part of a rule or law enforceable by a federal agency.

Noise criterion: A quantitative measure or relationship which reflects established effects of exposure to noise. Noise criteria are utilized in standards and regulations to give an indication of the acceptability of a noise environment; hence they are used for evaluating noise environments and in engineering calculations and designs for noise control.

Rating schemes: Methods and procedures employing noise criteria for estimating community response to noise. Rating schemes can be separated into two types: (1) rating *scales*, which describe some aspect of the noise stimulus itself (e.g., A-weighted level); and (2) rating *procedures*, which describe some aspect of the noise stimulus and, in addition, introduce corrections for peculiarities of the noise (tones, impulses, etc.) and special features of the background environment (type of neighborhood, time of day, ambient level, etc.).

Noise indices: The quantitative aspect of a rating scheme which gives a measure of community response to noise (for example, L_{dn}, L_{eq}, NEF*). This term is synonymous with criteria but is usually associated with community noise.

In the federal regulatory process the Congress of the United States approves a bill (piece of legislation); after signature by the President, the legislation becomes law. The law may designate one or more agencies of the federal government as responsible for the preparation and promulgation of regulations to implement the law [1]. The three primary agencies designated to issue noise control regulations under the two acts mentioned above are the Environmental

---

* These quantities will be defined later.

Protection Agency (EPA), the Department of Labor (DOL), and the Department of Transportation (DOT).

The DOL has responsibility for implementing the Occupational Safety and Health Act (1970), which was enacted to ensure safe and healthful conditions at the workplace. The EPA, under the Noise Control Act (1972), has responsibility for controlling environmental noise to protect the health and welfare of the general public. Its primary responsibility is to establish national, uniform (federal) noise standards for major products and sources which are involved in interstate commerce; state and local governments still retain the right to establish and to enforce controls on environmental noise by regulating the use, operation, or movement of noise sources and by establishing the levels of noise permitted in specified environments. A list of major products and sources considered by EPA for possible regulatory action is given in Table 7.1.

The DOT, through the Federal Aviation Administration (FAA) and the Federal Highway Administration (FHWA), is required to work closely with EPA in establishing aircraft regulations and in undertaking programs to control truck and highway noise. Other federal agencies concerned with noise regulations include the Department of Defense (DOD), the Department of Housing and Urban Development (HUD), the Department of Interior, and the General Services Administration (GSA). However, the regulations issued by these agencies are usually applicable in limited areas (for example, coal mines) or for special purposes (such as federal procurements or federally insured housing).

The study of environmental noise is an intrinsically complicated subject requiring different acoustic measures and descriptors to quantify each particular situation. Consequently, a certain degree of standardization is required in order to arrive at workable noise regulations which reflect consistency in method and application. Moreover, regulations can be enforced most effectively when based on fair, equitable, and uniform measurement methodology. For this reason, regulatory bodies rely heavily on the work of standards organizations responsible for developing measurement techniques, calibration methods, definitions, rating schemes, and equipment and product specifications concerned with noise.

The majority of standards are normally not a matter of law. However, widely accepted standards can become mandatory when incorporated into contracts, codes, and regulations. An exception occurs in the area of health and safety, where mandatory standards are issued by the federal government.

Most noise standards are developed by committees within industrial and trade associations, technical and scientific societies, and special government agencies who have a particular interest and expertise in acoustics. Organizations developing noise standards, and a representative listing of their documents, are given in Appendix A. (See Ref. 2 for a brief description of the standards listed in this table.)

Noise standards provide the engineer with noise criteria and procedures which are essential for (1) assessing a noise environment and (2) initiating and evaluating noise control programs in a consistent and generally accepted manner. In the discussions which follow we will emphasize noise criteria which

Table 7.1 Possible candidates for identification as major noise sources (EPA)*

Lawn Care
Edgers
Garden tractors
Hedge clippers
Home tractors
Lawn mowers
Snow and leaf blowers
Tillers
Trimmers

Air Transportation (Not
Candidates for Section 6†
Regulation)
Business jet aircraft
Commercial subsonic jet aircraft
Commercial supersonic jet
aircraft
Helicopters
Propeller-driven small airplanes
Short-haul aircraft

Construction / Industrial
Equipment
Air compressors
Backhoes
Chain saws
Concrete vibrators
Cranes, derrick
Cranes, mobile
Dozers (truck and wheel)
Engine-driven industrial
equipment
Generators
Graders
Loaders (track and wheel)
Mixers
Pavement breakers
Pavers
Pile drivers
Pneumatic and hydraulic tools
Power saws
Pumps
Rock drills
Rollers
Scrapers
Shovels

Recreational Vehicles
Snowmobiles
Motorboats
Off-road motorcycles
(including minicycles)
Other off-highway vehicles

Surface Transportation
Automobiles (including sports
cars, compacts, and standard
passenger cars)
Buses
Medium-duty and heavy-duty
trucks
Light trucks
Motorcycles
Railroad locomotives
Rapid transit—rail
Special auxiliary equipment on
trucks
Tires

Household Appliances
Air conditioners
Clothes dryers
Clothes washers
Dehumidifiers
Dishwashers
Electric can openers
Electric heaters
Electric knives
Electric knife sharpeners
Electric shavers
Electric toothbrushes
Exhaust fans
Floor fans
Food blenders
Food disposals (grinders)
Food mixers
Freezers
Hair clippers
Hair dryers
Home shop tools
Humidifiers
Refrigerators
Sewing machines
Slide/movie projectors
Vacuum cleaners
Window fans

* See Ref. 1.
† Noise Control Act of 1972.

have been specified in standards for describing acceptability of various commonly encountered noise situations. The ideal criterion should provide a single-number noise scale or noise index which [3]:

- should be applicable to assess the long- and short-term aspects of the noise environment
- should correlate well with known effects of the noise environment on the individual and the public
- should be simple, practical, and accurate, and in principle useful for planning as well as for enforcement or monitoring
- should be measurable with standardized, commercially available equipment
- should be closely related to methods currently in use
- should be predictable within acceptable tolerance from a knowledge of the physical phenomena producing the noise
- should lend itself to the use of small simple monitors

However, because of the complexity of the environmental noise problem and variability in the subjective response of people to noise, a universally acceptable criterion does not exist. Consequently, there has been a proliferation of noise rating schemes and indices put forth by different investigative groups in an attempt to find acceptable criteria for a wide variety of noise situations. In the sections which follow we will present some of the most commonly used noise criteria for both indoor and outdoor spaces, followed by a description of appropriate standards and regulations. The noise control engineer must keep in mind when using these criteria that they are not universally accepted. This is particularly true in the case of environmental (community) noise criteria. It is therefore important that the engineer select the appropriate standard and/or criterion applicable to the particular noise problem being considered. In some cases several sets of criteria may have to be considered in dealing with a noise problem. This would be the case for an industrial noise problem where both community noise and noise at the workplace is in question. The OSHA Occupational Noise Standards would be used to evaluate the workplace noise, while criteria from (possibly) state, country, and city noise regulations would have to be considered in evaluating the community noise.

7.2 CRITERIA FOR INDOOR NOISE ENVIRONMENTS

When dealing with problems caused by noise, one must consider three aspects of its effects on people: (1) annoyance, (2) communication interference, and (3) hearing-damage risk. Many other factors must also be considered, such as the use of the space, the time of day and duration of exposure, the type of noise (impulsive, pure tones, continuous), the functions which must be performed by people in the noise environment, and so on. Some noise criteria are specified in standards related to all three aspects listed above, for both indoor and outdoor spaces. Hence, some criteria listed in this section for indoor spaces will also be listed in the section for outdoor environments. (See Refs. 4 and 5 for an extensive listing of criteria used in assessing noise environments.) Only those criteria which were felt to be of general use in noise control engineering are described in detail in this chapter.

Direct Ratings of Sound Level

Overall sound-pressure level, L_p The overall sound-pressure level is the value obtained with the linear response of the sound-level meter, which gives equal weight to all frequencies. This measure gives little information as to the human perception of noise but is useful when determining the total noise power of a source.

A-weighted sound-pressure level, L_A The A-weighted sound-pressure level is measured in decibels (dBA) with a standard sound-level meter, or it can be estimated by applying A-weighted values from Table 7.2 to either octave or 1/3-octave-band levels and summing them on an energy basis. The A-level provides a single-number rating that has been found to correlate well with people's subjective assessment of the loudness or noisiness of many types of sound and with hearing-damage risks due to continuous sound.

C-weighted sound-pressure level, L_C The C-weighted sound-pressure level is measured in decibels (dBC) with a standard sound-level meter, or it can be estimated by applying C-weighted values from Table 7.2 to octave or 1/3-octave-band levels and summing the results on an energy basis. The C-weighting is used as an overall measure of sound with equal weighting given to all frequencies from 31.5 to 8000 Hz, the average range of human hearing.

D-weighted sound-pressure level, L_D The D-weighted sound-pressure level is measured in decibels (dBD) with a standard sound-level meter which has a D-weighting network, or it can be estimated by applying D-weighted values from Table 7.2 to octave or 1/3-octave-band levels and summing on an energy basis. The D level was developed as a simple approximation of perceived noise level (PNL) which can be estimated from the D-level reading by the equation

$$\text{PNL} \simeq L_D + 7 \qquad \text{PNdB} \qquad (7.1)$$

This equation should only be used as an estimator for PNL for sounds having their energy predominantly above 355 Hz.

Loudness and Annoyance Ratings

Loudness level (Stevens Mark VI) LL_s The loudness level is a single-number rating (in phons), calculated from octave and 1/3-octave-band sound levels, which correlates with people's assessment of the *loudness* of a sound. The

Table 7.2 A-, C-, and D-weighting correction values

1/3-octave-band center frequency, Hz	A-weighting correction, dB	C-weighting correction, dB	D-weighting corrrection, dB
10	−70.4	−14.3	
12.5	−63.4	−11.2	
16	−56.7	−8.5	
20	−50.5	−6.2	
25	−44.7	−4.4	
31.5	−39.4*	−3.0*	
40	−34.6	−2.0	
50	−30.2	−1.3	−12.8
63	−26.2*	−0.8*	−10.9*
80	−22.5	−0.5	−9.0
100	−19.1	−0.3	−7.2
125	−16.1*	−0.2*	−5.5*
160	−13.4	−0.1	−4.0
200	−10.9	0.0	−2.6
250	−8.6*	0.0*	−1.6*
315	−6.6	0.0	−0.8
400	−4.8	0.0	−0.4
500	−3.2*	0.0*	−0.3*
630	−1.9	0.0	−0.5
800	−0.8	0.0	−0.6
1,000	0.0*	0.0*	−0.0*
1,250	+0.6	0.0	+2.0
1,600	+1.0	−0.1	+4.9
2,000	+1.2*	−0.2*	+7.9*
2,500	+1.3	−0.3	+10.6
3,150	+1.2	−0.5	+11.5
4,000	+1.0*	−0.8*	+11.1*
5,000	+0.5	−1.3	+9.6
6,300	−0.1	−2.0	+7.6
8,000	−1.1*	−3.0*	+5.5*
10,000	−2.5	−4.4	+3.4
12,500	−4.3	−6.2	−1.4
16,000	−6.6	−8.5	
20,000	−9.3	−11.2	

* Octave-band corrections.

Stevens Mark VI method for computing loudness level should be employed only for a diffuse sound field for which the sound spectrum is relatively smooth and contains no pure tones. The LL_s method converts band levels to loudness in sones (loudness index), sums the results, and converts the sum into phons—a logarithmically scaled quantity; an increase of 10 phons in a sound is roughly equivalent to a doubling of its loudness (as measured in sones). The calculation procedure for LL_s in phons is given in Sec. 2.3 of this text. For more general types of sound fields, the Zwicker method [4] is recommended for computing loudness level. The Zwicker method usually predicts slightly higher results than the Stevens method for the same sounds. Computed differences as great as 5 phons are possible.

Perceived noise level, PNL The perceived noise level is a single-number rating of the *noisiness* of a sound computed from octave- or 1/3-octave-band sound levels. The PNL is patterned after the loudness level, except that equal-noisiness curves are employed instead of equal-loudness curves. The perceived noise level is most accurate in estimating the perceived noisiness of broadband sounds which do not contain strong discrete frequency components; it is used mainly for assessing the disturbance likely to be caused by aircraft flyover.

Methods available for determining PNL are similar to the Mark VI method for loudness level, except that one uses noy tables instead of sone tables. For a quick assessment of the noisiness of a sound we recommend using Eq. (7.1) and D-weighted sound levels for estimating PNC values. However, for more accurate computation of perceived noise levels, see Ref. 4.

Equivalent sound level, L_{eq} The equivalent sound level is the level in dBA of a hypothetical constant sound which, if substituted for the actual sound history over the same period of time, would represent the same amount of acoustic energy arriving at a given location. The purpose of L_{eq} is to provide a single-number measure of time-varying noise for a predetermined time period. The designation of *equivalent* signifies that the numerical value of the fluctuating sound is equivalent in level to a steady-state sound with the same total energy.

The equivalent sound level can be measured directly using an integrating sound-level meter which performs a continuous time integration of the sound being sampled over a specified period of time. Alternatively, one can estimate L_{eq} from a recording of A-weighted sound level versus time by using the definition

$$L_{eq} = 10 \log \left[\frac{1}{T} \int_0^T 10^{0.1 L_A(t)} \, dt \right] \tag{7.2}$$

where $L_A(t)$ = instantaneous A-level of sound and T = specified time period during which sound is sampled. By breaking the sound-level record into n equal increments of time Δt_i, Eq. (7.2) can be approximated by

$$L_{eq} \simeq 10 \log \left[\frac{1}{T} \sum_{i=1}^n 10^{0.1 L_{Ai}} \Delta t_i \right] \tag{7.3}$$

where L_{Ai} is the average A level over the ith increment of time.

Day-night level, L_{dn} The day-night level is the average A-weighted sound level (summed on an energy basis), integrated over a 24-h (86,400-s) period, with a 10-dB penalty added to night-time sound levels to account for more noise-sensitive activities (TV viewing, sleeping) during that period. It was originally developed for long-time noise exposure surveillance as an aid in land-use planning. The day-night level was later adopted by the Environmental Protection Agency in establishing levels of environmental noise requisite for protection of public health and welfare with an adequate margin of safety, for both indoor and outdoor noise exposure [5].

The day-night sound level can be measured directly using special sound-level meters designed for averaging sound levels (on an energy basis) over a long period of time. Alternatively, one can estimate L_{dn} from a recording of A-weighted sound level versus time by using the definition

$$L_{dn} = 10 \log \left[\frac{\int_0^{86,400} W(t) 10^{0.1 L_A(t)} \, dt}{86,400} \right] \qquad (7.4)$$

where $W(t) = \begin{cases} 1.0 \text{ during the period 7 A.M. to 10 P.M.} \\ 10 \text{ during the period 10 P.M. to 7 A.M.} \end{cases}$

$L_A(t) =$ instantaneous A level of sound

$t =$ time, s.

For discrete sampling of the A-weighted sound level over the 24-h interval, this equation becomes

$$L_{dn} = 10 \log \left[\frac{\sum_{i=1}^{n} W_i 10^{0.10 L_{Ai}} \Delta t_i}{86,400} \right] \qquad (7.5)$$

where $W_i =$ weighting factor defined in Eq. (7.4)

$L_{Ai} =$ A-level over the ith time interval

$\Delta t_i = i$th time interval, s.

Communication Interference Criteria

Preferred speech-interference level (PSIL) This is a simplified method for quantifying background noise in terms of communication interference. It is calculated from the arithmetic average of octave bands in the speech frequency range, that is, 500, 1000, and 2000 Hz.

$$\text{PSIL} = \frac{L_{500} + L_{1000} + L_{2000}}{3} \qquad (7.6)$$

Empirical graphs or tables (see Sec. 7.3) which indicate conversing distance over which speech is satisfactorily intelligible must be used to interpret the PSIL. The preferred* speech-interference level was developed as a simplified substitute for the Articulation Index, which is a more complicated rating scheme for which certain background noise levels were assumed. In cases where data on octave-band levels are not available, the PSIL can be approximated from A-levels by

---

* Speech-interference level (SIL) was initially defined in terms of the old octave bands: 600–1200 Hz, 1200–2400 Hz, and 2400–4800 Hz. With the advent of preferred frequencies for octave bands, the *preferred* speech-interference level (PSIL) was introduced which uses 500-, 1000-, and 2000-Hz octave bands.

the equation

$$PSIL \simeq L_A - 7 \quad dB \qquad (7.7)$$

Noise criterion curves Noise criterion curves define sets of octave-band levels which were established to provide a single-number rating for the octave-band spectra of a given noise environment. The NC method, which is based both on the speech-interference level and the loudness level, is used in setting specifications of acceptable ambient-noise levels in various noise environments. The NC number which is assigned to each curve (see Fig. 7.1) is the speech-interference level (SIL) value, obtained by averaging the values in the appropriate octave bands of the curve.

The NC rating of a given noise environment is determined by superimposing its octave-band sound spectrum on the family of NC curves. The NC rating is obtained from its tangential relationship to the NC curve having the largest integer value. For example, consider a noise environment with the octave-band levels given in Table 7.3. The spectrum of these band levels is plotted on the family of NC curves in Fig. 7.2. For this sound environment a rating of NC-61 is obtained. This can be determined by the level in the 1000-Hz band which is 1 dB more than the NC-60 curve.

Preferred noise criterion (PNC) Preferred noise criterion curves are revisions of NC curves and are used for similar situations in rating the noise environments of indoor spaces (see Table 7.6). The PNC curves were developed in answer to many objections made about the adequacy of the NC curves at low and high frequencies; they are based on both the preferred speech-interference level and the loudness level. The PNC number assigned to each curve is the PSIL which is obtained from an average of the values in appropriate octave bands.

The PNC rating of a given noise environment is determined in the same way as for NC curves—by superimposing the octave-band spectrum of the noise on the family of PNC curves given in Fig. 7.3. The PNC rating is obtained from its tangential relationship to the PNC curve having the largest integer value.

Criteria for Hearing-Damage Risk

Hearing damage can result from exposure to excessive noise levels over a prolonged period of time. Hence, hearing-damage risk associated with continuous noise is related to cumulative exposure to excessive levels. The energy-equivalent sound level, L_{eq}, has received wide acceptance in Europe as a measure of hearing-damage risk. L_{eq} was defined earlier using Eqs. (7.2) and (7.3). Since energy is the basis for determining the equivalent sound level, a 3-dB change in equivalent level represents a doubling or halving of energy.

On the other hand, hearing-damage-risk criteria proposed by OSHA use a 5-dB tradeoff for noise exposure rather than the equal-energy 3-dB tradeoff. Hence, if the OSHA criteria allow 8 h of exposure to continuous noise at 90

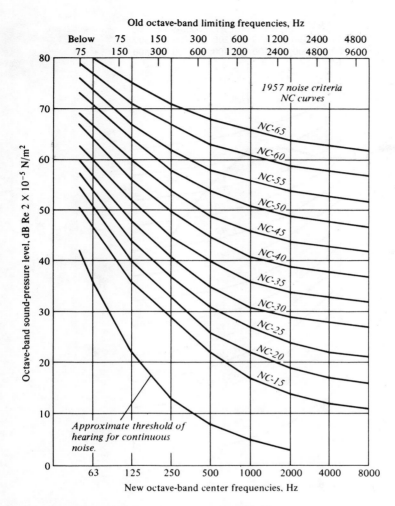

Figure 7.1 Indoor noise criteria (NC) curves (1957) [9].

Table 7.3 Octave-band levels use in calculating NC rating

Octave-band center frequency, Hz	63	125	250	500	1000	2000	4000	8000
Band level, dB	63	61	60	62	62	55	45	40

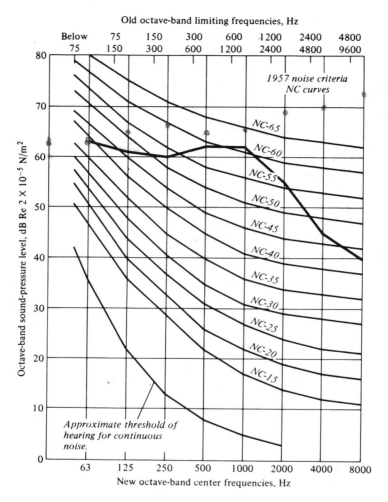

Old octave-band limiting frequencies, Hz

Figure 7.2 Sample calculation of NC value for specified noise environment [9].

dBA, 4 h of exposure would be allowed at 95 dBA, and supposedly would carry the same hearing-damage risk.

The OSHA equivalent level, L_{eq} (OSHA),* can be measured directly by using an integrating sound-level meter which performs continuous time integra-

---

* The OSHA "equivalent" level, L_{eq} (OSHA), is the level in dBA of a hypothetical constant sound which, if substituted for the actual sound, would represent the same hearing-damage risk at the given position. In this case the designation of *equivalent* implies *equal hearing-damage risk*. Thus, while energy is the basis for determining the equivalent sound level L_{eq}, hearing-damage risk is the basis for determining the OSHA equivalent sound level L_{eq} (OSHA).

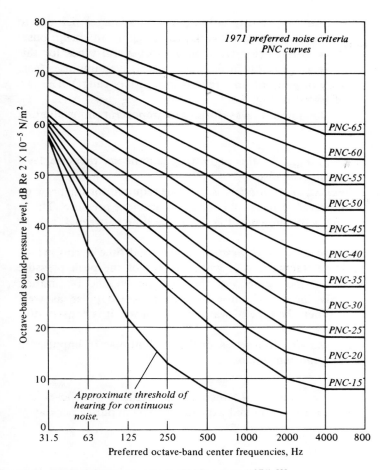

Figure 7.3 Preferred noise criteria (PNC) curves (1971) [9].

tion, with a 5-dBA tradeoff, of the A-weighted sound being sampled. Alternatively, one can estimate L_{eq} (OSHA) from a recording of the A-weighted sound level versus time by using the definition [6]:

$$L_{eq}(OSHA) = 16.7 \log\left[\frac{1}{T} \int_0^T 10^{\frac{L_A(t)}{16.7}} dt \right] \qquad (7.8)$$

where $L_A(t)$ = instantaneous A-level of sound and T = time period over which sound is sampled. By breaking the sound level into n equal increments of time Δt_i, Eq. (7.8) can be approximated by

$$L_{eq}(OSHA) = 16.7 \log\left[\frac{1}{T} \sum_{i=1}^n 10^{\frac{L_{Ai}}{16.7}} \Delta t_i \right] \qquad (7.9)$$

where L_{Ai} is the average A-level in the ith increment of time.

Guidelines have also been prepared to estimate hearing-damage risk due to impulsive noise of short duration (typically less than 1 s) having an abrupt onset and rapid decay. Impulsive noises are divided into two general types for this analysis: A-type impulses (e.g., gunshots in the open) and B-type impulses (e.g., metallic impacts in industry or gunshots in a reverberant indoor range). The two types of impulses are illustrated in Fig. 7.4.

Four parameters of the impulse waveform are important in evaluating hearing-damage risk:

1. *The peak pressure level*, L_{peak}, is the highest instantaneous pressure level reached at any time by the impulse.
2. *The pressure-wave duration, or A duration*, is the time required for the pressure wave to rise to its first positive peak and return to ambient pressure. The A duration of the pressure wave shown in Fig. 7.4 is the time between V and W on the time axis.
3. *The pressure-envelope duration, or B duration*, is the total time during which the envelope of pressure fluctuations is within 20 dB of the peak pressure level, as demonstrated in the figure. For the case shown, the B duration would include not only the initial pulse but the reflected pulse as well, $(X - V) + (Z - Y)$. When the type of wave is not known, it is conservative to assume a B-type wave.
4. *The number of repeated impulses* in a series, or the total number of impulses in a daily exposure, is an important factor.

Damage-risk criteria shown in Fig. 7.5 recommend limits to peak level as a function of impulse duration for a nominal exposure of 100 impulses per day at

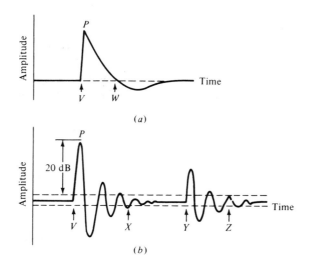

Figure 7.4 Two principal types of impulse noise: (*a*) A duration and (*b*) B duration [7].

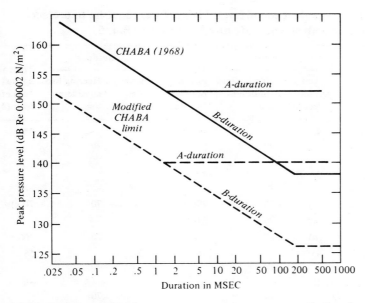

Figure 7.5 The CHABA Damage-Risk Criterion for impulse noise based on 100 exposures per day [5].

normal incidence. These criteria were recommended by the CHABA* working group. The solid curve (1968) is intended to protect 95% of those exposed from receiving more than a 20-dB noise-induced permanent threshold shift (NIPT) in their hearing acuity, after 20 years. The modified CHABA limits would protect 90% of those exposed against a 5-dB NIPT, after 20 years [5].

7.3 INDOOR NOISE STANDARDS AND REGULATIONS

The Noise Control Act of 1972 required the Environmental Protection Agency to publish *information* as to levels of noise "requisite to protect the public health and welfare with an adequate margin of safety." This information was published in 1974 [5], but it was not concluded by the EPA that the levels identified should be adopted as criteria for regulations. This decision was left to state and local governments. Nevertheless, the EPA document on noise levels does provide the noise control engineer with a set of criteria for evaluating a given noise environment in a situation where a set of codes or regulations is not available.

Table 7.4 presents the levels identified by EPA as requisite to protect public health and welfare with an adequate margin of safety for both activity interference and hearing loss. Three versions of equivalent sound level are used: L_{eq}

* Committee on Hearing, Bioacoustics, and Biomechanics.

Table 7.4 Yearly average* equivalent sound levels identified as requisite to protect the public health and welfare with an adequate margin of safety (Ref. 5)

		Indoor			Outdoor		
	Measure	Activity interference	Hearing loss consideration	To protect against both effects (b)	Activity interference	Hearing loss consideration	To protect against both effects (b)
Residential with outside space and farm residences	L_{dn}	45		45	55		55
	$L_{eq(24)}$		70			70	
Residential with no outside space	L_{dn}	45		45			
	$L_{eq(24)}$		70				
Commercial	$L_{eq(24)}$	(a)	70	70(c)	(a)	70	70(c)
Inside transportation	$L_{eq(24)}$	(a)	70	(a)			
Industrial	$L_{eq(24)}(d)$	(a)	70	70(c)	(a)	70	70(c)
Hospitals	L_{dn}	45		45	55		55
	$L_{eq(24)}$		70			70	
Educational	$L_{eq(24)}$	45		45	55		55
	$L_{eq(24)}(d)$		70			70	
Recreational areas	$L_{eq(24)}$	(a)	70	70(c)	(a)	70	70(c)
Farmland and general unpopulated land	$L_{eq(24)}$				(a)	70	70(c)

Code: (a) Since different types of activities appear to be associated with different levels, identification of a maximum level for activity interference may be difficult except in those circumstances where speech communication is a critical activity.

(b) Based on lowest level.

(c) Based only on hearing loss.

(d) An $L_{eq(8)}$ of 75 dB may be identified in these situations so long as the exposure over the remaining 16 h per day is low enough to result in a negligible contribution to the 24-h average, i.e., no greater than an L_{eq} of 60 dB.

Note: Explanation of identified level for hearing loss: the exposure period which results in hearing loss at the identified level is a period of 40 years.

* Refers to energy rather than arithmetic averages.

for an 8-h period, $L_{eq(8)}$; L_{eq} for a 24-h period, $L_{eq(24)}$; and day-night levels, L_{dn}, defined in Sec. 7.2. The maximum allowable levels identified in this table do not account for the effects of impulse noise, which, according to the EPA document on noise levels, should be evaluated using the CHABA damage-risk criteria given in Fig. 7.4. The EPA document recommends the following rules in evaluating impulsive-type noise [5]:

• Measure or predict the peak level (SPL) and A- or B-type duration of the impulse, using proper oscillographic technique. (*Note*: If the noise is rapidly repetitive, it may be treated and measured as continuous noise and evaluated accordingly in dBA. This usually means a repetition rate exceeding 10 times per second.)

• Use the "modified CHABA limit" in Fig. 7.4 to determine the maximum permissible peak SPL. If in doubt as to impulse type, assume B duration.

• If the number of similar impulses N experienced per day exceeds 100, reduce the permissible level by 10 dB for every tenfold increase in N (e.g., 10 dB when $N = 1000$; 20 dB when $N = 10,000$).

• If N is less than 100, a higher peak level may be allowed in accordance with the same rule (e.g., 10 dB more when $N = 10$), provided that an absolute maximum value of 167 dB for durations of less than 25-μs grazing incidence (or 162-dB normal incidence) is not exceeded.

• If the average repetition rate of impulses falls in the range 0.1 to 1 per second (i.e., the average interval between impulses is 1 to 10 s), reduce the permissible peak level by 5 dB.

• If the impulses are known to reach human ears in the vicinity at grazing incidence, the permissible peak level may be raised by 5 dB. *Note*: This allowance should be used with caution and must not be applied if the surroundings are reverberant. If in doubt, assume normal incidence.

Direct Rating Guides and Standards

The cumulative noise exposure level used in the EPA document on noise levels is difficult to measure. Moreover, it has been found that if the sound-frequency spectrum is continuous, contains no sharp peaks or dips, and extends over a wide frequency range, the A-level correlates as well with human response as any of the more complicated rating schemes. For this reason the A-level has been adopted in many standards and codes for rating both indoor and outdoor environments. Some typical A-weighted sound levels associated with commonly encountered noise sources are given in Table 7.5.

Although there is no single widely accepted standard for indoor noise environments, with the exception of the OSHA noise standard, there have been numerous studies which provide recommended A-levels for specific situations. For example, Table 7.6 lists A-level indoor design goals recommended in the ASHRAE* Systems Guide for steady background noise in various indoor spaces [10]. Other recommended A-level criteria are reported in the EPA levels document [5].

The Department of Housing and Urban Development (HUD) has established acceptable interior noise levels for new construction sites. The levels prescribed in the HUD standard for new and rehabilitated residential construction are given in Table 7.7. A builder cannot obtain federal funds or federal guarantees unless the noise levels conform to these criteria.

Finally, a comparison of A-level limits recommended by various sources, together with suggested cumulative level limits for several indoor spaces, is given in Table 7.8.

---

* American Society of Heating, Refrigerating, and Air-Conditioning Engineers.

Table 7.5 A-weighted level and relative loudness of typical noises in indoor and outdoor environments [9]

L_A (dBA)	Subjective impression	Community (outdoor)	Home or industry (indoor)	Relative loudness (human judgment of different sound levels)
130				32 times as loud
		Military jet aircraft takeoff with afterburner from aircraft carrier at 50 ft (130 dBA)		
	Uncomfortably		Oxygen torch (121 dBA)	
120	loud			16 times as loud
		Turbofan aircraft at takeoff power under flight path at 200 ft (118 dBA)		
			Riveting machine (110 dBA). Rock-n-roll band (108–114 dBA)	
110				8 times as loud
		Same jet flyover at 1000 ft (103 dBA). Boeing 707, DC-8 at 6080 ft before landing (106 dBA). Bell J-2A helicopter at 100 ft (100 dBA)		
	Very			
100	loud	Boeing 737, DC-9 at 6080 ft before landing (97 dBA). Motorcycle at 25 ft (90 dBA)	Newspaper press (97 dBA)	4 times as loud
90				2 times as loud
		Car wash at 20 ft (89 dBA). Prop. plane flyover at 1000 ft (88 dBA). Diesel truck, 40 mph at 50 ft (84 dBA). Diesel train, 45 mi/h at 100 ft (83 dBA). Power mower at 25 ft (85 dBA)	Food blender (88 dBA) Milling machine (85 dBA) Garbage disposal (80 dBA)	
	Moderately			
80	loud			Reference loudness
		High urban ambient sound (80 dBA). Passenger car, 65 mph at 25 ft (77 dBA). Freeway at 50 ft from pavement edge 10 A.M. (76 ± 6 dBA)	Living-room music (76 dBA) TV-audio, vacuum cleaner (70 dBA)	
70				$\frac{1}{2}$ as loud

Table 7.5 (continued) A-weighted level and relative loudness of typical noises in indoor and outdoor environments [9]

L_A (dBA)	Subjective impression	Community (outdoor)	Home or industry (indoor)	Relative loudness (human judgment of different sound levels)
			Cash register at 10 ft (65–70 dBA). Electric typewriter at 10 ft (64 dBA). Dishwasher, rinse at 110 ft (60 dBA). Conversation (60 dBA)	
60				$\frac{1}{4}$ as loud
		Air-conditioning condensing unit at 15 ft (55 dBA). Large transformers at 100 ft (50 to 60 dBA)		
50	Quiet	Birdcalls (44 dBA). Lower-limit urban daytime ambient noise (40 dBA)		$\frac{1}{8}$ as loud
40				$\frac{1}{16}$ as loud
		[Scale interrupted]		
	Just audible			
10	Threshold of hearing			
0				

Annoyance and Communication Interference Guides and Standards

Speech interference is a quantifiable phenomenon which can be clearly defined and measured under closely controlled environmental conditions; and general laws have been developed which allow rather accurate prediction of whether or not a speech sound will be masked by a particular noise. Figure 2.13, repeated here for convenience, gives maximum permissible levels of background noise for satisfactory intelligibility of difficult speech material. These levels are for persons with average voice strengths speaking face to face, with the spoken material not already familiar to the listener. A value of 5 dB should be subtracted from these levels for formal speakers. This chart assumes that there are no reflecting surfaces nearby, i.e., the listener is in the direct sound field. The values on this chart should not be used for a reverberant room, since the voice sounds will add to the existing background levels. On the other hand, if the speech material is familiar, or if the speaker uses gestures and other nonverbal communication, the speech interference will decrease.

Table 7.6 Ranges of indoor design goals recommended by ASHRAE* for unoccupied spaces, with all systems operating [10]

Type of area	Range of A-sound levels, dB	Range of NC criteria curves
Residences		
Private homes (rural and suburban)	25–35	20–30
Private homes (urban)	30–40	25–35
Apartment houses, 2- and 3-family units	35–45	30–40
Hotels		
Individual rooms or suites	35–45	30–40
Ballrooms, banquet rooms	35–45	30–40
Halls and corridors, lobbies	40–50	35–45
Garages	45–55	40–50
Kitchens and laundries	45–55	40–50
Hospitals and clinics		
Private rooms	30–40	25–35
Operating rooms, wards	35–45	30–40
Laboratories, halls and corridors		
Lobbies and waiting rooms	40–50	35–45
Washrooms and toilets	45–55	40–50
Offices		
Board room	25–35	20–30
Conference rooms	30–40	25–35
Executive office	35–45	30–40
Supervisor office, reception room	35–50	30–45
General open offices, drafting rooms	40–50	35–45
Halls and corridors	40–55	35–50
Tabulation and computation	45–65	40–60
	40–55	40–50
Auditoriums and music halls		
Concert and opera halls		
Studios for sound reproduction	20–30	15–22
Legitimate theaters, multipurpose halls	30–35	25–30
Movie theaters, TV audience studios		
Semi-outdoor amphitheaters	35–45	30–35
Lecture halls, planetariums		
Lobbies	40–50	35–45
Churches and schools		
Sanctuaries	25–35	20–30
Libraries	35–45	30–40
Schools and classrooms	35–45	30–40
Laboratories	40–50	35–45
Recreation halls	40–55	35–50
Corridors and halls	40–55	35–50
Kitchens	45–55	40–50

Table 7.6 (continued) Ranges of indoor design goals recommended by ASHRAE* for unoccupied spaces, with all systems operating [10]

Type of area	Range of A-sound levels, dB	Range of NC criteria curves
Public buildings		
Public libraries, museums, courtrooms	35–45	30–40
Post offices, general banking areas, lobbies	40–50	35–45
Washrooms and toilets	45–55	40–50
Restaurants, cafeterias, lounges		
Restaurants	40–50	35–45
Cocktail lounges	40–55	35–50
Nightclubs	40–50	35–45
Cafeterias	45–55	40–50
Stores, retail		
Clothing stores	40–50	35–45
Department stores (upper floors)	40–50	35–45
Department stores (main floor)	45–55	40–50
Small retail stores	45–55	40–50
Supermarkets	45–55	40–50
Sports activities, indoor		
Coliseums	35–45	30–40
Bowling alleys, gymnasiums	40–50	35–45
Swimming pools	45–60	40–55
Transportation (rail, bus, plane)		
Ticket sales offices	35–45	30–40
Lounges and waiting rooms	40–55	35–50
Equipment rooms		
8-h/day exposure	<90	
3-h/day exposure	<97	
(or per OSHA requirement)		

* American Society of Heating, Refrigerating, and Air-Conditioning Engineers.

Table 7.7 Acceptable interior noise levels for new and rehabilitated residential construction (HUD)

Location	Noise level
Sleeping quarters	Does not exceed 55 dBA for 60 min in 24 h; does not exceed 45 dBA for 30 min between 11 P.M. and 7 A.M.; does not exceed 45 dBA for 8 h in 24 h
Other interior areas	At discretion of HUD personnel

Table 7.8 Comparison of A-weighted sound-level limits in decibels recommended by various sources, together with current suggestions by author [11]

Space	Range of average values min	Range of average values max	Grand average value	Current suggestion*
Bedroom	25	40	35	L_{dn} 35–40
Living room	25	40	37	L_{dn} 40–45
Hotel	35	45	39	L_{dn} 45
Restaurant	45	55	52	$L_{eq}(1)$ 50–55
Private office	35	50	41	$L_{eq}(1)$ 40–45
General office	38	60	50	$L_{eq}(1)$ 45–55
Light industry	50	60	53	$L_{eq}(8)$ 50–75
Heavy industry	70	85	71	$L_{eq}(8)$ 65–85
Classroom	35	40	37	$L_{eq}(1)$ 45–50

* $L_{eq}(1)$ is L_{eq} measured in any hour when the space is occupied.
$L_{eq}(8)$ is L_{eq} measured in an 8-h period.

Figure 7.6 suggests a rating scheme for offices based on subjective tests which relate measured background speech-interference levels (PSIL) to subjective responses of listeners in the room. One would expect less complaints about noise in an office rated "moderately noisy" than in one rated "very noisy." The chart also indicates the level of difficulty in using the telephone for different background levels.

Recommended specifications for acceptable ambient-noise levels based on both speech interference and loudness (annoyance) are given in terms of noise criterion curves. Acceptable NC values for various indoor noise environments are listed in the ASHRAE guidelines presented earlier in Table 7.6.

Regulations for Hearing-Damage Risk—OSHA Noise Standard

Passage of the Social Security Act of 1935 assured the acceptance in the United States of the philosophy that the worker has the right to earn a living in an environment which does not endanger his or her health. In the period which followed, many states adopted codes and regulations governing control of the working environment. But it was not until the Walsh-Healey Public Contracts Act was amended in 1969 that allowable occupational noise levels were established on a national basis, applicable only to industries which had government contracts in excess of $10,000. These occupational noise levels were carried over into the Occupational Safety and Health Act of 1970 to cover all businesses which affect interstate commerce and have one or more employees. This law has had very far-reaching effects since most businesses use materials or components that require transport across state boundaries.

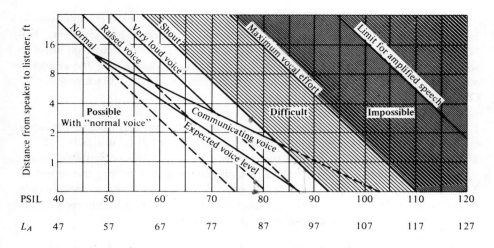

Figure 2.11 Rating chart for determining speech communication capability from speech-interference levels [12]. *(By permission, Webster, 1969.)*

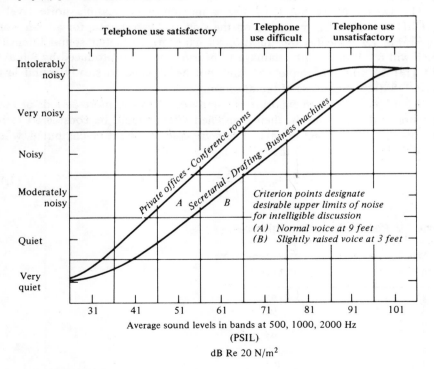

Figure 7.6 Rating chart for office noises. Data were determined by an octave-band analysis an correlated with subjective tests [12]. *(Courtesy Beranek and Newman, but modified for preferred banc From GenRad.)*

The OSHA Noise Standards are designed to protect workers exposed to hazardous noise environments from incurring permanent hearing loss. The regulation does basically two things: It *sets maximum levels* of industrial noise to which an employee may be exposed, and it *indicates what action the employer must take* if these levels are exceeded. The action required of the employer by OSHA can be summarized in three steps:

1. When employees are subjected to sounds exceeding permissible exposure levels, feasible *administrative* or *engineering* control shall be utilized.
2. If such controls fail to reduce sound levels to within the permissible limits, personal protective equipment shall be *provided* and the proper use *enforced*.
3. In all cases where the sound levels exceed values specified as permissible limits, an *effective hearing conservation program* shall be administered for as long as the noise levels exceed those permitted by law.

In this section we will deal with the maximum levels set by OSHA. A detailed discussion about implementing a noise control program, to come into compliance with OSHA noise regulations, is given in Chap. 11.

The OSHA Noise Standard sets a maximum permissible noise level of L_{eq}(OSHA) = 90 dBA, measured on the slow meter response, for an 8-h workday. Table 7.9 indicates the duration of exposure to higher sound intensities which will result in no more damage to hearing than that produced by 8 h at 90 dBA [13]. In addition employees must not be exposed to steady sound levels above 115 dBA, regardless of the duration.

When the daily noise exposure is composed of two or more periods of noise exposure at different levels, their combined effect should be considered rather than the individual effect of each. The *noise dose D* should be computed, where D is defined as the sum of the following fractions:

$$D = \frac{C_1}{T_1} + \frac{C_2}{T_2} + \cdots + \frac{C_n}{T_n} \qquad (7.10)$$

Table 7.9 Permissible noise exposures

Duration per day, h	Sound level, dBA (slow)
8	90
6	92
4	95
3	97
2	100
$1\frac{1}{2}$	102
1	105
$\frac{1}{2}$	110
$\frac{1}{4}$ or less	115

where C_n is the total time of exposure at the specified noise level, and T_n is the total time of exposure permitted at that level. Values of T_n can be obtained from Table 7.9 or from the equation

$$T_n = 16 \div 2^{(L_n - 85)/5} \qquad (7.11)$$

where L_n = A-level at nth time interval. Only levels of 90 dBA and above should be considered when computing noise dose. If the noise dose exceeds unity, the mixed exposure should be considered to exceed the limit value.

For impulse or impact noise the OSHA Noise Standard states that:

Exposure to impulsive or impact noise should not exceed 140 dB peak sound-pressure level.

This sets the upper limit of sound level to which a person should be exposed, regardless of the brevity of the exposure. Impact noise levels are to be measured only with an impact meter, a type 1 sound-level meter with true-peak-measuring capability, or an oscilloscope.

It is sometimes necessary to distinguish between short-duration intermittent sounds and impulse sounds of very short duration resulting from impacts or explosions. Regardless of the mechanism of noise generation, the Noise Standard states that:

If the variations in noise level involve maxima at intervals of 1 second or less, it is to be considered continuous.

This suggests that when the sound-level meter, set on the A scale at slow response, moves up from a generally steady reading at intervals of 1 s or less, say from 88 to 92 dBA, the high reading shall be taken as that to be used in Table 7.9 [13]. On the other hand, the intensity and duration of intermittent sounds of brief duration at intervals greater than 1 s should, as far as practical, be measured and the total duration over a day be determined. This total should then be entered in Eq. (7.10) to determine the permissible limit.

The impact noise standard does not take into account the hearing-damage risk associated with exposure to a large number of impact noises, nor the influence of A- and B-duration impulses discussed in Sec. 7.2. A revised OSHA Noise Standard was proposed (*Federal Register*, October 24, 1974) which would remedy these shortcomings. However, the wheels of the federal legislative process turn slowly, and as of this writing the new regulation has not been adopted. Very briefly, the major changes which will occur if the proposed standard is adopted are [14]:

1. Table 7.9 will be replaced by Table 7.10, given below.

This table is based on a permissible 8-h time-weighted average of L_{eq} (OSHA) equal to 90 dBA, but all exposure levels of 85 dBA and above will be used when determining permissible exposure to continuous noise.
2. The exposure limit for impulsive or impact noise will take into account both

Table 7.10

Sound level, dBA	Time permitted (h, min)	Sound level, dBA	Time permitted (h, min)
85	16, 0	101	1, 44
86	13, 56	102	1, 31
87	12, 8	103	1, 19
88	10, 34	104	1, 9
89	9, 11	105	1, 0
90	8, 0	106	0, 52
91	6, 58	107	0, 46
92	6, 4	108	0, 40
93	5, 17	109	0, 34
94	4, 36	110	0, 30
95	4, 0	111	0, 26
96	3, 29	112	0, 23
97	3, 2	113	0, 20
98	2, 50	114	0, 17
100	2, 0	115	0, 15

peak levels and number of impacts per day, as follows:

(a) Exposures to impulse or impact noise shall not exceed a peak sound-pressure level of 140 dB.

(b) Exposures to impulses of 140 dB shall not exceed 100 such pulses per day. For each decrease of 10 dB in peak sound-pressure level of the impulse, the number of impulses to which employees are exposed may be increased by a factor of 10.

The effect which the proposed changes would have on assessing industrial noise environments is discussed in detail in Chap. 11.

7.4 RATING SCHEMES FOR OUTDOOR NOISE ENVIRONMENTS

Central to all efforts in community noise abatement is the need to relate the subjective community response to its environment to some readily measured aspect of that environment. Both physical and social aspects of the environment must be considered when assessing the noise. Physical parameters of the sound field which affect people include the amplitude of the sound, its frequency content, and the variation of both with time. Hence, to get a complete physical description of a noise environment it would be necessary to obtain a continuous recording of the frequency spectrum, its overall pressure level, and the variation of both with time. This would require obtaining large amounts of data which would be very complex and difficult to analyze. Consequently, much effort has been put into the development of rating schemes which would *simplify data acquisition* and *identify essential descriptors* needed to predict community response. The goal of these efforts has been to develop single-number ratings which would allow one to order noise exposure along a one-dimensional scale and, subsequently, to select a criterion of acceptability on that scale.

The first major simplification in most rating schemes is to combine frequency-spectrum information and overall level by means of a weighting network. The A-weighting is most commonly used and has been found to correlate reasonably well with community response to noise. The temporal pattern of the A-weighted noise level is then needed in order to complete the description of the outdoor noise environment. This can be obtained by use of a graphic level recorder. Figure 7.7 shows two 8-min samples of outdoor noise of a typical suburban neighborhood [15].

Three features of these two samples should be noted.

- The noise level varies with time over a range of 33 dBA.
- The noise appears to be characterized by a fairly steady lower *residual* level, on which are superimposed higher *intrusive* levels associated with discrete single events.
- There is a duration factor associated with each of the discrete single events which could affect the degree of annoyance.

The next major simplification in characterizing the noise environment is to eliminate much of the temporal detail. There are typically three ways by which this is accomplished.

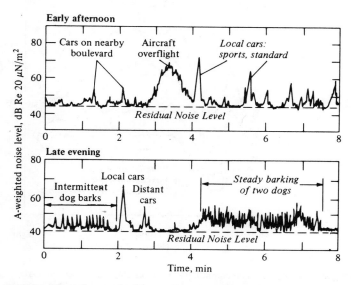

Figure 7.7 Two samples of outdoor noise in a normal suburban neighborhood with microphone located 20 ft from the curb [15].

- The noise-level history is broken into several periods:

Day	7 A.M. to 7 P.M.
Evening	7 P.M. to 10 P.M.
Night	10 P.M. to 7 A.M.

- Both the values of residual noise level and the values of the maximum noise level of single-event intrusive sounds are measured.
- Statistical properties of the noise level are determined.

The statistical properties most commonly used in rating schemes are defined below:

L_{max} = maximum sound level over a sampling period
L_{min} = minimum sound level over a sampling period
L_n = percentile level, the sound level exceeded n percent of the time over the sampling period
L_{eq} = equivalent noise level, the constant level which would have the same energy as the time-varying level over equal sampling periods

A statistical portrayal of community noise, for a particular day and location in the community, can be obtained by plotting these data over a 24-h period. An example is shown in Fig. 7.8, which plots statistical measures obtained on an

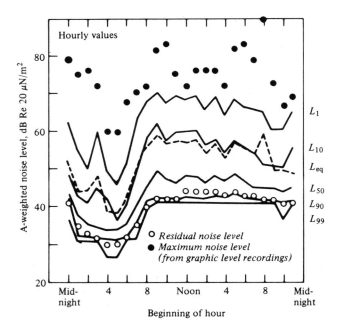

Figure 7.8 Statistical portrayal of community noise within a 24-h period. Data include maximum and residual noise levels read from a graphic level recorder, together with hourly and periodic values of the levels which are exceeded 99, 90, 50, 10, and 1 percent of the time, and the equivalent level (L_{eq}) [15].

hourly basis, along with the maximum and minimum values read from a continuous-level recorder. All statistical measures exhibit a typical temporal pattern in which the residual-noise level drops sharply after midnight, reaching a minimum between 4:00 and 5:00 A.M., thereafter rising to its almost constant daytime value by 8:00 A.M. This temporal pattern correlates well with the amount of human activity and in particular the vehicular traffic in urban areas.

The percentile levels L_1 and L_{90} are used in some noise rating schemes to represent the intrusive- and ambient-noise levels, respectively. The results in Fig. 7.8 show that the L_{90}, the level exceeded 90 percent of the time sampled, is a good estimate of the residual-noise (or ambient-noise) level. However, the maximum levels of the intrusive noise can be considerably greater than those predicted by the L_1 level. This is particularly true if the duration of the event is very short.

The above spectral and temporal simplifications provide practical methods for describing a community noise environment, but only to the extent that it is possible to correlate these descriptions with community reaction to the environment. Numerous techniques have been devised to measure annoyance; individual responses of people to noise are often studied in the laboratory, while community annoyance regarding noise is usually determined through social surveys. These studies show three types of annoyance factors [8]:

1. Physical parameters of the noise
   - Intensity level and spectral characteristics
   - Duration of the event
   - Presence of discrete frequency components
   - Presence of impulses
   - Abruptness of onset or cessation of the noise event
   - Degree of "harshness" or "roughness"
   - Degree of intermittency of loudness, pitch, or rhythm
   - Information content
   - Degree of interference with activity
2. Community factors
   - Noise climate (background noise) against which the event occurs
   - Previous experience of the community with the particular noise
   - Time of day during which the event occurs
   - Attitude of people toward the noise maker
   - Socioeconomic status of the community
3. Personal factors
   - Fear associated with activities of noise sources
   - Socioeconomic status and educational level
   - Extent to which resident of community believes he or she is being treated fairly
   - Attitude of resident regarding the contribution of activities associated with noise source to the general well-being of the community
   - Extent to which the resident believes the noise source could be controlled

The many rating schemes available attest to the fact that identifying the key factors which are strongly correlated with community response to given noise environments is an elusive task. The procedure involved in developing such rating schemes may be carried out as follows:

1. Make extensive noise surveys.
2. Conduct social surveys in the community.
3. Review the history of noise complaints found in civil records of the community.
4. Perform a statistical analysis to establish correlations between descriptors and community response to the noise.
5. Devise a scheme, drawing on a few essential descriptors, which will provide reasonable correlation between the community response to noise for the type of community noise problem studied.
6. Establish criteria of acceptability based on this scheme.

The rating schemes which have been developed provide the noise control engineer with the tools needed either to *predict* the community response to a proposed new intrusive noise source (such as a plant or airport) which would alter its noise environment in a known way, or to *assess* the attitude of another similar community toward its noise environment. The results from 55 case studies are compared in Fig. 7.9 to show the community response to many types of intrusive noise as a function of three different rating schemes. Presenting the

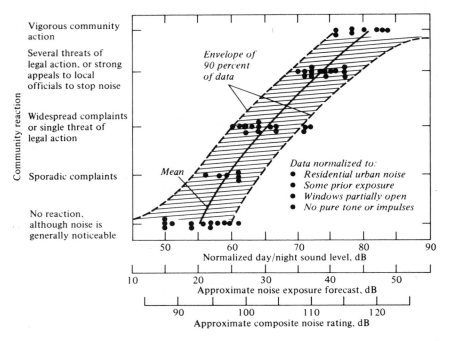

Figure 7.9 Community reaction to many types of intrusive noise as a function of normalized day/night equivalent level [15].

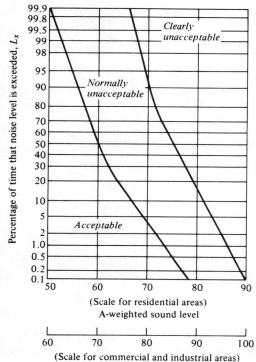

Figure 7.10 Proposed community noise standard [8].

data in this way can help to establish acceptability criteria for the rating schemes being studied; an example is the proposed standard shown in Fig. 7.10.

Because of the complexities involved in developing rating schemes for community noise, there has been a proliferation of such schemes, each one developed to satisfy some particular situation. Many studies have been undertaken to relate these different schemes; one of the more complete is given in Ref. 16. The rating schemes can be classified into two groups: (1) rating scales and (2) rating procedures. The rating scale uses descriptors of the noise stimulus itself. The rating procedures also use descriptors of the noise stimulus, but in addition introduce *corrections* to account for other aspects of the environment. The most important of these rating schemes are discussed below. When reviewing these it is important to keep in mind that *any* rating scheme developed for community noise will at best give the expected response of a large population (10,000 or more people) and cannot predict how an individual will react to a given noise environment.

Rating Scales

A rating scale describes only some aspect of the noise exposure itself. The maximum value of A-weighted sound level during a transient noisy event is a simple example. A more complicated scale is the *noise pollution level*, which is defined in terms of a sum of several statistical measures of the sound.

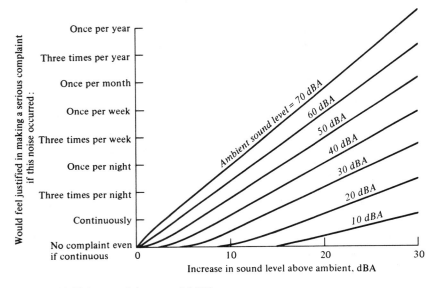

Figure 7.11 Noise complaint potential [17].

1. A-level The A-weighted sound-pressure level has been defined earlier for indoor noise. A single-number rating scale which uses the A-level to assess acceptability of an outdoor environment is given in terms of noise complaint potential in Fig. 7.11. In developing this scale it was assumed that the community response to the intrusive noise would depend upon the number of intrusions and also on the amount by which the A-level of the intrusive noise exceeded previous background or ambient levels.

The Department of Housing and Urban Development has established environmental noise standards for new construction sites which make use of the A-level scale. Noise measurements are to be made at appropriate heights above the boundaries of a construction site. The builder may not obtain federal funds

Table 7.11 External noise levels for new construction sites (HUD)

Description	Noise level
Unacceptable	Exceeds 80 dBA for 6 min in 24 h, or exceeds 75 dBA for 8 h in 24 h
Normally unacceptable	Exceeds 65 dBA for 8 h in 24 h, or loud repetitive sounds
Normally acceptable	Does not exceed 65 dBA for 8 h in 24 h
Acceptable	Does not exceed 45 dBA for 30 min in 24 h

Table 7.12 Limit levels for indoor A-weighted noise levels, dBA

Listening to radio and TV		Sleeping	
L_{50}	35–45	L_{50}	25–50—depends on surroundings (rural versus urban)
L_{10}	41–51	L_{10}	31–56 (same comment)
NPL	50–60	NPL	40–65 (same comment)

or federal guarantees unless the measured noise levels conform to the prescribed levels given in Table 7.11.

2. Noise pollution level (NPL-dBNP) The noise pollution level was developed in an effort to improve upon other single-number noise rating systems which consider only intensity. The NPL attempts to acount for the effect of fluctuations of the noise environment; it is defined by

$$NPL = L_{eq} + \sigma k \tag{7.11}$$

where $k = 2.56$ and $\sigma =$ standard deviation of the time-varying sound level over the sampling time.* The value for k leads to the best fit with results from studies of subjective response to noise. An alternate expression for NPL is

$$NPL = L_{50} + d + \frac{d^2}{60} \tag{7.12}$$

where $d = L_{10} - L_{90}$. In both equations for NPL, the first term is a measure of the intensity of the intruding noise, while the remaining terms measure the fluctuation in background noise. There have been many studies to determine acceptable noise levels for dwellings. These studies in general indicate that the *indoor* levels should not exceed those listed in Table 7.12 [9]. The indoor limits can be converted to acceptable *outdoor limits* by the following changes:

Open windows—add 10 dB to the indoor limits
Closed windows—add 20 dB to the indoor limits

Acceptability criteria for outdoor noise environments as a function of noise pollution level and A-level have been adopted by the U.S. Department of Housing and Urban Development, as shown in Fig. 7.12.

* Standard deviation can be computed from the equations

$$\sigma^2 = \frac{\Sigma(L_{Ai} - \mu)^2 \Delta t_i}{24} \qquad L_{Ai} = \text{A-level}$$

$$\mu = \frac{\Sigma L_{Ai} \Delta t_i}{24} = \bar{L}_A$$

where 24 is the duration of the survey in hours and L_{Ai} is the A-level during the time interval Δt_i.

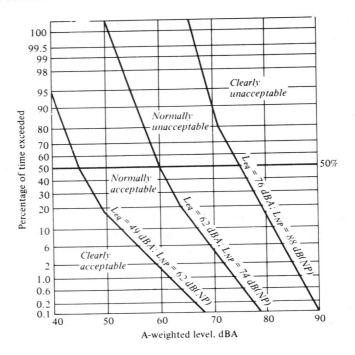

Figure 7.12 Criteria adopted by U.S. Department of Housing and Urban Development for non-aircraft noise measured outdoors in residential areas. L_{eq} is the mean square A-weighted sound level; L_{NP} is the noise pollution level [9].

3. A-weighted L_{10} (ten-percentile level) The Federal Highway Administration (FHWA) adopted the A-weighted L_{10} level as the principal indicator for assessing the impact of highway noise. Table 7.13 summarizes recommended L_{10} levels that should not be exceeded when a planned highway reaches its maximum traffic capacity. Essentially, federal funds cannot be obtained if the levels for the different land uses are exceeded. Hence, this standard has important economic implications, since most major highways are 90 percent federally funded.

Rating Procedures

A rating procedure describes some aspect of the noise stimulus, but in addition it attempts to account for the context in which the noise is experienced. This is accomplished by introducing corrections—both for peculiarities of the noise (pure tones, impulses, duration, rumbling, etc.) and for the situation into which it intrudes (ambient-noise level, type of neighborhood, time of day during which event occurs, etc.).

1. Day-night level, L_{dn} The day-night level was defined earlier for describing indoor noise environments. This rating procedure was developed as a single-

NOISE CRITERIA, STANDARDS, AND REGULATIONS **195**

Table 7.13 Federal Highway Administration Noise Standards for New Highway Construction*

Activity category	Exterior noise level, dBA		Description of activity category
	L_{eq}	L_{10}	
A	57	60	Tracts where serenity and quiet are especially important
B	67	70	Residences, motels, schools, churches, hospitals, etc.
C	72	75	Developed lands other than those above

* Either L_{eq} or L_{10} may be used (not both), measured in *any* hour.

number measure of community noise exposure in an attempt to improve upon the equivalent sound level (L_{eq}). This was accomplished by adding a correction of 10 dB to nighttime (10 P.M. to 7 A.M.) noise intrusions, to account for the increased annoyance caused by noise during that period.

L_{dn} was not designed as a single-source measure, and therefore it should not be used in determining source standards or for certification of product noise. Rather, it is a method best suited for predicting the long-term noise exposure effects on a community. Table 7.4, presented earlier, gives L_{dn} levels for outdoor environments identified by EPA as requisite to protect public health and welfare against long-term noise exposure.

2. Composite noise rating (CNR) The composite noise rating is a measure using octave-band sound-level data with appropriate corrections for spectral characteristics, background noise interference, and time of day. It has been used to assess the influence of various intruding noises such as traffic noise, industrial noise, and aircraft noise on the community.

The composite noise rating is calculated as follows:

• Measure or estimate the octave-band levels of the intruding noise source. Each band level is assumed averaged (on an energy basis) over a reasonable time interval, and over a reasonable number of locations in the community.
• The noise-level rank of the source (in terms of a letter) is determined by plotting the octave levels on the chart of curves given in Fig. 7.13. The highest zone into which the octave spectrum protrudes establishes the noise-level rank.
• Corrections are made for background noise by using either Fig. 7.14 or Table 7.14.
• Make corrections for the repetitiveness of the noise using Fig. 7.15.
• Make final corrections according to the community information and the procedure outlined in Table 7.15. (Note that a total correction of ±3 means that the level rank should be moved up or down by three letters, respectively.)

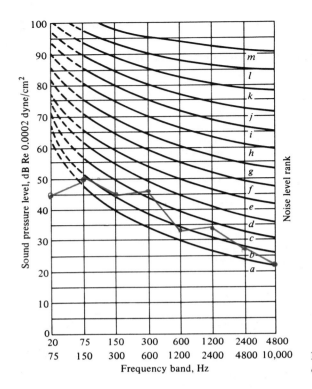

Figure 7.13 Family of curves used to determine the noise-level rank [4].

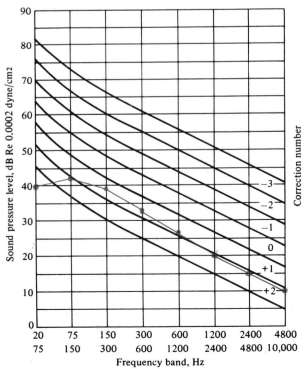

Figure 7.14 Family of curves used to determine the correction number for background noise [4].

Table 7.14 Corrections for background noise [4]

Neighborhood	Correction number
Very quiet suburban	+1
Suburban	0
Residential urban	−1
Urban near some industry	−2
Area of heavy industry	−3

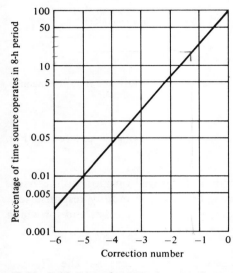

Figure 7.15 Proposed correction numbers for repetitiveness of the noise when the source operates on a reasonably regular daily schedule [4].

Table 7.15 List of correction numbers to be applied to noise-level rank to give CNR_C [4]

Influencing factor	Correction number
1. Background noise (see Fig. 7.14 or Table 7.13)	+2 to −3
2. Temporal and seasonal factors	
(*a*) Daytime only	−1
Nighttime	0
(*b*) Repetitiveness (see Fig. 7.15)	0 to −6
(*c*) Winter	−1
Summer	0
3. Detailed description of the noise	
(*a*) Continuous spectrum	0
Pure-tone components	+1
(*b*) Smooth time character	0
Impulsive	+1
4. Previous exposure	
None	0
Some	−1

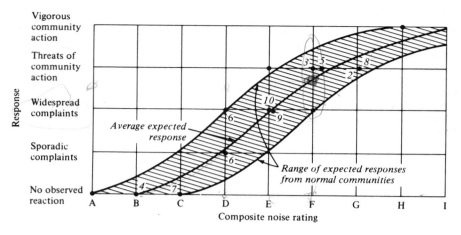

Figure 7.16 The wide curve shows the range of responses that can be expected from communities exposed to noises of increasing severity [4].

• The final level rank obtained for the intrusive noise is entered in Fig. 7.16 to obtain the response expected from the community.

The composite noise rating scheme works fairly well on an absolute basis. The scheme works better, however, in predicting the community response to a change (for better or worse) in a noise source which already exists and for which the response is known [16].

3. Noise exposure forecast (NEF) The noise exposure forecast uses the effective perceived noise level (EPNL) as its basic measure. EPNL is a single-number measure of complex aircraft flyover noise which approximates laboratory annoyance responses. It includes corrections for both the duration and tonal components of the spectra for different types of non-sonic-boom aircraft flyover noise. EPNL is used by the Federal Aviation Administration (FAA) in aircraft certification. The calculation procedures are complicated and can be found in Ref. 4.*

The noise exposure forecast (NEF) is the total summation (on an energy basis) over a 24-h period (weighted for the time of day) of EPNL minus a constant. Let $EPNL_{ij}$ be the effective perceived noise level at a particular ground location for aircraft of type i using flight path j. Then

$$NEF_{ij} = EPNL_{ij} + 10 \log\left[\frac{n_D(ij)}{20} + \frac{n_N(ij)}{1.2}\right] - 75 \text{ dB} \quad (7.13)$$

---

* Tables and graphs showing EPNL versus distance are available for known aircraft types, to facilitate construction of NEF contour maps; see "Noise Exposure Forecast Contours for 1967, 1970 and 1975 Operations at Selected Airports," DOT/FAA Office of Noise Abatement, FA68WA-1900, Sept. 1970, BBN Report No. 1863.

where $n_D(i\,j)$ is the number of daytime flights and $n_N(i\,j)$ is the number of nighttime flights. Then, summing for all classes of aircraft using a particular airport and including all possible flight paths, the NEF value at the particular ground location of interest is

$$\text{NEF} = 10 \log\left(\sum_i \sum_j 10^{0.1\,\text{NEF}_{i\,j}} \right) \tag{7.14}$$

It has been shown that NEF can be approximated by the day-night level by the following equation:

$$L_{dn} = (\text{NEF} + 35) \pm 3 \text{ dBA} \tag{7.15}$$

NEF contours have been used by HUD in evaluating land uses around airports, and they are usually included in environmental impact statements dealing with noise from jet aircraft operations around airport communities. Approximate construction of NEF contours is accomplished as follows:

- Calculate airport traffic index $= X = n_D + 17\ n_N$, where n_D, $n_N =$ number of jet takeoffs plus landings during daytime and nighttime at the airport, respectively.
- Take the value of X and refer to Fig. 7.17 to construct approximate NEF contours about each runway.
- Locate a point at the center of principal runways, then construct a straight line between the center point and the ground site of interest.
- Refer to Table 7.16 to establish HUD's acceptability category of the site.

As an example, consider the case of an airport which has 150 daytime and 30 nighttime jet aircraft operations. This gives a value of $X = 660$, $L/W = 2.5/2000$ ft for the NEF-40 contour. Figure 7.18 shows the two contours plotted. In accordance with the HUD criteria, site 1 is "clearly acceptable," but site 2 is rated "normally accepted," which would require that a building constructed there must include acoustical treatment to attenuate airport noise.

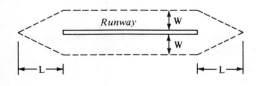

	Recommended L/W ratios for approximate construction of NEF contours for airport traffic indices	
	Contour size	
X	NEF-30 L/W	NEF-40 L/W
50	1 mi/0.5 mi	None
50–500	3 mi/0.5 mi	1 mi/1000 ft
500–1300	6 mi/1.5 mi	2.5 mi/2000 ft
1300	10 mi/2 mi	4 mi/3000 ft

Figure 7.17 Approximate construction of the NEF contours in which L and W are prescribed in the table. *(Source: Edward Magrab, Environmental Noise Control, 1975. Reprinted by permission of John Wiley & Sons, Inc.)*

Table 7.16 Site exposure to aircraft noise

Distance from site to the center of the area covered by the principal runways	Acceptability category
Outside the NEF-30 (CNR-100) contour, at a distance greater than or equal to the distance between the NEF-30 and NEF-40 (CNR-100, CNR-115) contours	Clearly acceptable
Outside the NEF-30 (CNR-100) contour, at a distance less than the distance between the NEF-30 and NEF-40 (CNR-100, CNR-115) contours	Normally acceptable
Between the NEF-30 and NEF-40 (CNR-100, CNR-115) contours	Normally unacceptable
Within the NEF-40 (CNR-115) contour	Clearly unacceptable

Source: Noise Assessment Guidelines, U.S. Dept. of Housing and Urban Development, 1971.

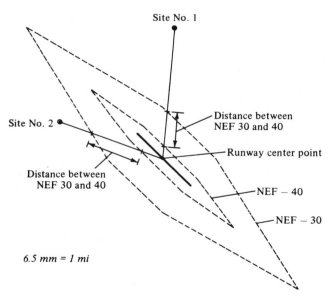

Figure 7.18 Construction of NEF contours in the example. *(Source: Edward Magrab, Environmental Noise Control, 1975. Reprinted by permission of John Wiley & Sons, Inc.)*

7.5 COMMUNITY (ENVIRONMENTAL) NOISE REGULATIONS

In early industrial America, urban communities grew up around industrial plants because factory workers wanted to live within easy reach of their place of employment. For these people the noise from industrial plants was acceptable. However, as new generations grew up, and as new people moved into these areas, the "sounds of progress" emanating from the factory began to take on a sour note. This same pattern of industrial and community development has been repeated more recently in areas having ready access to superhighways and commercial airports. Associated with these patterns of change has been an accelerating growth of the population in urban areas. The growth of the noise problem occurring with this shift in population is brought into focus if we note that the outdoor daytime residual-noise level in a wilderness area, such as the Grand Canyon Rim, is on the order of 16 dBA; the level on a farm is 30 to 35 dBA, and in a city 60 to 75 dBA. Consequently, there is a need to control the ever-increasing noise levels which threaten the health and welfare of the population in their workplaces and in their communities. In this section we attempt to outline the types of regulations which exist at federal, state, and local levels of government for the control of community noise.

Types of Regulations at Federal, State, and Local Levels

Federal and state regulations are necessary to deal with major noise sources which require statewide or national uniformity of treatment. Public transportation, such as air service, is an example where federal regulation is needed, while noise emission characteristics of new automobiles sold to private citizens are best regulated at the state level. In contrast, noise regulations which deal with community noise must be suited to the local needs and conditions of the community and should, therefore, be generated at the local level of government.

Nuisance ordinances The word "nuisance," in the legal sense, refers to "any annoying, unpleasant, or obnoxious thing or practice." Many of the laws currently in existence were developed to restrict activities which arouse discomfort, dissatisfaction, or annoyance among the public; these are called *nuisance ordinances*. The majority of us have experienced the roaring of the neighbor's lawnmower, the staccato of pneumatic hammers or pavement breakers at a construction site, the incessant barking of a neighbor's dog at night, the unmuffled engine of a passing automobile or motorcycle, or the boisterous party in the apartment above (to which we were not invited). These are all commonly encountered noise nuisances. Noise nuisance ordinances are regulations designed to restrict such unpleasant or annoying noises that are not easily measured or that are difficult to control by physical means.

Noise nuisance ordinances are one of the most common types of regulations for controlling community noise. However, because of their broad application, and since they are highly subjective in nature, these laws are difficult to administer and enforce. In a survey of noise regulations in 79 cities in 33 states [18], virtually every noise nuisance ordinance surveyed contained either explicitly or implicitly the following section:

> No person within the city shall make, or cause the making of, or suffer or permit to be made, upon any premises owned, occupied, or controlled by such person any unreasonably loud, disturbing, unusual, penetrating, boisterous, or unnecessary noise, disturbance, or commotion, as to be detrimental to the life or health of any individual or cause discomfort or annoyance to a reasonable person of normal sensitivities.

For this section to be effectively enforced it would be necessary to establish that the noise is *unreasonably loud, unnecessary*, and that it has caused annoyance to a reasonable person of *normal sensitivities*. The definitions of "unreasonably loud," "unnecessary," and "normal sensitivities" have frequently led to problems for lawmakers, courts, noise makers, law enforcement officials, and the citizens who object to the noise. Although the first two terms can presumably be established by inspection, establishment of the last term can often be an embarrassing procedure regardless of whether the noise is unreasonably loud and unnecessary.

Often additional criteria must be provided in a nuisance ordinance in order to unify and clarify phraseology and to help establish whether a violation has occurred; for example,

> The standards which shall be considered in determining whether a violation of this section exists shall include, but shall not be limited to, the following: (*a*) the volume of the noise, (*b*) the intensity of the noise, (*c*) whether the nature of the noise is usual or unusual, (*d*) the proximity of the noise to residential sleeping facilities, (*e*) the time of the day or night during which the noise occurs, (*f*) whether the noise is recurrent, intermittent or constant . . . [*etc.*].

On the other hand, it may be possible to state explicitly the means of establishing violation of an ordinance for specific noise sources, as was done in the following case:

> Using, operating, or permitting to be played any radio, television set, musical instrument, or other device for producing sound in such a manner as to disturb the peace, quiet, and comfort of the inhabitants of a residence district shall be unlawful . . . and it is declared that the operation of the foregoing between the hours of 10:00 P.M. and 7:00 A.M. in such a manner as to be plainly audible at a distance of 100 feet from where it is located shall be prima facie evidence of a violation of this section.

Although the noise nuisance ordinance has subjective limitations, it is often the best means of abatement since it can be adjusted to suit the particular needs of a community. Almost all nuisance ordinances specify [18]:

1. Those activities which are strictly prohibited
2. Those activities which are restricted to certain hours of the day

3. Those activities which require permits or licenses
4. The creation of "quiet zones"

A common pattern is to explicitly enumerate those actions and activities within these areas which have been deemed acceptable. Then, as the community grows and changes, sections within the ordinance can be added to or revised in order to control any new annoyance or unacceptable action. The primary shortcoming of this type of regulation is its subjective nature, which results in difficulty in administering and enforcing it.

Performance codes Performance codes have been added to noise legislation in an attempt to improve and remedy the drawbacks of subjective criteria and connotations which are characteristic of nuisance ordinances. By specifying limiting sound levels that are permissible at specified locations, the performance code provides a quick and easy means of assessing whether or not a violation exists.

An underlying basis of the performance code is the existence of separate ambient-noise levels associated with different areas of a community. Hence, individual performance codes can be specified which reflect the type of activities anticipated within these areas and the maximum sound level that persons within these areas are willing to accept. Three areas typically designated in performance codes are *residential, commercial* (business), and *industrial* (manufacturing). The performance code as it applies to noise in these areas exists in three basic formats [18]:

1. Codes which specify *limiting octave-band levels* at district, area, or zone boundaries
2. Codes which specify *limiting sound levels* at district, area, or zone boundaries
3. Codes which specify *limiting octave-band levels* but also employ *equivalent "A" or "C" sound levels* for monitoring or quick checking purposes

An example of a performance code which specifies limiting sound levels reads as follows:

A noise shall be deemed to be unreasonably loud and a violation of this ordinance under the following circumstances: Any sound radiated for continuous or recurrent periods from any premises which sound-pressure levels at any point on the property line of said premises in excess of the following "A"-scale limits:

	"A"-scale limit	
District	Day	Night
Residential	51	46
Business	56	51
Industrial	61	56

On the other hand, a typical performance code which specifies limiting octave-band levels might read as follows:

The maximum sound-pressure level along the boundary separating the M (general industry) district from such districts (residential, commercial) shall not exceed the standards set forth in the table below.

Octave-band center frequency, Hz	Maximum band level, dB Re 2×10^5 N/m^2
63.5	72
125	67
250	59
500	52
1000	46
2000	40
4000	34
Above 4000	32

Some performance codes may list corrections which should be applied to permissible levels for specific conditions. A sample list is given below:

Corrections to be applied to limiting octave-band levels	
Condition	Correction
Noise is present at nighttime	-7 dB
Noise contains pure tones or is impulsive	-7 dB
Noise has an "on time" of no more than 0.5 s, and an "off time" between successive "on times" of at least 30 min	$+10$ dB
[etc.]	

Although the addition of performance codes to noise control regulations has the potential for reducing the difficulty of administration and enforcement, the wording and all supporting information must be as complete and explicit as possible. A survey of existing noise ordinances reveals that there are several common deficiencies found in many performance codes which make them at least difficult to apply and enforce, if not invalid. Several errors or omissions that occur most frequently are listed below:

1. The weighting network and meter response setting for measuring the sound level are not specified.
2. The acoustic reference level is not given when specifying levels.
3. Calibration of and standards for instruments are not specified.

4. The measurement locations specified in the code may be acoustically unreliable or unacceptable.
5. Limiting octave-band levels are set too low.

An example of the difficulties encountered when the weighting network and method of measuring the sound levels are not specified is demonstrated in this zoning ordinance for a township in southern Michigan:

> The emission of measurable noises from industrial use shall not exceed seventy (70) decibels as measured at the boundary property lines, except that when normal street traffic noises exceed seventy (70) decibels, the measurable noise emanating from the use may equal but not exceed traffic noises. In addition, objectionable sounds of an intermittent nature, or characterized by high frequencies even if falling below the aforementioned decibel reading, shall be controlled so as not to become a nuisance to adjacent uses.

Sound-level measurements were taken at the property line of a forging manufacturing company where this ordinance applies in order to show the shortcomings of the performance code. The sound measured was the impulsive noise of a forging hammer. The results of these measurements are tabulated here to show the effect of instrument settings on noise levels.

Sound-level meter setting	Sound level, dB
A weighting, slow response, maximum meter reading	65 dBA$_{sm}$
A weighting, fast response, maximum meter reading	68 dBA$_{fm}$
A weighting, impulse-hold	71 dBA$_p$ (rms)
A weighting, true-peak-hold	82 dBA$_p$ (true)
Flat response, impulse-hold	90 dB$_p$ (rms)
Flat response, true-peak-hold	97 dB$_p$ (true)

The figures show a range of values from 65 to 97 dB obtained at one location, for the same source, using six different instrument settings. The difficulty in administering and enforcing this ordinance is clearly seen. It is interesting to note that for this particular ordinance, the performance code was backed up by a nuisance code which was equally difficult to enforce.

Land-use concepts and urban planning Effective land use and municipal planning is a very important alternative in urban noise control, particularly in regions where inner-city renewal and suburban community developments are contemplated. However, these measures are less effective in established communities where the noise sources (transportation, industrial) and their paths are, for practical purposes, fixed.

The basic concept in effective land use for community noise control is the creation of "buffer" zones. The objective of noise zoning is to separate the noise source from the receiver by some scheme of controlled land use. Methods for accomplishing this objective fall into three categories:

1. Land-use planning
2. Zoning
3. Municipal building codes

Much forethought and knowledgeable judgment are necessary in planning community layout, design, and renewal. Land development within and in the region of a local community can be directed toward various purposes such as industrial/commercial, recreational, health, educational, and residential activities. Restricting the use of parcels of land for noise control purposes can have a socioeconomic impact on the community and on occupants of the affected land (e.g., property devaluation or appreciation, change in tax base, costs of implementation and enforcement). On the other hand, the lack of regulation of land use according to activity can result in a lopsided development of the area, with silence-oriented educational activities interspersed with noisy industrial and commercial activities. Therefore, planning the land use for noise abatement and control requires the local government to formulate a comprehensive location (zoning) plan. Figure 7.19 shows a hypothetical land-use arrangement designed to separate the community into compatible groups and to protect residential areas from both aircraft and traffic noise through the use of buffer zones.

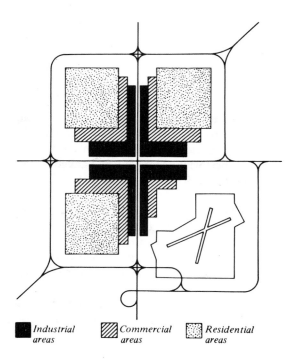

■ *Industrial areas*   ▨ *Commercial areas*   ⬚ *Residential areas*

Figure 7.19 Use of buffer zones in community planning [18].

Zoning refers to the regulation or location of specific socioeconomic activities within a land-use plan. For example, zoning would control the distribution of single- and multifamily units within a residential area, or the distribution of light versus heavy industry in an area designated for industrial use.

In cases where land-use planning and zoning do not provide sufficient protection for the community, building codes may be required to reduce interior noise levels in buildings. Building codes are particularly effective (1) in situations where major renewal of existing structures is planned and (2) with new construction. Enforcement of building codes can protect the inhabitants from exterior noise sources, such as airports and highways, and from noise produced in adjacent dwellings in multifamily buildings. However, there are two major obstacles to the effectiveness of building codes for noise protection: (1) There is still a lack of technical information on the actual noise reduction afforded by various constructions and (2) there is a severe lack of suitably trained personnel at the local level of government to implement such programs successfully. These obstacles must be overcome before building codes can be used successfully in noise control.

7.6 EPA MODEL COMMUNITY NOISE CONTROL ORDINANCE AND STRATEGY GUIDELINE MANUAL

The shortcomings of performance codes listed earlier can sometimes be attributed to oversights, but most often they come about because the people responsible for preparing the ordinance have insufficient understanding of the technical and legal problems associated with implementing and enforcing a noise control program. The same statement is true for those responsible for land-use planning and developing building codes. The U.S. Environmental Protection Agency, which has the primary role for controlling environmental noise under Section 4 of the Noise Control Act of 1972, has developed a Model Community Noise Control Ordinance [20] and a Community Noise Strategy Guideline Manual [21] which should help communities cope with their noise problems.

The model ordinance is intended as a basic tool which communities, both large and small, can use to construct noise control ordinances suited to local needs and conditions. Although the model ordinance is most suitable for larger communities (100,000 population or greater), smaller communities (and large ones with limited resources) need adopt only those provisions which address their pressing noise problems. The model ordinance maintains provision for a nuisance law for prohibiting noise disturbances, but also provides definitive operation and use standards for motor vehicles and other sources of community noise which, with the increasing availability of reliable monitoring equipment, should result in ordinances that are more easily implemented and enforced than many have been in the past.

Specific values of sound levels in the performance standards, and permitted hours for the conduct of activities or the operation of equipment, have been omitted in the model ordinance in order to allow the level and extent of such control to be decided locally. This is a necessary aspect of any model ordinance since each community has its own set of environmental, health, economic, and other goals which it wishes to attain; and each has its own configuration of noise sources which it wishes to control.

The EPA recognizes that the successful implementation and enforcement of a community noise control program requires the careful selection of cost-effective abatement measures based on economic and acoustical data gathered in the community. To this end the EPA has prepared a Community Noise Strategy Guideline Manual designed to help local governments determine in an objective manner the best allocation of funds for reducing the adverse effects of noise in their communities.

The approach taken in the strategy guidelines manual has three basic steps [21]:

1. Find out what the problems are.
   - What noises are people complaining about?
   - What noises are people annoyed by?
   - How loud are the noise sources?
   - Which ones should be considered as problems, and therefore candidates for noise reduction?

   EPA has devised two surveys, an attitudinal survey [22] and an acoustical monitoring survey [23], which help determine how many people are annoyed and by what noise sources, what types of noise abatement solutions they support, and how much they are willing to pay. The acoustical survey provides information on the levels of noise produced by various sources in the community.

2. Find out what the solutions are.
   - What solutions are appropriate for the identified problems?
   - How much do they cost?
   - How effective are they?
   - Are they politically and socially feasible?

   The EPA guidelines manual outlines a series of steps which help to identify the most promising solutions, estimate costs of each solution, estimate noise-level reduction of each solution, eliminate abatement measures which are politically or socially infeasible, and identify additional measures which the community wishes to support.

3. Choose the best solutions.
   - How much money should be spent on each solution to achieve the maximum benefit while still remaining within the budget?

   The procedures described in the manual utilize an optimization computer program to select the most cost-effective abatement measures and the amount of money which should be spent on each, based on the economic and acoustical data gathered in the community.

Although the steps described in the guidelines manual for carrying out the three tasks are somewhat detailed, the overall approach is quite simple in concept and can be used by local governments as a guideline for devising individually tailored noise control strategies.

REFERENCES

1. Lang, William W., "The Status of Noise Control Regulations in the USA," *Noise Control Eng.*, November–December 1975.
2. *Standards on Noise Measurements, Rating Schemes, and Definitions: A Compilation*, National Bureau of Standards Special Publication 38C, 1976 ed.
3. Robinson, D. W., "Practice and Principle in Environmental Noise Rating," *Noise/News* **6** (5):96–104 (1977).
4. Pearsons, Karl S., and Ricarda L. Bennett, *Handbook of Noise Ratings*, NASA Contractor Report, NASA CR-2376, National Aeronautics and Space Administration, Washington, D.C., April 1974.
5. *Information on Levels of Environmental Noise Requisite to Protect Public Health and Welfare with an Adequate Margin of Safety*, U.S. Environmental Protection Agency, 550/9-74-004, March 1974.
6. Ostergaard, Paul B., "Machine Tool Noise Measurement," *Sound and Vibration*, October 1976.
7. Magrab, E., *Environmental Noise Control*, Wiley, New York, 1975.
8. Franken, P. A., "Criteria, Standards and Regulations," *Noise Control Eng.*, 1973, pp. 86–89.
9. Beranek, L. L. (ed.), *Noise and Vibration Control*, McGraw-Hill, New York, 1971.
10. *ASHRAE Handbook & Product Directory 1976 Systems*, American Society of Heating, Refrigerating and Air Conditioning Engineers, Inc., New York, 1976.
11. Eldred, K. M., *Standards and Criteria for Noise Control*, Proceedings of Inter-Noise Conference, 1978, San Francisco, Calif.
12. Peterson, A. P. G., and E. E. Gross, *Handbook of Noise Measurement*, 7th ed., General Radio Company, Concord, Mass., 1972.
13. *Guidelines to the Department of Labor's Occupational Noise Standards*, U.S. Department of Labor, Occupational Safety and Health Administration, Bulletin 334.
14. "Proposed OSHA Industrial Noise Regulations," *Noise/News* **3** (6):135–159 (1974).
15. Eldred, Kenneth M., "Assessment of Community Noise," *Noise Control Eng.*, September–October 1974, pp. 88–95.
16. Schultz, T. J., *Community Noise Ratings*, Applied Science Publications, London, 1972.
17. Wells, R. J., *Noise Complaint Potential—Ambient Noise versus Intrusive Noise*, Proceedings of the 7th International Congress on Acoustics, 1971.
18. Gatley, William S., and Edwin E. Frye, "Regulation of Noise in Urban Areas," manual prepared for Workshops, Continuing Education Series, University of Missouri, Rolla, 1971.
19. Sharp, H., and H. G. Lakhani, "Information Needed in Development of Local Noise-Protective Measures," Wyle Research Dept. WR 76-28, for U.S. Environmental Protection Agency, September 1977.
20. *Model Noise Control Ordinance*, U.S. Environmental Protection Agency, 1976.
21. First Draft—"Community Noise Strategy Guidelines Manual," Wyle Research Dept. WR 78-1, for U.S. Environmental Protection Agency, February 1978.
22. Levine, N., and S. Bush, "An Attitudinal Assessment of Community Noise—Vol. IV, A Manual for Coding Questionnaires," Wyle Research Dept. WR 77-4, for U.S. Environmental Protection Agency, October 1977.
23. "Community Noise Monitoring Manual," Wyle Research Dept. (draft), for U.S. Environmental Protection Agency, November 1977.
24. Cunniff, P. F., *Environmental Noise Pollution*, Wiley, New York, 1977.

IMPORTANT TERMS AND FORMULAS

Noise regulation, noise ordinance, noise standard
Noise criteria, rating schemes, noise indices
Direct ratings: L_p, L_A, L_C, L_D
Annoyance ratings: LL_s, PNL, L_{eq}, L_{dn}
Communication interference level: PSIL, NC curves, PNC curves
Hearing-damage risk criteria: L_{eq} (OSHA), CHABA
OSHA Noise Standard
Statistical descriptors of noise: L_{max}, L_{min}, L_n, L_{eq}
Rating scales: L_A, NPL, L_{10} dBA
Rating procedures: L_{dn}, CNR, NEF, EPNL
Nuisance ordinance
Performance code
Land-use concepts

$$L_{eq} = 10 \log\left[\frac{1}{T} \sum_{i=1}^{n} 10^{0.1 L_{Ai}} \Delta t_i\right] \quad L_{eq}(\text{OSHA}) = 16.7 \log\left[\frac{1}{T} \sum_{i=1}^{n} 10^{L_{Ai}/16.7} \Delta t_i\right]$$

$$\text{PSIL} = \frac{L_{500} + L_{1000} + L_{2000}}{3} \qquad D = \sum \frac{C_i}{T_i} \qquad \text{NPL} = L_{50} + d + \frac{d^2}{60}$$

PROBLEMS

7.1 Give a brief definition of each of the following terms: (*a*) noise regulation, (*b*) noise ordinance, (*c*) noise standard, (*d*) noise criteria, (*e*) rating schemes, (*f*) noise indices.

7.2 Given the following noise data:

Center frequency, Hz	Band level, dB
31.5	80
63	80
125	75
250	74
500	73
1000	82
2000	80
4000	76
8000	75

(*a*) What is the PSIL?
Answer: 78 dB

(*b*) What is the A-level?
Answer: 86 dB
(*c*) What is the PNC value?
(*d*) What is the loudness level?
Answer: 96 dB
(*e*) Would the noise be acceptable in an office?
Answer: No
(*f*) What attenuation at each octave band would be necessary to achieve an NC value of 35?
    Answer: 31.5—18; 63—25; 125—25; 250—29; 500—33; 1000—47; 2000—50; 4000—48; 8000—47
(*g*) What distance apart can people be understood (talking) if they speak in:
    (1) normal voices
        Answer: Can't be heard
    (2) raised voices
        Answer: 9 in
    (3) shouting voices
        Answer: 3 ft
(*h*) Can telephone conversation be carried on?
Answer: With great difficulty

7.3 A local bank has determined that it will no longer give mortgages to developers who propose to put housing on land next to highways, airports, commercial areas, etc., whenever the L_{NP} at the boundary of the site exceeds 74 dB. A noise survey is made at one site where development is proposed, and the following data are collected for a "typical" day:

Level, dBA	Total	Day	Night
90–95	1	1.0	0.0
85–90	4	3.5	0.5
80–85	2	1.5	0.5
75–80	8	7.5	0.5
70–75	5	0.5	4.5
65–70	3	0.5	2.5
60–65	1	0.5	0.5
		15.0	9.0

(*a*) What is the noise pollution level (i.e., is the site acceptable)?
Answer: 102.2 dB (no)
(*b*) What are the L_{90}, L_{50}, L_{10}, L_{eq}, L_{dn} levels?
Answer: 68 dB, 77 dB, 88 dB, 83.4 dBA, 86 dBA
(*c*) Would this site be acceptable under the HUD criteria for new residential construction?

7.4 Given the following hourly L_{eq} readings:

Time	L_{eq}, dBA	Time	L_{eq}, dBA	Time	L_{eq}, dBA
0700	50	1500	65	2300	50
0800	50	1600	65	2400	40
0900	50	1700	65	0100	40
1000	65	1800	65	0200	40
1100	65	1900	60	0300	40
1200	65	2000	60	0900	40
1300	65	2100	55	0500	40
1400	65	2200	55	0600	40

(a) Find the L_{dn}.

(b) Estimate L_{10}, L_{50}, L_{90}.

(c) Does the site meet the HUD criteria for new residential construction?

7.5 Given the following nighttime and daytime equivalent sound levels:

L_n = 45 dBA (between 10 P.M. and 7 A.M.)

L_d = 55 dBA (between 7 A.M. and 10 P.M.)

(a) Find the L_{dn} over the 24-h period.

(b) Find the L_{eq} over the 24-h period.

7.6 During an 8-h period a factory employee is exposed to 81 dBA for the first 2 h, 97 dBA for the next 2 h, 66 dBA during lunch, and 90 dBA for the remaining 3 h.

(a) Calculate the L_{eq} for the 8-h exposure.

(b) Calculate the L_{eq} (OSHA) for the 8-h exposure.

(c) Calculate the noise dose D.

(d) Is there a possible violation of the OSHA Noise Standard?

7.7 Consider the time history of community noise shown. Approximate the time history by breaking the response into equal 5-s intervals:

(a) Calculate L_{eq} for the sound-level record.

(b) Estimate L_{10}, L_{50}, L_{90}.

(c) Compute the noise pollution level (NPL).

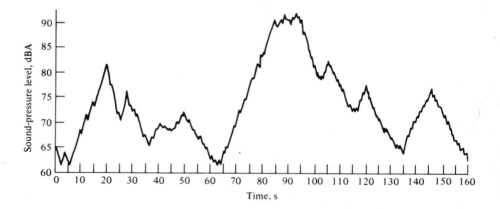

7.8 Octave-band noise levels resulting from a factory that plans to operate continuously at night in a suburban community from 8:00 P.M. to 10:00 P.M. are given in the table below. Also shown are background levels without the factory operating. Time of year is summer. The noise is impulsive and contains a whine (pure tone).

Octave-band frequency, Hz	Factory noise, dB	Background noise, dB
20–75	45	40
75–150	50	42
150–300	45	39
300–600	41	33
600–1200	33	27
1200–2400	34	20
2400–4800	27	15
4800–10,000	22	10

Use the composite noise rating scheme (CNR) to predict the community response to the factory noise.

Answer: Except "widespread complaints" with the possibility of "threats of community action."

7.9 When a fan is turned on in a room, the octave-level spectrum of the noise in the room changes as follows:

Octave-band center frequency	I_p W/m² Before	After
31.5	60	63
63	62	63
125	65	65
250	65	67
500	62	65
1000	60	66
2000	65	69
4000	68	70
8000	67	72

(*a*) What are the octave-band levels due to the fan alone, at the point in question?

(*b*) With the fan on, at about what distance can a person be heard talking in a normal voice? *Answer:* Approximately 1 ft

(*c*) What would you expect the subjective response to this total noise to be?

(*d*) What is the approximate overall sound-pressure-level reading of the total noise? *Answer:* 77 dB

(*e*) What is the approximate dBA reading of the total noise? *Answer:* 76 dBA

(*f*) What is the NC value of the total noise? The PNC value?

(*g*) What is the loudness level, LL_s, of the fan noise? *Answer:* 90 phons

(*h*) What must the noise reduction be across a wall separating the fan room from a supervisor's office in order to achieve a specification of NC-55 in the supervisor's office?

7.10 A survey is made to determine the noise levels at a site proposed for a housing development. Data were taken for a 24-h period, and are as follows:

L_{A_i}	t_i (h) total	t_i (day)	t_i (night) (10 P.M.–7 A.M.)
90–95	0.75	0.75	0.0
85–90	2.00	1.50	0.5
80–85	4.00	3.00	1.0
75–80	9.00	8.00	1.0
70–75	5.00	1.00	4.0
65–70	2.75	0.75	2.0
60–65	0.50	0.00	0.5
	21.00	15.33	9.0

(*a*) Estimate L_{10}, L_{50}, L_{90}. *Answer:* 86 dBA, 77 dBA, 68 dBA

(*b*) Estimate L_{eq}, L_{dn}. *Answer:* 82 dBA, 86 dBA

(*c*) Estimate the standard deviation σ.

(*d*) Estimate the noise pollution level, NPL. *Answer:* 99 dB

(*e*) Does the site comply with HUD criteria?

EIGHT

ACOUSTICAL MATERIALS AND STRUCTURES

8.1 INTRODUCTION

A working knowledge of acoustical materials and structures is essential for the practicing noise control engineer. Without this knowledge, cost-effective control of noise becomes more a matter of chance than of intelligent design. In this chapter we will describe and compare absorptive and barrier materials, silencers, damping treatments, and vibration isolators.

The major characteristics of each of these categories are summarized in Table 8.1. The function of the first three categories is to absorb or attenuate airborne sound waves. In other words, some vibrating object in contact with a medium (usually air) has created sound waves whose propagation through the medium is to be minimized. The function of the last category (vibration isolation) is to minimize the transmission of shaking forces (from rotating machinery, for example) into a floor or other solid structure. These forces, if not attenuated, can cause vibration of the structure and consequent widespread generation of sound waves. The function of the fourth category (damping treatments) is (1) to reduce the amplitudes of resonant vibrations that generate airborne sound and/or (2) to minimize the transfer of vibratory energy at panel edges or attachment points to adjoining structural elements.

Table 8.1 Materials and structures for noise control

Category	Description of	Purpose of	Representative uses of
Absorptive materials	Relatively lightweight (0.5 to 20 lb/ft³); porous, with interconnecting passages; poor barrier	Dissipation of acoustic energy, through conversion to minute amounts of heat	Reduction of reverberant sound energy; dissipation of acoustic energy in silencers
Silencers	Series or parallel combination of reactive or dissipative elements	Dissipation of acoustic energy in the presence of steady flow	Duct silencers in HVAC systems; inlet and exhaust silencers for engines, compressors, fans, turbines
Barrier materials	Relatively dense (20 to 80 lb/ft² of surface area); nonporous; poor absorber	Attenuation of acoustic energy	Containment of sound; reduction of acoustic transmission
Damping treatments	Flexible viscoelastic material with relatively large internal losses	Dissipation of vibratory energy	Reduction of acoustic energy generated by resonant panel vibrations
Vibration isolators	Resilient pads; metallic springs	Reduction of transmitted forces and structural vibrations	Mounts for fans, compressors, engines, machinery

215

8.2 ABSORPTIVE MATERIALS AND STRUCTURES

Mechanisms for Dissipation of Acoustic Energy

The function of absorptive materials and structures is to transform impinging acoustic energy into heat. Because the energy contained in sound waves is normally very small, the quantity of heat generated is also small. The two mechanisms by which energy is dissipated are:

- *Viscous-flow losses.* An effective absorber structure consists of a series of interconnected pores or voids, by means of which sound waves propagate into and through the structure. During propagation, the particle velocity associated with the sound wave causes *relative* motion between the medium (usually air) and the surrounding material. As a result, boundary-layer losses occur within the structure.
- *Internal friction.* Some absorptive materials have resilient fibrous or porous structures that are compressed or flexed by sound-wave propagation. In these structures, dissipation occurs not only from viscous-flow losses but also from the internal friction of the material itself.

The absorptive characteristics of an acoustical material are determined to a large extent by the pore or void size, interconnections between pores or voids, and material thickness. Although engineers interested in noise control do not require complete knowledge of these loss mechanisms, a general understanding of the relationship between material properties and dissipation of acoustic energy is essential. The acoustical impedance at the material surface and at various frequencies and angles of incidence is probably the best descriptor of this relationship. (Recall that the acoustical impedance defines the magnitude and phase relationship between acoustic pressure and particle velocity.) If a particular combination of frequency and material structure results in a high impedance, the reflected wave amplitude will be relatively large and the absorption coefficient will be correspondingly small.* On the other hand, material with an impedance equal to the impedance of the medium will produce no reflected waves. In other words, when the impedances of the material and structure are "matched," all of the incident energy is dissipated within the material structure.

Dissipation of acoustic energy for a given material requires that the *relative* velocity between the material structure and the medium be as large as possible. For a material placed directly over a solid backing, a thickness of at least one-tenth of the wavelength of impinging sound is required. Figure 8.1a shows the approximate particle-velocity distribution in a material with thickness $t = \lambda/10$. Note that the particle velocity within the material (the vector sum of incident- and reflected-wave particle velocities) is zero at the solid backing and relatively small at the other locations. As the t/λ ratio increases, the particle

---

* Actually, the reflected wave at a given frequency is a combination of many waves reflected from the material surface, the interior structure, and the backing which supports the material.

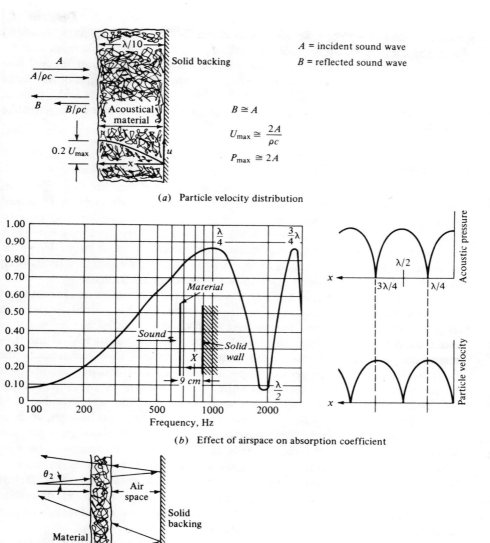

A = incident sound wave
B = reflected sound wave

$$B \cong A$$

$$U_{max} \cong \frac{2A}{\rho c}$$

$$P_{max} \cong 2A$$

(a) Particle velocity distribution

(b) Effect of airspace on absorption coefficient

(c) Effect of angle of incidence Θ on effective depth of airspace

Figure 8.1 Effects of material thickness, airspace, and angle of incidence on acoustical performance. *From B & K Instruments, Inc.*

velocity approaches a maximum value within the material. In fact, the normal-incidence absorption of a thin material increases dramatically if it is separated from the backing by an air space with $\lambda/4$ (Fig. 8.1b). The performance of the material approaches that of a material thickness equal to $\lambda/4$, at much lower cost. In the usual case, sound waves arrive at many different angles of incidence (Fig. 8.1c). At each angle, sound waves "see" a different thickness and air space. As a result, a material backed by an air space of 1 or 2 in can be an effective absorber at relatively low frequencies.

Properties of Absorptive Structures

The ability of a given material to dissipate energy is a function not only of its thickness but also of its internal structure. If the structure consists of closed pores or voids, acoustic waves cannot propagate into the interior, and viscous-flow losses are negligible. At low frequencies the entire structure may move as a unit, and the resulting flexure may cause some internal friction losses. However, at higher frequencies the inertia of the structure virtually eliminates its motion; the structure surface becomes essentially a reflector of acoustic energy.*

If an acoustical material has interconnecting pores or voids, its absorption at a given frequency is a function of its "flow resistance." This quantity is the ratio of the static-pressure drop across a sample of the material to the resulting steady-flow velocity through the sample. "Specific flow resistance" is the flow resistance per unit thickness of the material. Note that flow resistance is the in-phase (resistive) component of impedance for a zero-frequency sound wave. In addition to flow resistance, other structural characteristics affect the dissipative properties of an acoustical material. These are the size, number, and distribution of surface openings; the extent of interconnections between voids or pores within the structure; and the tortuosity of internal flow passages (described by the "structure factor"). Although all of these characteristics have an influence on flow resistance, they are also significant in and of themselves. These parameters, in combination with material thickness and other factors (such as resilience of the material and the presence of an air space), determine the acoustic impedance at a given frequency. The acoustic impedance is in turn directly related to the absorption coefficient.

A simplified but nonetheless useful description of the interaction between a sound wave and an absorbing structure proceeds as follows.

· If the resistance of the structure to acoustic-wave propagation is too low, energy dissipation will be small, and most of the energy will be reflected from the backing material into the surroundings. Low resistance can occur because the material structure is too "open" or because the ratio of thickness to wavelength is too small, in which case the material is essentially "transparent" to sound waves.

* For this reason, closed-cell structures such as styrofoam are poor absorbers of airborne sound.

• If the resistance of the structure to acoustic-wave propagation is too high, most of the energy will be reflected from the surface of the structure. Energy dissipation within the structure will be correspondingly small. High resistance can occur because surface openings are too few or too small to allow adequate wave propagation, or because of insufficient "openness" between internal voids or pores.

Mechanical Model of Absorptive Materials

A simplified mechanical model which illustrates the dissipation process is shown in Fig. 8.2a. In this model, mass M represents the mass of the medium in the internal void structure (and a fraction of the material mass if the structure is resilient); K represents the compressibility of the medium in the internal void structure (and the resilience of the material); C represents the energy-dissipation properties of the structure (viscous-flow losses and internal friction). A normalized plot of the average energy dissipated per unit of time versus frequency ratio

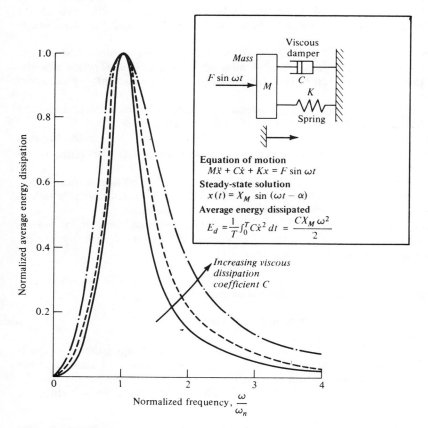

Figure 8.2 Simplified mechanical model of energy dissipation in an acoustical material.

is also shown. Although the actual dissipation process is more complex than that predicted by the model, it does illustrate some important facts for the noise control engineer:

- The frequency range over which a given structure provides maximum energy dissipation is a function of material properties and geometry (indicated by the undamped natural frequency ω_n of the model).
- The dissipative properties of a structure may be relatively poor outside the frequency range of maximum performance.
- Matching of structure performance to the specific noise control problem at hand is essential if an effective solution at the lowest cost is desired.

Summary: Energy Dissipation and Material Properties

We can summarize the discussion in this section as follows:

- Viscous-flow losses and internal friction are the primary means of energy dissipation in an acoustical material. These mechanisms are effective to the extent that a relative flow velocity between the medium and the structure is present.
- Important material properties are surface openings, internal structure, flow resistance, and thickness. The combined effects of these properties determine the acoustical impedance (and absorption coefficient) of a given material.
- Energy dissipation within a material less than $\lambda/10$ thick, placed directly over a solid backing, is usually too small to be of value.
- An air space of 1 to 4 in behind a material with a $\frac{1}{2}$- to 2-in thickness is frequently an effective way to improve the low-frequency performance of an acoustical material.
- Compression of a given material (such as glass fibers) into a more dense structure during manufacture increases the density and flow resistivity, which in turn improves low-frequency absorption for a given thickness.
- Limiting the number of interconnections between cells in a porous material (such as polyurethane foam) can improve the low-frequency performance, for material thicknesses less than 2 in.

Types and Characteristics of Absorbing Structures

The most common types of absorbing materials are:

- Interlaced glass fibers with a resinous binder, forming either a resilient structure (such as house insulation) or a rigid structure (such as acoustical tile and lay-in panels), depending on density
- Spun lava-rock fibers ("rock wool"), which form a resilient structure

- Interlaced wood or other plant fibers cemented together to form a rigid structure with internal voids
- Cellulose fibers formed with a binder into a rigid porous structure
- Cellulose fibers mixed in a slurry that is sprayed in place to form a porous resilient structure
- Open-cell resilient foams (usually polyurethane), in which pore size and interconnecting passages are controlled.

These materials are illustrated in Fig. 8.3, and typical thicknesses, weight densities, and absorption coefficients are shown in Table 8.2.

Other dissipative materials of value in specific applications are:

- Interlaced and compressed cotton textile waste (used extensively in the automotive industry)
- Heavy drapery material
- Deep-pile carpeting
- Sintered metal fibers formed into a rigid structure, 1/16 to 1.4 in thick, with carefully controlled flow resistance (for use with an air space in silencers for high-flow, high-temperature applications such as gas turbines)

All of these materials can be combined with other elements into a structure with enhanced acoustical or physical properties. The most common of these elements are air spaces and surface treatments—the latter including paint, cloth, a thin impervious membrane, or a perforated cover fabricated from metal, fiberboard, thermoplastic, or vinyl. The function of an air space has already been discussed. We will now describe the functions and acoustical effects of surface treatments.

Functional effects of surface treatments include improved appearance; washability; resistance to weather; improved durability; resistance to abrasion and erosion (as by flow, for example); and prevention of contact between the material (especially glass fiber) and people or animals. The effects of surface treatments on absorption of acoustic energy are summarized below.

A thin coating of paint, with open perforations equal to 6 to 15 percent of the surface area, will not materially affect the absorption of ceiling tile or lay-in panels. A coarse-weave cloth stretched over or cemented to the surface of glass-fiber board also has little if any effect. However, a close-weave cloth can add appreciable flow resistance, with a corresponding increase in low-frequency absorption and some decrease at higher frequencies. The method of attachment (at the edges, or by adhesive or chemical bonding of the surfaces) also influences the acoustical performance. In general, the most effective methods are bonding at the edges or in strips over the surface. (If the bonding agent creates an impervious coating over all or any part of the surface, the absorptive characteristics of the affected material will be seriously degraded.)

Polyurethane

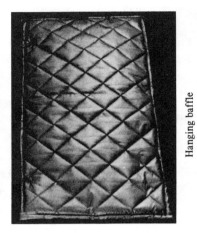

Hanging baffle

Glass fiber building insulation

Glass fiber ceiling panels

Loaded vinyl sheet

Loaded vinyl-urethane foam composites

Glass fiber boards

Glass fiber pipe wrap

Figure 8.3 Representative acoustical materials. *Glass fiber products courtesy of Owen-Corning Fiberglas Corporation; foam and vinyl products courtesy of Ferro Corporation, Composites Division.*

An impervious membrane (usually between 1/2 and 1 1/2 mils thick), bonded to or stretched over the material surface, will enhance low-frequency absorption and degrade high-frequency absorption. The method of attachment produces effects similar to those described for a cloth cover.

The effect of a perforated cover on absorption depends upon the percentage of open area, the size of individual openings, and the spacing between them. In most cases, the open area ranges between 10 and 30 percent; a typical arrangement (20 percent open) has 3/16-in-diameter holes spaced on staggered 3/8-in centers. A cover of this type increases low-frequency absorption, with decreases occuring at higher frequencies. As the percentage of open area decreases, additional improvement occurs at low frequencies; however, the cover may be essentially a reflector of energy at high frequencies.

Representative absorptive characteristics of the materials and structures described in this section, and of common construction materials, are illustrated in Figs. 8.4 to 8.6 and Tables 8.2 to 8.6. Those readers interested in more complete data should refer to manufacturers' brochures or to Ref. 14.

Table 8.2 Representative physical characteristics and absorption coefficients for acoustical materials

Material	Range of weight density, lb/ft^3	Range of thickness, in	Random-incidence absorption coefficient with solid backing (no. 4 mounting)*							
			Thickness, in	Density, lb/ft^3	Absorption coefficients					
					125	250	500	1000	2000	4000
Resilient glass fiber with resinous binder	1–3	$\frac{1}{2}$–6	1	1.5	.12	.28	.73	.89	.92	.93
			2	1.5	.24	.77	.99	.99	.99	.99
			2	3.0	.22	.82	.99	.99	.99	.99
Rigid glass-fiber boards and lay-in panels	3–6	$\frac{1}{2}$–2	1	6	.08	.25	.74	.95	.97	.99
Molded panels and boards	8–25	$\frac{1}{2}$–1	$\frac{1}{2}$	18	.20	.18	.64	.61	.59	.56
Interlaced plant fibers cemented into a rigid structure	24	1–3	2	24	.32	.37	.77	.99	.79	.88
Open-cell resilient polyurethane foams	1.8–2.5	$\frac{1}{4}$–2	1	1.8	.22	.35	.60	.98	.94	.99
Sprayed-in-place fibrous slurry	10–20	$\frac{1}{2}$–1$\frac{1}{2}$	1	12	.08	.29	.75	.98	.93	.76

*Data for molded panels obtained for 1/8-in air space between panel and solid backing (no. 1 mounting).

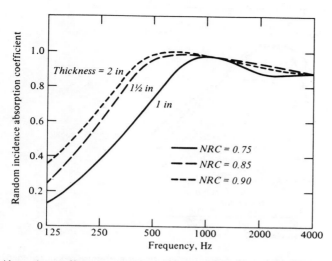

(a) Absorption coefficients and noise-reduction coefficients of porous rigid glassfiber formboard mounted directly on hard backing

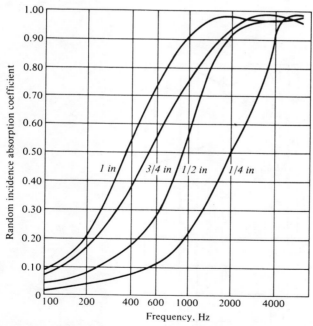

(b) Random incidence sound absorption as a function of frequency for polyurethane foams of various thicknesses.

Figure 8.4 Effect of thickness on absorption coefficient. *(a) From L. L. Beranek (ed.),* Noise and Vibration Control, *McGraw-Hill, New York, 1971. (b) From J. Emme, "Composite Materials for Noise and Vibration Control,"* Sound and Vibration, *July 1970.*

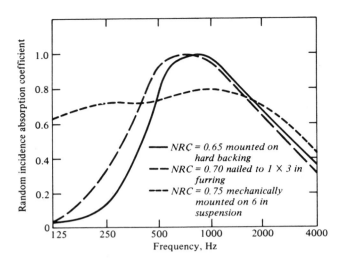

Figure 8.5 Effect of mounting conditions on absorption coefficient and noise-reduction coefficient of 3/4-in textured acoustical tile. The decrease in absorption at these frequencies is due to the nonopen nature of the textured surface. *From L. L. Beranek (ed.),* Noise and Vibration Control, *McGraw-Hill, New York, 1971.*

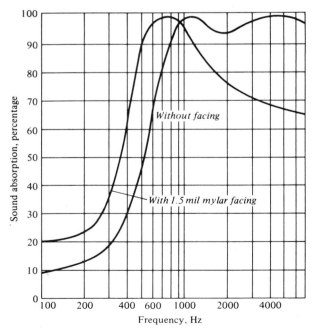

Figure 8.6 Effect of a facing on the random-incidence sound absorption of 1-in-thick polyurethane foam. *From B & K Instruments, Inc.*

Table 8.3 Effects of density and air space on acoustical absorption

Structure	Absorption coefficients					
	125	250	500	1000	2000	4000
1.5 lb/ft³ glass fiber, 1 in thick, solid backing	0.06	0.20	0.65	0.90	0.95	0.98
6 lb/ft³ rigid glass-fiber board:						
1 in thick, solid backing	0.03	0.17	0.63	0.87	0.96	0.96
1 in thick, 1-in air space	0.04	0.26	0.78	0.99	0.99	0.98
1 in thick, 2-in air space	0.17	0.40	0.94	0.99	0.97	0.99
2-×4-ft rigid glass-fiber ceiling panel, 5/8 in thick, 16-in air space (no. 7 mounting)	0.40	0.46	0.60	0.99	0.87	0.58

Table 8.4 Random-incidence absorption coefficientsfor common construction materials, and absorption of seats and audience

Material	Frequency, Hz					
	125	250	500	1000	2000	4000
Brick						
Unglazed	0.03	0.03	0.03	0.04	0.04	0.05
Painted	0.01	0.01	0.02	0.02	0.02	0.02
Concrete block, painted	0.10	0.05	0.06	0.07	0.09	0.08
Concrete	0.01	0.01	0.015	0.02	0.02	0.02
Wood	0.15	0.11	0.10	0.07	0.06	0.07
Glass	0.35	0.25	0.18	0.12	0.08	0.04
Gypsum board	0.29	0.10	0.05	0.04	0.07	0.09
Plywood	0.28	0.22	0.17	0.09	0.10	0.11
"Soundblox" concrete block						
Type A (slotted), 6-in	0.62	0.84	0.36	0.43	0.27	0.50
Type B, 6-in	0.31	0.97	0.56	0.47	0.51	0.53
Carpet, heavy, on concrete	0.02	0.06	0.14	0.37	0.60	0.65

Absorption of seats and audience*

	125	250	500	1000	2000	4000
Audience, seated in upholstered seats, per square foot of floor area	0.60	0.74	0.88	0.96	0.93	0.85
Unoccupied cloth-covered upholstered seats, per square foot of floor area	0.49	0.66	0.80	0.88	0.82	0.70
Unoccupied leather-covered upholstered seats, per square foot of floor area	0.44	0.54	0.60	0.62	0.58	0.50
Wooden pews, occupied, per square foot of floor area	0.57	0.61	0.75	0.86	0.91	0.86
Chairs, metal or wood seats, each, unoccupied	0.15	0.19	0.22	0.39	0.38	0.30

*Values given are in sabins per square foot of seating area or per unit.

Table 8.5 Effect of kraft-paper backing on absorption of house insulation

Product thickness, in	Mounting	Octave-band center frequencies, Hz					
		125	250	500	1000	2000	4000
3.5 (R-11), paper exposed to sound	4	0.38	0.98	0.99	0.62	0.36	0.24
3.5 (R-11), insulation exposed to sound	4	0.34	0.85	0.99	0.97	0.97	0.99
6.0 (R-19), paper exposed to sound	4	0.71	0.99	0.85	0.61	0.41	0.26
6.0 (R-19), insulation exposed to sound	4	0.64	0.99	0.99	0.99	0.99	0.99
3.5 (R-11), paper exposed to sound	7	0.78	0.87	0.90	0.71	0.40	0.32
3.5 (R-11), insulation exposed to sound	7	0.80	0.98	0.99	0.99	0.98	0.99
6.0 (R-19), paper exposed to sound	7	0.84	0.92	0.94	0.64	0.45	0.34
6.0 (R-19), insulation exposed to sound	7	0.86	0.99	0.99	0.99	0.99	0.99

Table 8.6 Absorption data for various structures

Description	Octave-band center frequency, Hz					
	125	250	500	1000	2000	4000
$23 \times 48 \times 1\frac{1}{2}$ in glass-fiber board (4.7 lb/ft^3) wrapped with Mylar film and hung vertically in rows 4 ft on center; sabins/unit	2.1	5.9	9.8	13.3	11.6	7.6
Acoustical panels, 16-gauge steel back panel, 20-gauge perforated-steel front panel, septum filled with 4-in-thick glass-fiber insulation; random-incidence absorption coefficient	0.55	0.99	0.99	0.99	0.99	0.97

8.3 DISSIPATIVE AND REACTIVE SILENCERS

Acoustic silencers are devices designed to attenuate sound waves propagated in a flowing medium. Typical applications include HVAC systems (in which fan noise is usually dominant); automotive exhaust and intake systems; gas turbines and compressors; rotary and reciprocating pumps; and air discharge lines. Two types of silencers are in common use:

  • Dissipative silencers are "straight-through" devices incorporating a flow channel (or several flow channels) lined with absorptive material (Fig. 8.7a).
  • Reactive silencers consist of one or more nondissipative elements arranged either in parallel or in series. Typical elements include expansion chambers, side-branch resonators, bends, and perforated tubes (Fig. 8.7b).

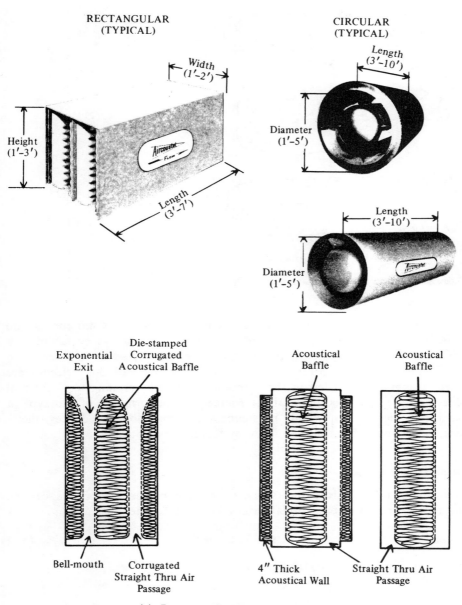

RECTANGULAR
(TYPICAL)

Width
(1'-2')

Height
(1'-3')

Length
(3'-7')

Aircoustat
Flow

CIRCULAR
(TYPICAL)

Length
(3'-10')

Diameter
(1'-5')

Length
(3'-10')

Diameter
(1'-5')

Aircoustat

Exponential
Exit

Die-stamped
Corrugated
Acoustical Baffle

Acoustical
Baffle

Acoustical
Baffle

Bell-mouth

Corrugated
Straight Thru Air
Passage

4" Thick
Acoustical Wall

Straight Thru Air
Passage

(*a*) Representative dissipative silencers

Figure 8.7 Dissipative and reactive silencers. (*a*) *From Koppers Company.* (*b*) *From L. L. Beranek (ed.),* Noise and Vibration Control, *McGraw-Hill, New York, 1971.*

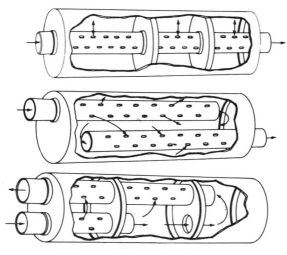

(*b*) Representative reactive silencers

Figure 8.7 (continued) Dissipative and reactive silencers.

Dissipative silencers, as the name implies, transform acoustic energy into heat. Sound waves impinge upon absorbing material that lines all or part of each flow channel. By comparison, the primary function of reactive silencers is to reflect sound waves toward the source. Losses associated with this reflection are small; energy is dissipated in the extended flow path resulting from internal reflections, and by absorption at the source. The performance of this type of silencer is affected significantly by source and termination impedances; therefore, the location of the silencer in the system may be critical.

Dissipative Silencers

The attenuation of dissipative silencers meeting certain restrictions can be calculated from an empirical relation developed by Sabine:

$$A = 12.6 \frac{P}{S} \alpha^{1.4} \tag{8.1}$$

where A = attenuation, dB/ft of length
P = perimeter of flow area, in
S = flow area, in^2
α = random-incidence absorption coefficient in a given frequency band

The restrictions are that:

• The length of each flow channel should be at least twice its smaller transverse dimension.

· Flow velocities should be less than 4000 ft/min (to minimize noise generation within the duct)

· The smaller transverse dimension of the duct should be sized to prevent "beaming" (line-of-sight propagation) of higher frequencies; Eq. (8.1) does not account for this effect. Beaming will occur at frequencies with wavelengths less than about 7 times the smaller transverse dimension. In this case, the maximum attenuation for any duct length will be about 10 dB. Some commercial silencers overcome this difficulty by using "wavy" flow passages to prevent line-of-sight propagation.

Figure 8.8 is used to design lined parallel baffle silencers, in which the dissipative structure is placed on two surfaces of each flow channel. The dissipative structure consists of an absorbing material (frequently glass fiber with a density of 1 to 4 lb/ft^3) protected by a perforated metal cover. The flow-resistance parameter $R_f t / \rho c$ is the ratio of the material flow resistance to the acoustical impedance of the medium. The specific flow resistance for glass-fiber materials can be estimated from Fig. 8.9. (In practice, parameter $R_f t / \rho c$ can vary from one-half to twice the values shown without significant effect on attenuation.) The vertical scale of Fig. 8.8a is the attenuation of each flow channel, in decibels, for a length equal to the channel width.* However, the chart should not be used for silencer lengths less than three to four duct widths. Figure 8.8b shows additional attenuations to be added to those obtained from Fig. 8.8a. These additions result because Fig. 8.8a assumes normally incident sound waves; in practice, oblique waves will still be present at frequencies whose wavelengths approach (or are less than) the width of the flow channel. (Oblique waves are more readily absorbed than normally incident waves.)

A wide variety of dissipative duct silencers are commercially available. Representative performance data are shown in Table 8.7.

Lined Ducts, Bends, and Plenums in HVAC Systems

The attenuation of fan noise and duct transmission between adjoining spaces are important for noise control in buildings. Lined ducts, bends, and (to a lesser extent) plenums are commonly used for these purposes. Duct lining is a commercial material consisting of glass-fiber insulation (1.5 lb/ft^3 density) with a treated surface to minimize erosion by flow. Recommended thicknesses are 1 in for ductwork and 2 to 4 in for plenums. Typical random-incidence absorption coefficients and representative attenuation data are listed in Table 8.8.

Right-angle square or rectangular bends are normally fabricated with turning vanes to reduce turbulence noise generated by flow around the bend. A lined bend is not acoustically effective unless the lining extends at least three (preferably four) transverse duct dimensions downstream and upstream. This requirement can be explained by referring to Fig. 8.10. Oblique waves are readily

---

* The curves in Fig. 8.8a include the effects from line-of-sight propagation.

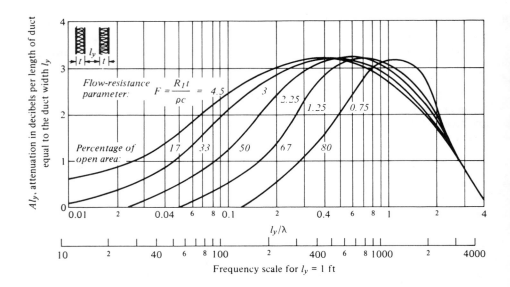

Attenuation for ducts lined on two sides with a flow-resistive material. The flow-resistance parameter F is nondimensional so that R_1 (the flow resistance per unit length), t (the thickness of the lining), and ρc (the characteristic impedance of air) must be in consistent units. A is the attenuation in decibels per unit length of duct. To find the attenuation for a duct length l_e multiply the ordinate by l_e/l_y. To achieve the attenuations shown for each percentage open area indicated, the flow resistance of the lining should be chosen to yield the proper flow-resistance parameter.

(a)   Attenuation curves for axial inputs.

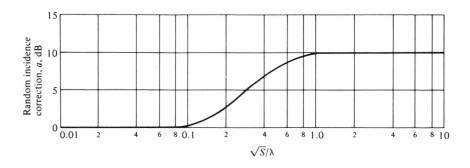

Correction a to be added to plane-axial-wave TL of a duct to obtain the TL for a random incidence input. S = open area of duct; λ = wavelength of sound.

(b)   Correction curve for random inputs.

Figure 8.8 Design curves for lined parallel-baffle silencers. *(a) From L. L. Beranek (ed.),* Noise and Vibration Control, *McGraw-Hill, New York, 1970. (b) From L. L. Beranek (ed.),* Noise Reduction, *McGraw-Hill, New York, 1960*

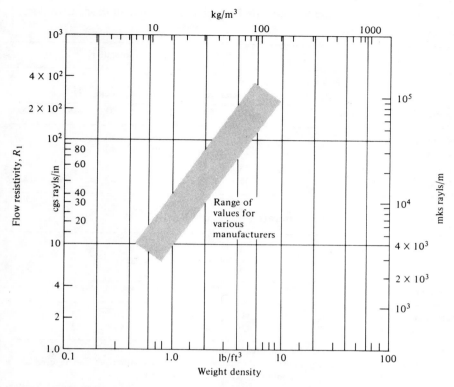

Figure 8.9 Specific flow resistivity for representative glass-fiber materials.

propagated around (and produced by) the bend but are also rapidly attenutated by the downstream lining. The upstream lining attenuates incident oblique waves, so that arriving sound waves are primarily axial. These waves are partially reflected and partially absorbed at the bend; much of the transmitted energy is converted into oblique waves by the bend. Representative attenuations for lined round and square bends are listed in Table 8.9. If the bend and adjacent ductwork are unlined, the attenuation is negligible at frequencies below 500 Hz.

Attenuation data for lined 180° bends are presented in Fig. 8.11. The insertion loss can be significant, but space and pressure-drop requirements may prevent the use of 180° bends in some applications.

A plenum is a relatively large chamber, usually fabricated from sheet metal, that is normally used to attenuate acoustic energy generated by a fan or transmitted through ductwork (Fig. 8.12). An approximate expression for the

Table 8.7 Dynamic insertion loss and air-flow-generated noise of dissipative duct silencers

| Description | Face-velocity,* ft/min | Dynamic insertion loss, dB† | | | | | | |
| | | Octave-band center frequencies, Hz | | | | | | |
		125	250	500	1000	2000	4000	8000
Rectangular,	750	13	28	36	39	40	39	27
5 ft long	2000	11	25	34	39	40	39	27
Circular,	1000	6	18	31	38	36	25	16
3 ft long	2500	5	15	28	35	33	24	14

Air-flow-generated noise, dB Re 10^{-12} W

| Description | Face velocity, ft/min | Octave-band frequencies, Hz | | | | | | |
		125	250	500	1000	2000	4000	8000
Rectangular	1500	62	55	54	54	52	56	54
Circular	2000	52	43	42	42	46	44	42

* Air flow in ft³/min divided by face area of silencer.
† Difference in radiated sound levels when silencer is installed in duct. A fan is used as a noise source, and the discharge duct terminates in a reverberation room.

attenuation (insertion loss) of a plenum is given by

$$A = 10 \log_{10} \left[\frac{1}{S_e \left(\dfrac{\cos \theta}{2\pi d^2} + \dfrac{1 - \alpha}{\alpha S_w} \right)} \right] \quad \text{dB} \qquad (8.2)$$

where $\alpha =$ random-incidence absorption coefficient of plenum lining
$S_e =$ plenum exit area, ft²
$S_w =$ plenum wall area, ft²

Note that this equation merely compares the arriving sound power to that produced at the plenum exit by free-field and reverberant-field sound levels.

Reactive Silencers

Reactive silencers are used for low-frequency applications where dissipative silencers are ineffective and in cases where eventual disintegration of absorptive materials may occur. The insertion-loss characteristics of reactive silencers tend to vary widely with frequency and location within the system, whereas those of

Table 8.8 Absorption coefficient of duct liner and attenuation of lined ducts

Description	Octave-band center frequencies, Hz					
	125	250	500	1000	2000	4000
Random-incidence absorption coefficient:						
1-in-thick duct liner	0.06	0.24	0.47	0.71	0.85	0.97
2-in-thick duct liner	0.20	0.51	0.88	0.99	0.99	0.99
Attenuation of lined duct, dB/ft Round, 5 to 10 in flow diameter						
1-in-thick lining	0.30	1.20	2.00	3.00	3.00	2.40
Round, 18 to 24 in flow diameter						
1-in-thick lining	0.22	0.78	1.30	1.80	1.80	1.24
2-in-thick lining	0.29	1.05	2.00	2.80	2.70	2.30
Unlined	0.06	0.03	0.02	0.02	0.02	0.02
Rectangular, smaller flow dimension 5 to 10 in						
1-in-thick lining	0.30	1.20	2.00	3.00	3.00	2.40
Rectangular, smaller flow dimension 18 to 24 in						
1-in-thick lining	0.25	0.50	1.20	1.80	1.80	1.40
2-in-thick lining	0.33	0.87	1.80	2.40	2.30	1.90
Unlined	0.12	0.06	0.05	0.04	0.04	0.04

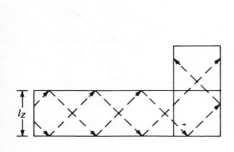

(a) Propagation of oblique waves around an unlined 90° bend.

(b) Lined 90° bend.

Figure 8.10 Lined and unlined 90° bends.

Table 8.9 Attenuation of round and rectangular 90° lined bends*

Description	Dimension D, in	Octave-band center frequency, Hz						
		63	125	250	500	1000	2000	4000
Round duct of	5–10	0	0	1	2	3	4	6
diameter D, or	11–20	0	1	2	3	4	6	8
rectangular duct	21–40	1	2	3	4	5	6	8
with dimension D								
in plane of bend								

* Lining thickness equals 0.1 D.
  Lining extends for minimum distance 3 D on both sides of bend. Rectangular bends have turning vanes.

dissipative silencers tend to be more uniform. Typical examples of reactive silencers include automotive exhaust mufflers and silencers for industrial processes.

Two common reactive elements are a simple expansion chamber and a side-branch resonator. Analysis of these elements usually assumes plane waves throughout (transverse dimensions less than λ), sound levels less than 120 dB, no

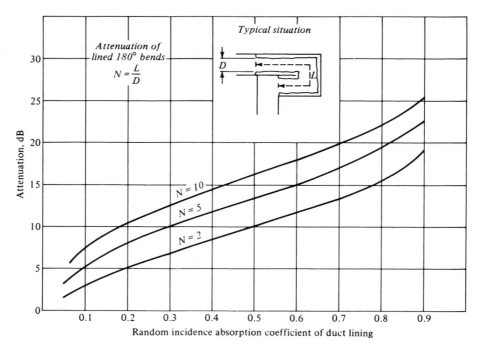

Figure 8.11 Design curves for lined 180° bends. *From C. M. Harris (ed.),* Handbook of Noise Control, *McGraw-Hill, New York, 1957.*

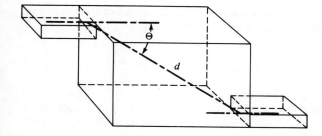

Figure 8.12 Plenum for reduction of airborne duct noise. *From the National Institute for Occupational Safety and Health*, Compendium of Materials for Noise Control, *Cincinnati, June 1975.*

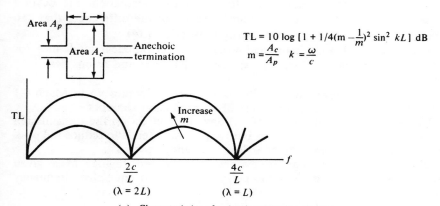

$$TL = 10 \log \left[1 + 1/4(m - \frac{1}{m})^2 \sin^2 kL \right] dB$$

$$m = \frac{A_c}{A_p} \quad k = \frac{\omega}{c}$$

(a) Characteristics of a simple expansion chamber.

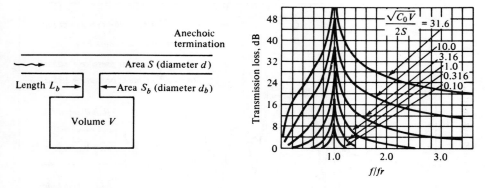

C_0 = conductivity of neck

$\quad = S_b/L_b'$ where L_b' = effective length of neck $\cong L_b + 0.82 \, d_b$

f_r = resonant frequency

$\quad = \frac{c}{2\pi} \sqrt{C_0/V}$ where c = propagation velocity

(b) Characteristics of a simple sidebranch (Helmholtz) resonator.

Figure 8.13 Performance characteristics of reactive silencers. *From C. M. Harris (ed.)*, Handbook of Noise Control, *McGraw-Hill, New York, 1957.*

237

flow velocity, and no temperature gradients. Performance data are shown in Fig. 8.13. Note that the ordinate, transmission loss, is defined by

$$\text{TL} = 10 \log_{10} \frac{A_1^2/\rho c}{A_2^2/\rho c} \tag{8.3}$$

where $A_1^2/\rho c$ = intensity of incident wave, with rms amplitude A_1, and $A_2^2/\rho c$ = intensity transmitted into an anechoic termination, where A_2 is the rms amplitude of transmitted wave. A measure of greater practical interest is insertion loss, which includes the effects of the actual termination and the source impedances on silencer performance. Although these calculations are beyond the scope of this book, the reader should be aware of the differences that can occur between transmission loss and insertion loss (Fig. 8.14).

Both experimental and theoretical work suggests practical guidelines for predicting the performance of simple expansion chambers and resonators:

• Incident sound levels up to 150 dB and flow velocities up to Mach 0.1 have little effect on the transmission loss of an expansion chamber.
• Incident sound levels up to 150 dB have little effect on the transmission loss of a simple side-branch resonator, but flow velocity tends to reduce the peak loss at resonance and to shift the peak-loss frequency upward.
• The effect of a change in temperature on performance at a given frequency can be predicted from the performance at an equivalent frequency

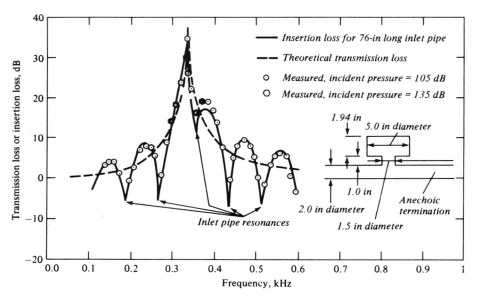

Figure 8.14 Comparison of transmission loss and insertion loss of a side-branch resonator. *From Richard Oboka, Ph.D. thesis, University of Missouri, Rolla, 1973.*

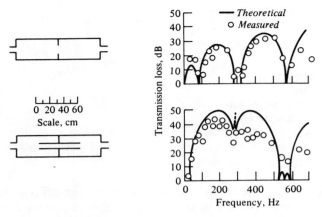

(*a*) Performance of expansion chambers in series, with anechoic termination.

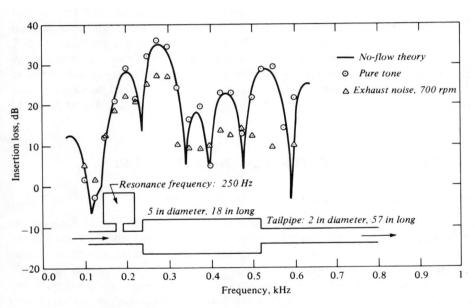

(*b*) Performance of resonator and expansion chamber in series, with tailpipe termination.

Figure 8.15 Performance characteristics of combinations of elements. *(a) From C. M. Harris (ed.), Handbook of Noise Control, McGraw-Hill, New York, 1957. (b) From Richard Oboka, Ph.D. thesis, University of Missouri, Rolla, 1973.*

given by

$$f_2 = f_1 \frac{\sqrt{T_1 + \Delta T}}{\sqrt{T_1}}$$

where f_2 = equivalent frequency
$\quad f_1$ = given frequency
$\quad T_1$ = initial absolute temperature
$\quad \Delta T$ = change in absolute temperature
(This equation states that the performance of a given silencer is dependent on the wavelength of incident sound waves; the wavelength at a given frequency is proportional to the square root of the absolute temperature.)

A common practice (evidenced by automotive exhaust mufflers) is to combine a number of reactive elements in series or in parallel to provide a more uniform transmission loss over a specified frequency range. An example is shown in Fig. 8.15.

Another type of reactive element consists of concentric outer and perforated inner tubes. The annular space between the tubes is divided into independent closed volumes by the use of baffles. Although no absorptive material is used, the propagation of sound waves into the annular volumes does result in energy loss. Insertion-loss values for an element 10 ft long, consisting of a 4-in (inner diameter) outer tube and a 3-in (outer diameter) perforated inner tube that varies from 5 to 19 percent open area, range from 5 dB at 250 Hz to 25 dB at 2000 Hz.

8.4 ATTENUATING MATERIALS AND STRUCTURES

Attenuation versus Dissipation of Acoustic Energy

A material or structure for attenuating sound is designed to restrict the passage of an airborne acoustic disturbance from one side to the other. By nature, an acoustical absorber is a poor attenuator (or barrier) because too much of the incident acoustic energy propagates through its porous structure. On the other hand, the dense, nonporous characteristics of a barrier make it a good reflector (and a poor absorber) of incident sound waves. Typical barrier materials are steel, lead, plywood, gypsum wallboard, glass, brick, concrete, concrete block, and sheet vinyl that has been weighted or "loaded" with lead powder or other material during manufacture.

The principal measure of the performance of a barrier material or structure is its transmission loss at various frequencies. The meaning and measurement of both sound transmission loss (STL) and sound transmission class (STC) were described in Chap. 6. A common although not particularly useful measure of barrier performance is "average transmission loss," the arithmetic average of transmission-loss values in the 125- to 4000-Hz range. The relationships between average STL, STC, and speech privacy are summarized in Table 8.10. Note that

Table 8.10 Comparison of average transmission loss and STC ratings

Average transmission loss required for various levels of speech privacy

Average transmission loss of wall, dB	Hearing conditions	Rating
30 or less	Normal speech can be understood quite easily and distinctly through the wall.	Poor
30–35	Loud speech can be understood fairly well. Normal speech can be heard but not easily understood.	Fair
35–40	Loud speech can be heard, but is not easily intelligible. Normal speech can be heard only faintly, if at all.	Good
40–45	Loud speech can be faintly heard but not understood. Normal speech is inaudible.	Very good—recommended for dividing walls between apartments.
45 or greater	Very loud sounds, such as loud singing, brass musical instruments, or a radio at full volume can be heard only faintly or not at all.	Excellent—recommended for band rooms, music practice rooms, radio and sound studios.

STC ratings for various levels of speech privacy

25	30	35	42	45	48	50
Normal speech can be understood quite easily	Loud speech can be understood fairly well	Loud speech audible but not intelligible	Loud speech audible as a murmur	Must strain to hear loud speech	Some loud speech barely audible	Loud speech not audible

STC ratings for common building materials

Material	STC rating
1/4-in steel plate	36
1/4-in plate glass	26
3/4-in plywood	28
4-in brick wall	41
6-in concrete-block wall	42
1/2-in gypsum board on both sides of 2 × 4 studs	33
12-in reinforced-concrete wall	56
14-in cavity wall	
8-in brick—2-in air space—4-in brick	65

an average STL of 30 dB or less is classified as "poor" from a speech privacy standpoint, although the resulting attenuation may be perfectly acceptable for other applications, such as machinery enclosures.

The guideline that "a good absorber is a poor barrier" is illustrated by the following example. Consider a sound wave impinging on the surface of an absorbing structure. If 80 percent of the incident intensity is absorbed, 10 percent is reflected, and 10 percent is transmitted, then

$$STL = 10 \log_{10} \frac{1.0}{0.1} = 10 \text{ dB}$$

On a speech privacy basis, the performance of the structure would be rated as poor.

Transmission Loss of Homogeneous Panels

Transmission-loss data for representative barrier structures will be presented later in this chapter. First, however, we will discuss the theoretical calculation of transmission loss for large homogeneous panels.[*]

A complete derivation indicates that the panel bending stiffness per unit width

$$\frac{EI}{b}(1 - \mu^2) \tag{8.4}$$

where $E=$ Young's modulus
$\mu=$ Poisson's ratio
$I/b= t^3/12$, the area moment of inertia per unit width b of the panel
$t=$ panel thickness
has a negligible effect on transmission loss, at frequencies below a "critical" frequency. Therefore, the theoretical transmission loss in the "mass-controlled" region can be derived by considering only the acoustic pressure and normal component of velocity acting on a small mass element of the panel (Fig. 8.16a). The transmitted wave angle is equal to the incident wave angle; the ratio of transmitted intensity to incident intensity is given by

$$\tau = \frac{1}{1 + \left(\dfrac{\omega \rho_s}{2\rho c} \cos \theta \right)^2} \tag{8.5}$$

where $\rho_s=$ mass of panel per unit surface area
$\omega=$ frequency of sound wave, rad/s
$\theta=$ angle of incidence of impinging sound wave, rad
$\rho c=$ characteristic impedance of medium (415 rayls for air at standard temperature and pressure)

---

[*] For a more detailed treatment, see Refs. 1 and 2.

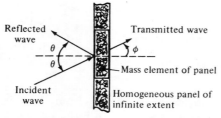

(a) Model for calculation of theoretical transmission loss in mass controlled region.

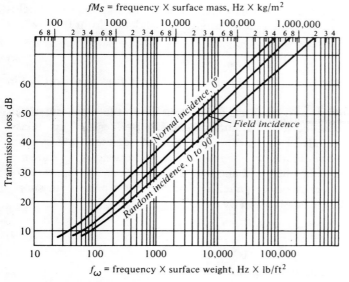

(b) Normal, field, and random incidence transmission loss in mass-controlled region.

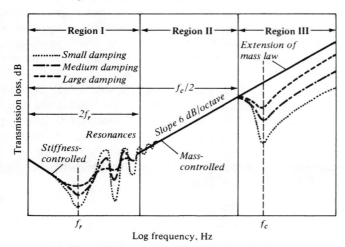

(c) Theoretical transmission loss. Mass-controlled region is bounded by $f_c/2$ and $2f_r$, approximately.

Figure 8.16 Transmission loss of homogeneous infinite panel. (b, c) *From L. L. Beranek (ed.),* **Noise Reduction,** *McGraw-Hill, New York, 1960.*

The transmission loss for normal incidence is given by

$$TL_0 = 10 \log_{10} \frac{1}{\tau} = 10 \log_{10}\left[1 + \left(\frac{\omega \rho_s}{2\rho c}\right)^2\right] \; dB \qquad (8.6)$$

If the transmission coefficients for angles of incidence from 0 to 90° are averaged, the random-incidence transmission loss is given by

$$TL \simeq TL_0 - 10 \log_{10}(0.23 \, TL_0) \qquad dB \qquad (8.7)$$

for values of TL_0 greater than 15 dB. In many practical situations, the "field-incidence" transmission loss, obtained for angles of incidence from 0 to 78°, is more accurate:

$$TL_f = TL_0 - 5 \; dB \qquad (8.8)$$

for values of TL_0 greater than 15 dB. Figure 8.16b shows Eqs. (8.6) to (8.8) in graphic form.

Note that the normal- and field-incidence transmission-loss characteristics increase by 6 dB for each doubling of surface mass or frequency. This "mass-controlled" region is bounded by a "stiffness-controlled" region at low frequencies and by a "coincidence-frequency" region at higher frequencies, as shown in Fig. 8.16c. The stiffness-controlled and mass-controlled regions are separated by the lowest resonant frequency of the panel in bending. For a panel with simply supported edges, this frequency is given by

$$f_r = \frac{\pi}{2}\left(\frac{B}{\rho_s}\right)^{1/2}\left[\left(\frac{1}{L_x}\right)^2 + \left(\frac{1}{L_y}\right)^2\right] \qquad (8.9)$$

where $B = EI/L_y$, the panel bending stiffness per unit width
$\quad L_x$ = panel length
$\quad L_y$ = panel width
(The corresponding frequency for the same panel with clamped edges is twice this value.) In many practical cases, the lowest resonant frequency is well below the lowest frequency of interest. However, enclosures for small lightweight machines are sometimes designed to provide desired attenuation in the stiffness-controlled region.

At frequencies above the lowest resonant frequency, additional bending resonances occur in increasing numbers. These bending resonances are the result of an in-phase combination of waves traveling toward and away from the edges of the panel. The situation is in fact analogous to the production of resonant frequencies and mode shapes in a reverberant space (see Sec. 4.3).

An interesting characteristic of bending waves is the frequency-dependence of their propagation velocity in the panel, given by

$$C_p = \sqrt[4]{\frac{\omega^2 B}{\rho_s}} \qquad (8.10)$$

By comparison, the speed of propagation of longitudinal (acoustic) waves in gaseous media is virtually independent of frequency. (Gaseous media are incapable of propagating bending waves.) As the frequency of impinging sound waves increases, the bending wavelength in the panel approaches the airborne-sound wavelength. "Coincidence," or equality of the wavelengths, first occurs at grazing (parallel) incidence; when this happens, incident sound waves and bending waves in the panel reinforce each other. The resultant increase in panel vibration causes a decrease in transmission loss. The "critical" or "coincidence" frequency of a homogeneous panel can be calculated from

$$f_c = \frac{c^2}{2\pi}\sqrt{\frac{\rho_s}{B}} \quad \text{or} \quad f_c = \frac{c^2}{2\pi}\sqrt{\frac{W_s}{gB}} \qquad (8.11)$$

where c = propagation velocity of incident sound waves
 W_s = surface weight of panel
 g = gravitational constant
An equivalent expression, for air at standard conditions, is given by

$$f_c = \frac{5.2 \cdot 10^{10}}{t} \frac{w}{E} \qquad (8.12)$$

where t = homogeneous panel thickness, in
 w = weight density of panel, lb/in^3
 E = Young's modulus of panel, lb/in^2
The conditions for coincidence are shown in Fig. 8.17. Note that f_c depends on the bending stiffness per unit panel width; as bending stiffness decreases, the critical frequency increases. In general, a panel with low bending stiffness (such

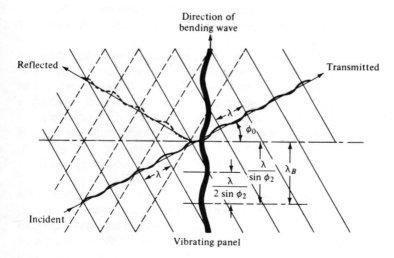

Figure 8.17 Vibrating panel with bending wavelength λ_b. Wave coincidence occurs when the projected wavelength of an incident sound wave $\lambda/\sin\phi_0$ equals the bending wavelength λ_b in the panel. *From L. L. Beranek (ed.)*, Noise Reduction, *McGraw-Hill, New York, 1960.*

as lead sheet) is desirable because its critical frequency will often lie outside the range of interest. Therefore the decrease in transmission loss that normally occurs near f_c will not affect the performance of the panel. The coincidence phenomenon occurs at and above f_c, whenever the projection of the airborne-sound wavelength equals the bending wavelength in the panel. Thus there is always an angle of incidence for arriving sound waves at which coincidence will occur, for frequencies greater than the critical frequency (Fig. 8.17).

The effect of coincidence is a reinforcement of bending waves in the panel by incident sound waves. As a result, large panel amplitudes and reduced transmission loss occur over a wide range of frequencies near and above f_c, as shown in Fig. 8.16c. The amount of reduction is usually greatest for panels with small internal damping and large bending stiffness, such as glass.

Effects of Panel Mounting on Transmission Loss

The equations developed above apply to homogeneous panels of infinite extent; in practical situations, the effects of panel size and mounting must be considered. As already discussed, bending waves produced by impinging sound are reflected from the panel edges.* The combination of incident and reflected waves produces standing waves in the panel; at certain "forced-resonance" frequencies these waves reinforce each other, and relatively large displacements occur. The number of resonant frequencies in a given band increases rapidly above the lowest possible resonance. We have already learned that the bending stiffness of a panel has no appreciable effect on its transmission loss in the mass-controlled region. In other words, the panel behaves as a membrane whose displacement is inversely proportional to its surface mass. Although forced-resonance bending waves are present in the panel surface, they are not effective radiators of airborne sound in the mass-controlled region. Let us discuss this phenomenon in greater detail.

We already know that the bending wavelength in the panel is less than the corresponding wavelength of airborne sound, at frequencies below f_c. Therefore, the distance between adjacent regions of maximum panel displacement is less than an acoustic wavelength. This means that there is no direction in which a sound wave with the correct wavelength can be propagated. Instead, the pressures created by panel displacements cause a transfer of energy between areas of positive pressure and adjoining areas of "negative" pressure. As a result, "pressure cancellation" occurs, and very little airborne acoustic energy is created.

A different situation exists at the corners and edges of the panel, because pressure cancellation from adjoining panel segments is incomplete. As a result, corners of the panel radiate like monopoles and edges radiate like dipoles, when their separation distances approach or exceed the corresponding wavelength of

---

* In most cases panel mounting is approximated by simple supports, so that reflected bending waves are 180° out of phase with arriving waves.

airborne sound. However, in many practical situations corner and edge radiation does not cause significant changes in mass-controlled transmission loss at frequencies less than $f_c/2$. In the frequency range between $f_c/2$ and f_c, corner and edge radiation may affect the transmission loss to a noticeable extent. At frequencies near and above f_c, the separation between adjacent regions of maximum panel displacement equals or exceeds the corresponding wavelength of airborne sound, and bending waves become effective radiators of acoustic energy. The transmission loss of the panel is therefore controlled by combined radiation from coincidence and from resonant panel vibrations.

At low frequencies where the bending wavelength approaches or exceeds the dimensions of the panel surface, the panel stiffness (rather than its surface mass) controls the amplitude of vibration. The result is an increase in transmission loss, at frequencies less than the lowest resonant frequency of the panel. In fact, the theoretical increase in this "stiffness-controlled" region is 6 dB per halving of frequency, as shown in Fig. 8.16c. However, measured values usually indicate a smaller increase, or no increase at all.

Mechanical Point Loading of Homogeneous Panel

So far we have discussed the radiation of sound from one side of a homogeneous panel, the result of uniform loading from randomly incident sound on the opposite side. Now we will consider acoustic radiation from mechanical loading at a point of attachment on the surface of the panel. The principal characteristics of this radiation are:

• Near-field acoustic radiation from the attachment point is dominant up to an excitation frequency of about $f_c/4$. The acoustic power radiated from one side of the panel is given approximately by

$$W = \frac{8}{\pi^3} V_{\text{rms}}^2 \frac{\rho c^3}{f_c^2} \qquad (8.13)$$

where V_{rms}^2 = mean square panel velocity at point of excitation.
• In the frequency range between $f_c/4$ and f_c, both near-field and edge radiation may be significant.
• Near and above f_c, resonant vibrations of the panel surface become the dominant source of acoustic radiation.

Transmission Loss of Barrier Materials

Measured transmission-loss data for various materials are listed in Table 8.11. For other homogeneous materials or surface weights, the theoretical transmission-loss curve can be constructed as follows:

1. Plot the mass-controlled field TL from Eq. (8.8) or Fig. 8.16b. [An equivalent expression for field incidence is given by TL = $10 \log_{10}(f w_s)^2 - 33$ dB, where w_s = surface weight, lb/ft^2.] $\qquad (8.14)$

Table 8.11 Measured transmission-loss data for various materials

Material	lb/ft²	125	250	500	1000	2000	4000	8000
				Frequency, Hz				
Lead								
1/32 in thick	2	22	24	29	33	40	43	49
1/64 in thick	1	19	20	24	27	33	39	43
Plywood								
3/4 in thick	2	24	22	27	28	25	27	35
1/4 in thick	0.7	17	15	20	24	28	27	25
Lead vinyl	0.5	11	12	15	20	26	32	37
Lead vinyl	1.0	15	17	21	28	33	37	43
Steel								
18-gauge	2.0	15	19	31	32	35	48	53
16-gauge	2.5	21	30	34	37	40	47	52
Sheet metal (viscoelastic laminate-core)	2	15	25	28	32	39	42	47
Plexiglas								
1/4 in thick	1.45	16	17	22	28	33	35	35
1/2 in thick	2.9	21	23	26	32	32	37	37
1 in thick	5.8	25	28	32	32	34	46	46
Glass								
1/8 in thick	1.5	11	17	23	25	26	27	28
1/4 in thick	3	17	23	25	27	28	29	30
Double glass								
1/4 × 1/2 × 1/4 in		23	24	24	27	28	30	36
1/4 × 6 × 1/4 in		25	28	31	37	40	43	47
5/8-in gypsum								
On 2 ×2-in stud		23	28	33	43	50	49	50
On staggered stud		26	35	42	52	57	55	57
Concrete, 4 in thick	48	29	35	37	43	44	50	55
Concrete block, 6 in	36	33	34	35	38	46	52	55
Panels of 16-gauge steel, 4-in absorbent, 20-gauge steel		25	35	43	48	52	55	56

2. Calculate f_c from Eq. (8.11) or (8.12) and the lowest forced-resonance frequency from Eq. (8.9). These frequencies are the upper and lower bounds, respectively, of the mass-controlled region.
3. Sketch the stiffness-controlled curve and the curve for frequencies greater than f_c, as shown in Fig. 8.16c.

The resulting transmission-loss characteristic, although approximate, is a usable guide for predicting the performance of an actual panel.

An alternate procedure is shown in Fig. 8.18, for frequencies greater than the lowest forced-resonance frequency. In most cases, Fig. 8.18 is accurate

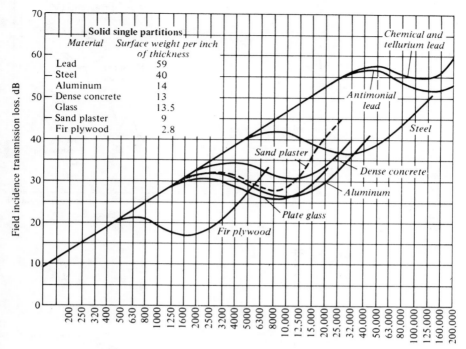

Figure 8.18 Chart for estimating the transmission loss of various homogeneous panels. *From Lead Industries Association. Calculated and plotted by Bolt, Beranek, and Newman, Inc.*

within ±4 dB. Note that the ordinate of Fig. 8.18 is the product of surface weight (in pounds per square foot) and frequency (in Hertz).

Attenuation of Composite Structures

The transmission loss predicted by the mass law for a homogeneous panel can often be increased, for a given surface weight, by a "sandwich" construction. Typical examples are:

· Two aluminum or steel panels (16- to 22-gauge) separated by 1 or 2 in styrofoam or glass-fiber board.
· Vinyl sheet, loaded (weighted) with lead or other substance, in 1/32-in or 1/16-in thickness; a urethane-foam layer 1/16 to 1/2 in thick is bonded to one side. A composite panel is formed by cementing the foam surface to a steel, plywood, or other panel.

The improved performance of a composite structure can be explained by the fact that the surfaces are isolated (or "decoupled") from each other. As the sandwich layer (which may be an air space) increases in thickness, the relative

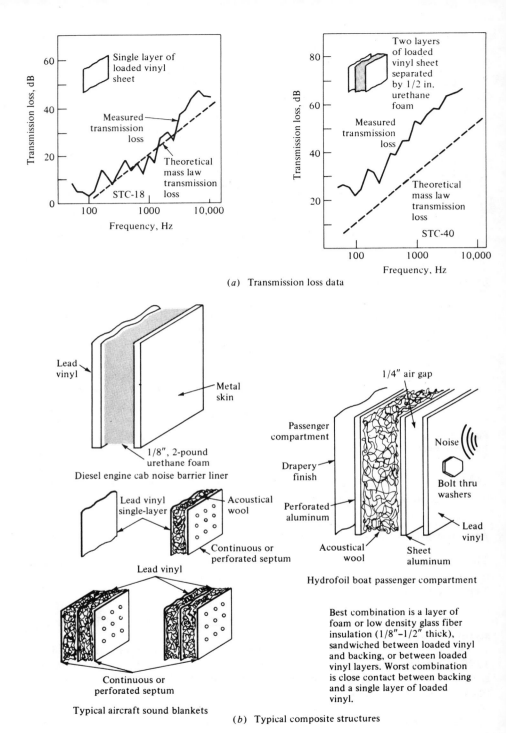

(a) Transmission loss data

Lead vinyl
Metal skin
1/8″, 2-pound urethane foam
Diesel engine cab noise barrier liner

Lead vinyl single-layer
Acoustical wool
Continuous or perforated septum

Lead vinyl
Continuous or perforated septum
Typical aircraft sound blankets

1/4″ air gap
Passenger compartment
Drapery finish
Perforated aluminum
Acoustical wool
Noise
Bolt thru washers
Lead vinyl
Sheet aluminum
Hydrofoil boat passenger compartment

Best combination is a layer of foam or low density glass fiber insulation (1/8″–1/2″ thick), sandwiched between loaded vinyl and backing, or between loaded vinyl layers. Worst combination is close contact between backing and a single layer of loaded vinyl.

(b) Typical composite structures

Figure 8.19 Composite structures using loaded vinyl. *From Ferro Corporation, Composites Division.*

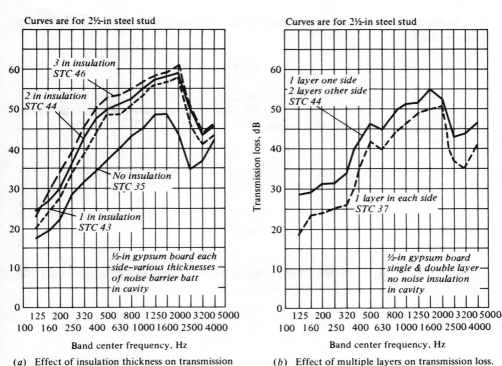

(a) Effect of insulation thickness on transmission loss (density unimportant).

(b) Effect of multiple layers on transmission loss.

Figure 8.20 Data for steel-stud walls. *From Owens-Corning Fiberglas Corporation.*

improvement increases. In fact, as the separation approaches $\lambda/4$, the transmission loss of the composite structure approaches the sum of the panel transmission losses. At higher frequencies, the transmission loss is further increased by attenuation of sound waves in the intermediate layer. For example, a blanket of fine-spun glass fiber with a density of 0.6 lb/ft^3 has an attenuation of about 5 dB/in at 1000 Hz, and about 14 dB/in at 8000 Hz.

Representative transmission-loss data for composite structures are shown in Figs. 8.19 and 8.20.

Attenuation of Noise in Piping

High-velocity gas flows in piping systems not only generate noise at bends, valves, and other discontinuities, but also transmit noise generated by fans, blowers, and compressors. Furthermore, the pipe surface can be an effective radiator of acoustic energy for large distances from the point of its generation. Pipe lagging (wrapping the pipe with rigid or flexible glass fiber and a protective metal or cloth cover) is probably the most effective method for reducing pipe-radiated noise. (However, using silencers at points of noise generation may be a more desirable alternative in some cases.)

The transmission loss of piping is nearly identical to that of a flat panel above the "ring frequency" f_r:

$$f_r = \frac{C_L}{\pi d} \text{ Hz} \tag{8.15}$$

where C_L = propagation velocity of longitudinal waves in the pipe wall (5100 m/s for steel) and d = nominal pipe diameter. The ring frequency is the lowest resonance of the pipe cross section. Pipe transmission loss is calculated as follows:

- Use the mass law transmission loss for a flat plate [Eq. (8.8) or Fig. 8.16b or Fig. 8.18] for all values greater than the limiting transmission loss indicated in Fig. 8.21.
- Subtract the values given in Fig. 8.21 for frequencies less than that corresponding to the limiting transmission loss.

Note that the radiation from piping behaves as a line source, i.e., a series of point sources. The corresponding decrease in free-field sound-pressure levels is about 3 dB per doubling of distance rather than 6 dB.

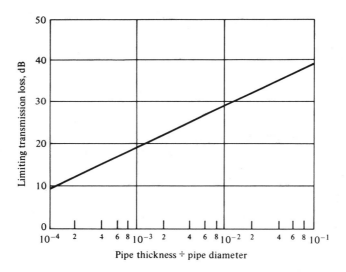

Corrections for Cylindrical Pipe Wall Transmission Loss below the Ring Frequency f_R

$\dfrac{f}{f_r}$	0.025	0.05	0.1	0.2	0.3	0.4	0.5	0.6	0.7	0.8
Correction, dB	−6	−5	−4	−3	−2	−2	−2	−2	−2	−3

Figure 8.21 Data for estimating the transmission loss of piping. *From L. L. Beranek (ed.)*, Noise and Vibration Control, *McGraw-Hill, New York, 1971.*

Table 8.12 Insertion loss of various pipe coverings

Material	Octave-band center frequencies, Hz				
	250	500	1000	2000	4000
Glass-fiber pipe insulation over 12-in-diameter steel pipe, covered with 0.25 lb/ft² aluminum jacket:					
1-in-thick insulation	1	6	14	19	26
2-in-thick insulation	1	6	15	21	28
3-in-thick insulation	2	8	18	23	30
Same as above, except for 1.40 lb/ft² jacket:					
1-in-thick insulation	2	9	18	22	20
2-in-thick insulation	4	11	18	23	29
3-in-thick insulation	4	13	18	24	30

The insertion loss of a completely sealed homogeneous pipe wrap is essentially that of the wrapping material itself. If the lagging is glass fiber wrapped with an impermeable membrane (such as thin aluminum sheet), the insertion loss is dependent on the lowest resonance frequency of the membrane and the space enclosed by the membrane, given by

$$f_0 = \frac{120}{\sqrt{w_s d}} \qquad (8.16)$$

where w_s = surface weight of membrane in pounds per square foot and d = thickness of airspace in inches. (This resonance assumes that the stiffness of the membrane is negligible.) The insertion loss L_{IL} is estimated as follows:

- Below $1.5 f_0$, L_{IL} is nearly zero.
- At frequencies where the attenuation of the wrap is greater than 9 dB, L_{IL} is given by the sum of blanket attenuation and membrane transmission loss.
- Connect the two regions just described by a straight line, on a plot of L_{IL} versus log frequency.

Insertion-loss data for various pipe coverings are listed in Table 8.12.

Transmission Loss of Door Constructions

The effective transmission loss of a wall or panel is often determined by the performance of a door or access panel. In turn, the performance of these structures depends heavily on the effectiveness of seals around the edges. Seals are usually resilient vinyl, foam, or rubber constructions that are compressed when the door or panel is closed. For maximum effectiveness, the sealing system

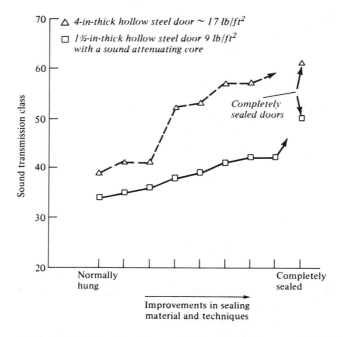

Figure 8.22 Effects of sealing materials and techniques on STC ratings of commerical steel doors. *From the National Institute for Occupational Safety and Health,* Compendium of Materials for Noise Control, *Cincinnati, June 1975.*

should be airtight. (Remember that air leaks are also "sound leaks," or paths by which airborne sound can propagate from one side of a barrier to the other.)

The effects of various sealing measures on the STC values of typical commercial steel doors are shown in Fig. 8.22. Note that the heavier 4-in-thick door, with its higher STC value, is more sensitive to improvements in sealing than the standard door. This behavior is discussed in greater detail in Sec. 9.5. Transmission-loss data for a standard 16-gauge metal door (1 3/4 in thick with paper honeycomb core), installed in a gasketed metal frame, are shown in Fig. 8.23. In this case, an automatic door bottom (or drop seal) was used; this device is a seal that is lowered into place as the door is closed. The seal is raised as the door is opened, to reduce friction and wear, by a cam mechanism attached to the lower door hinge.

Impact Performance of Floor-Ceiling Constructions

In Chap. 6 we compared the standard methods for measuring impact performance and transmission loss. The former is a measure of the attenuation of

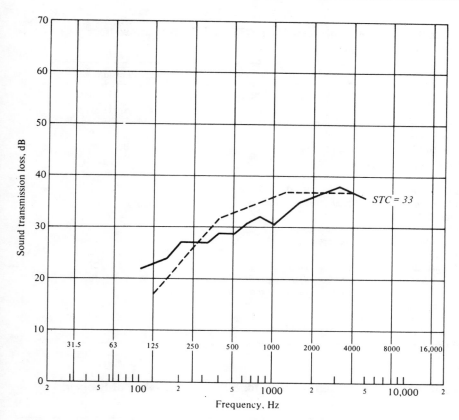

Figure 8.23 Transmission-loss data for commercial steel door in gasketed frame. *From Mesker Industries, Inc.*

mechanical impacts (such as footfalls or falling objects) for a given construction, whereas the latter describes the attenuation of airborne sound. Table 8.13 shows the improvements in STC and IIC that are provided by various floor and ceiling treatments. Note that:

• Carpet improves impact performance significantly, but its relatively low surface weight and open structure eliminate any improvement in STC.
• A resiliently mounted or isolated construction, such as an acoustical ceiling or floating floor, is particularly effective in improving impact performance, as measured by IIC.

Table 8.14 lists values for STC and IIC recommended by the Department of Housing and Urban Development (HUD). Grades I, II, and III refer to various classes of construction.

Table 8.13 Typical improvements in STC and IIC for various floor and ceiling treatments

Type of treatment	Change in ratings	
	Airborne, STC	Impact, IIC
2-in concrete topping, 24 lb/ft²	3	0
Standard 44-oz carpet and 40-oz pad	0	48
Other carpets and pads	0	44–56
Vinyl tile	0	3
1/2-in wood block adhered to concrete	0	20
1/2-in wood block and resilient-fiber underlay adhered to concrete	4	26
Floating concrete floor on fiberboard	7	15
Wood floor, sleepers on concrete	5	15
Wood floor on fiberboard	10	20
Acoustical ceiling resiliently mounted	5	27
Acoustical ceiling added to floor with carpet	5	10
Plaster or gypsum-board ceiling resiliently mounted	10	8
Plaster or gypsum-board ceiling with insulation in space above ceiling	13	13
Plaster direct to concrete	0	0

Table 8.14 HUD recommendations for STC and IIC values of floors in multifamily housing

Partition function between dwellings			Sound transmission class (STC)			Impact isolation class (IIC)		
Apt. A	above	Apt. B	Grade			Grade		
			I	II	III	I	II	III
Bedroom			55	52	48	55	52	48
Living room			57	54	50	60	57	53
Kitchen		Bedroom	58	55	52	65	62	58
Family room			60	56	52	65	62	58
Corridor			55	52	48	65	62	58
Bedroom			57	54	50	55	52	48
Living room			55	52	48	55	52	48
Kitchen		Living room	55	52	48	60	57	53
Family room			58	54	52	62	60	56
Corridor			55	52	48	60	57	53

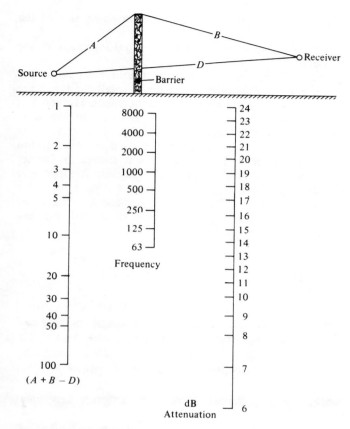

Figure 8.24 Nomogram for design of partial barriers. *From Owens-Corning Fiberglas Corporation.*

Design of Partial Barriers for Outdoor Environments

A partial barrier can provide significant attenuation of airborne noise,* particularly when the source and/or receiver are nearby. Successful applications include reduction of freeway and industrial noise in nearby residential areas. The function of a barrier is to provide a "shadow zone," or reduced noise region, on the receiver side. This region is limited by diffraction or scattering of sound waves at the top of the barrier, which gradually reduces the barrier effectiveness with increasing distance. A typical barrier geometry, and a design nomogram, are shown in Fig. 8.24. The following guidelines apply:

• The barrier structure should be airtight and should have a transmission loss that is at least 5 dB greater than the barrier attenuation, at each frequency of interest.

---

* The attenuation of partial barriers used indoors may be significantly lower because of reflections from the ceiling or other surfaces.

• The barrier should extend at least twice its height on either side of the source.
• Distances A and B (Fig. 8.24) should represent actual locations of the noise source and receiver's ear.
• The nomogram predicts barrier attenuation at various frequencies for zero wind and temperature gradients. If gradients do exist, a small change in the speed of sound occurs as the distance above ground level increases. The result is refraction or bending of sound waves with distance, so that the shadow zone beyond the barrier is either increased or decreased in size. Sound waves that propagate upwind are bent upward, which increases the shadow zone; sound waves propagating downwind are bent downward, which decreases barrier effectiveness somewhat. A strong negative temperature gradient (temperature decreasing with height) tends to produce a symmetric shadow zone around the source, with a corresponding increase in barrier effectiveness. On the other hand, a large temperature inversion (strong positive temperature gradient) may decrease barrier attenuation to some extent.

8.5 DAMPING OF THIN PANELS

We have seen that panel vibration can be an effective radiator of acoustical energy. Damping treatments are materials or structures attached to the panel surface for the purpose of transforming vibratory energy into heat. As a result, panel motion is reduced, and a corresponding decrease in radiated sound may occur. Damping treatments are most effective when applied to panels or other surfaces that are less than 1/4 in thick.

The effectiveness of a damping treatment for noise reduction is dependent on two conditions:

• Panel vibrations must occur at resonant frequencies; damping has relatively little effect on off-resonance vibrations (Fig. 8.29).
• Panel vibrations must be capable of generating sound waves. In the case of airborne sound excitation, bending waves contribute little to acoustic radiation at frequencies less than about half the critical frequency f_c. Therefore, a damping treatment applied to the panel surface will have little effect other than to increase the panel mass somewhat. However, application of a damping treatment to panel edges, corners, and other attachment points may be effective in reducing radiated noise, depending on mounting conditions. At frequencies greater than $f_c/2$, a damping treatment applied to the panel surface at locations of greatest displacement is often a useful noise control procedure.

In the case of mechanical excitation, near-field radiation from the attachment point is the dominant source at frequencies less than about $f_c/4$. At frequencies between $f_c/4$ and $f_c/2$, radiation from panel corners and edges may become significant. Bending waves in the panel surface become increasingly effective radiators at frequencies greater than $f_c/2$; they become the dominant source of radiation at frequencies greater than f_c. Although the transmission loss of a panel at frequencies less than $f_c/2$ may be improved by a damping treatment, the improvement results more from increased panel mass than from reduced panel vibrations.

The performance of damping treatments is measured by the "loss factor" η of the damped structure, where

$$\eta = \frac{\text{energy dissipated per radian of motion at a given excitation frequency}}{\text{maximum strain energy stored in system at the same frequency}}$$

The relationship between η and the equivalent viscous damping factor C/C_c (see Sec. 8.6) is

$$\eta \simeq 2\frac{C}{C_c} \tag{8.17}$$

The minimum loss factor for satisfactory performance is about 0.1; typical values lie between 0.1 and 0.3. If the panel surface is an effective radiator, a tenfold increase in η can reduce the radiated sound level by up to 10 dB.

Loss factor is usually measured in one of two ways:

• The damping treatment is attached to a 20-in-square, 1/4-in-thick steel plate (called a *Geiger plate*) which is supported at the midpoint of each side, as shown in Fig. 8.25a. A magnetic-force transducer drives the plate at its lowest flexural resonance (160 Hz); when the force is removed, the plate decay is measured by a capacitive-displacement transducer (located near one corner) and recorded on an oscilloscope screen or high-speed chart recorder. The loss factor is simply related to the logarithmic decrement δ:

$$n \simeq \frac{\delta}{\pi} \qquad \text{for } \eta \leqslant 0.25 \tag{8.18}$$

where $\delta = \ln(x_1/x_2)$ and $x_1/x_2 = $ the amplitude ratio of any two consecutive cycles of plate vibration. The loss factor obtained in this way must be corrected for different plate and treatment thicknesses encountered in actual applications.

• The damping treatment is attached to a supported beam (Fig. 8.25b); typical dimensions are 1/2 to 1 1/2 in wide, 5 to 12 in long, and 0.02 to 0.06 in thick. The beam length is adjusted so that a magnetic-force transducer located at its midpoint will excite one or more flexural resonances. The response of the beam at and near resonance is measured by a capacitive-displacement transducer. For values of $\eta < 0.25$,

$$\eta \simeq \frac{\Delta f}{f} \tag{8.19}$$

where $\Delta f = $ bandwidth of response and $f = $ resonant frequency, both in Hertz. This method has two advantages over the Geiger-plate method: the beam and damping-treatment thicknesses can be similar or equal to those of the actual application, and the variation of η with excitation frequency can be determined.

Three types of damping treatments are in common use—homogeneous damping, constrained-layer damping, and frictional damping. Homogeneous

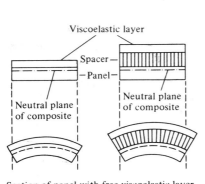

(a) Homogeneous damping.

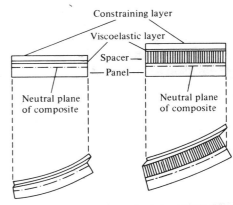

(b) Constrained layer damping.

Figure 8.25 Methods for measuring the loss factor of a damped structure. *From L. L. Beranek (ed.), Noise and Vibration Control, McGraw-Hill, New York, 1971.*

damping (Fig. 8.26*a*) is a single-layer treatment in which a "high-loss" material (usually asphaltic or plastic-based) is sprayed on, brushed on, or adhesively bonded (in sheet form) to the panel surface. As the panel surface flexes, the damping material undergoes extensional motion, which in turn produces significant losses. The composite loss factor of the treated panel is highly dependent on ambient temperature and the ratio of material thickness to panel thickness (Fig. 8.27). Note that ratios greater than 2 : 1 become increasingly impractical. Figure 8.27*c* shows only a small dependence between loss factor and excitation frequency.

The effectiveness of homogeneous damping can be increased by placing a stiff, rigidly bonded spacer between the panel and damping material, as shown in Fig. 8.26*a*. This construction places the material at a greater distance from the neutral axis of the structure; extension of the material and the composite loss factor increase accordingly.

Constrained-layer damping consists of a viscoelastic layer with a stiff (but thin) outer retaining layer, such as aluminum or steel (Fig. 8.26*b*). The constrained and retaining layers are usually about one-third of the panel thickness; the purpose is to resist extension and compression of the viscoelastic material, so that significant shear stresses are induced. These stresses in turn cause dissipation of vibratory energy. Spaced-layer constructions may also be used to increase shear in the viscoelastic layer. Constrained-layer damping treatments are available in sheet form with a magnetic base, for easy attachment to steel panels.

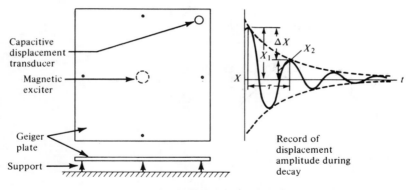

(*a*) Decay of resonant vibrations using Geiger plate.

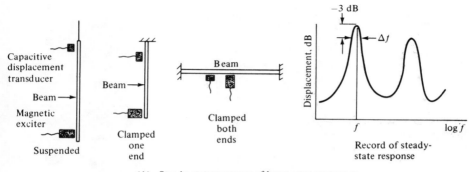

(*b*) Steady-state response of beam near resonance.

Figure 8.26 Homogeneous and constrained-layer damping.

Homogeneous and constrained-layer damping can be compared as follows:

• The loss factor with homogeneous damping depends approximately on the square of the weight of the damping treatment. With constrained-layer damping, the dependence of the loss factor on the treatment weight is approximately linear.

• The system loss factors provided by either type are approximately equal for treatment surface weights equal to 10 to 20 percent of the panel surface weight. For treatment weights less than 10 percent of panel weight, constrained-layer damping is probably more effective; for treatment weights greater than 20 percent of panel weight, homogeneous damping is probably more effective.

Frictional damping is proportional to the normal force and displacement between the damping material and the panel upon which it is placed. However, it can be approximated by an equivalent viscous-damping coefficient at or near

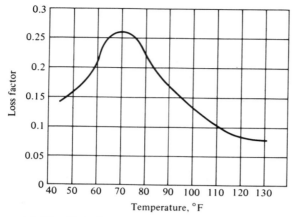

(a) The effect of temperature on the loss factor of a plastic-based vibration damping material (material/metal thickness ratio = 2, frequency = 200 Hz).

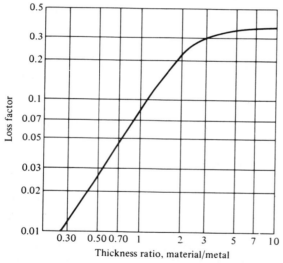

(b) The effect of thickness ratio on the loss factor of a plastic-based vibration damping material (temperature = 72°F, frequency = 200 Hz).

Figure 8.27 Effects of temperature, thickness ratio, and frequency on effectiveness of homogeneous damping. *From J. Emme, "Composite Materials for Noise and Vibrational Control," Sound and Vibration, July 1970.*

panel resonances; equivalence is determined by equating the average energies dissipated per cycle. Frictional damping requires relatively large values of both the normal force and the coefficient of friction between the surfaces. Three commonly used materials are jute, urethane foam, and cork.

Let us summarize the circumstances under which the energy-dissipation characteristics of damping treatments are effective for reducing airborne noise generated by panel vibrations.

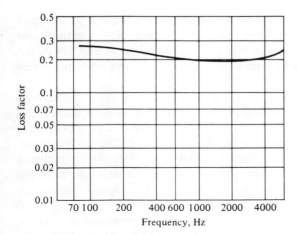

(c) Loss factor as a function of frequency of a plastic-based vibration damping material (temperature = 72°F, material/metal thickness ratio = 2).

Figure 8.27 (continued) Effects of temperature, thickness ratio, and frequency on effectiveness of homogeneous damping.

- The panel surface must be vibrating at or near one or more of its resonant frequencies.
- The resonant vibration of the panel surface must be an effective radiator of acoustic energy.
- For frequencies above $f_c/2$, the damping treatment should be attached to the panel surface and concentrated in regions of maximum resonant amplitude.
- For frequencies less than about $f_c/2$ for airborne sound excitation, or about $f_c/4$ for mechanical point excitation, damping treatments should be concentrated near panel mounting and structural attachment points.*
- The minimum length and width of damping material should be at least 40 percent of the flexural wavelength in the panel for homogeneous and frictional treatments, and at least 60 percent of the flexural wavelength for constrained-layer treatments.
- Homogeneous and constrained-layer treatments should be attached to the panel surface by a complete, rigid bond that fully transmits vibrations into the damping material.

8.6 VIBRATION ISOLATION

Operation of machinery can often produce one of two types of shaking forces—*harmonic forces* associated with rotating unbalance or *impulsive forces* associated with shearing, punching, or other forms of mechanical impact. The

---

* As mentioned earlier, a damping treatment applied over the entire panel surface can decrease radiation of sound by the panel. However, the improvement is primarily the result of increased surface weight rather than energy dissipation by the damping treatment. In these cases, less expensive materials will function as well or better.

forcing frequency from rotating unbalance usually occurs at the rotational speed of a shaft, impeller, etc. However, the frequency content of a repetitive but nonharmonic shaking force can span a wide frequency range at and above the repetition rate. (The frequency spectrum can be calculated from a Fourier-series expansion of the shaking force.)

The transfer of these forces to a floor or panel can cause significant structural response and acoustic radiation over a large area surrounding the point of excitation. We have seen in Sec. 8.4 that the surface of a panel becomes an effective radiator of acoustic energy when the structural excitation frequency is greater than about $f_c/2$. For a 6-in-thick concrete floor slab, the coincidence frequency is approximately 150 Hz; thus, frequencies greater than about 75 Hz will be radiated effectively. In addition, radiation will occur at lower frequencies in the vicinity of beams or other support points.

The purpose of vibration isolation is to reduce the transmission of shaking forces to a floor, roof, or other support to an acceptable level. In theory, the transmitted force should be infinite if it occurs at a frequency equal to a resonant frequency of the supporting structure. However, all structures possess a small amount of damping (the ability to dissipate energy), which limits the response amplitudes at resonant frequencies. In most cases both vibration of, and acoustic radiation by, supporting structures are adequately controlled if the vibration isolation system transmits between 1 and 30 percent of the shaking force, depending on the application. The corresponding "force transmissibility" (TR) is between 0.01 and 0.30, and the corresponding "isolation efficiency" is between 99 and 70 percent. Of course, the actual transmissibility required is a function of the type of equipment involved (i.e., magnitude and frequency content of the shaking forces) and of the space in which the equipment is operated. ("Critical" spaces are offices, churches, meeting rooms, auditoriums, etc.; "noncritical" spaces are garages, maintenance shops, manufacturing areas, indoor sports facilities, etc.)

The most common types of vibration isolators are:

- Helical springs wound from steel wire
- Pads made of neoprene, rubber, or compressed glass fiber and loaded in compression
- Neoprene or rubber loaded in shear

The first two categories are normally placed under machinery, while the third type (as well as helical springs) is used to suspend machinery or piping from an overhead structure. In almost all cases, the supported mass, the vibration isolator, and the supporting structure can be modeled as shown in Fig. 8.28. When the supporting structure is essentially rigid ($K_{support} \gg K_{isolator}$), Fig. 8.28a applies; Fig. 8.28b represents situations where the spring constant of the supporting structure is less than, say, $10K_{isolator}$. The following additional simplifying assumptions used to design the models illustrated in Fig. 8.28 should be

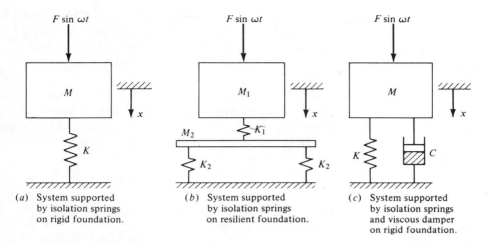

Figure 8.28 Models for vibration isolation systems

$F \sin \omega t$ = shaking force

m, M_1 = supported machine mass

m_2 = effective mass of resilient support

K, K_1 = effective spring constant of isolators

K_2 = spring constant of resilient support

C = viscous damping coefficient

X = displacement of supported mass

noted:

• The supported mass is rigid, and the mass of the spring is negligible compared with that of the supported mass.

• The shaking force is simple harmonic in the vertical direction, and motion occurs in this direction only. Actually, the shaking force is more often the result of rotating unbalance, so the force vector rotates and is simple harmonic in both the vertical and horizontal directions. The usual procedure is to select isolators with about the same stiffness in both directions, so that the corresponding transmissibilities are approximately equal. In any event, a horizontal shaking force is less able to excite flexural vibrations in the supporting structure than a vertical force.

• Energy dissipation in the vibration isolator or supporting structure is negligible. This assumption is valid except in those cases where damping (usually viscous, sometimes frictional) is deliberately incorporated into the isolation system. One primary application of damping is to reduce displacement and force transmission when the shaking-force frequency is near the natural frequency of the system (for example, when a fan or compressor is being brought up to its operating speed). In most cases, however, damping is not required for this purpose because the rotating element passes through the resonant frequency too rapidly for objectionable forces or displacements to occur. A second use for damping is to minimize the transmission of impulsive forces with low repetition rates—less than one per second. (Impulsive forces are characterized by a high amplitude and short duration—typically 1/2 s or less. Examples are operating a punch press or firing a bullet into a water-filled ballistics tank.) The disadvantages of damping are cost, possible variation with temperature, and an increase in transmissibility above resonance.

Let us consider the response of the system, shown in Fig. 8.28 *a*, to harmonic excitation. The differential equation of motion is obtained by equating the sum of external forces acting on M to the product $M\ddot{X}$ (Newton's second law for constant M):

$$- KX + F \sin \omega t = M\ddot{X} \qquad \text{or} \qquad M\ddot{X} + KX = F \sin \omega t \qquad (8.20)$$

The total response is a combination (or superposition) of the homogeneous (transient) and particular (steady-space) responses. We will assume that the system possesses enough inherent damping to quickly eliminate the transient response, but not enough to affect the steady-state response. The steady-state solution is

$$x(t) = \frac{F}{K - M\omega^2} \sin \omega t$$

$$= \frac{F/K}{1 - (M\omega^2/K)} \sin \omega t$$

$$= \frac{F/K}{1 - (\omega/\omega_n)^2} \sin \omega t \qquad (8.21)$$

where $\omega_n = \sqrt{K/M}$ rad/s, the undamped natural frequency of the system. (This is the frequency of vibration that occurs when the system is displaced from rest and allowed to vibrate naturally.) The force transmissibility is the ratio of the amplitude of the transmitted force to the amplitude of the shaking force:

$$\text{TR} = \left| \frac{KX_M}{F} \right| = \left| \frac{1}{1 - (\omega/\omega_n)^2} \right| \qquad (8.22)$$

A plot of Eq. (8.22) is shown in Fig. 8.29 ($\zeta = 0$). Note that TR < 1 only when $\omega/\omega_n > \sqrt{2}$. Thus significant vibration isolation occurs only when $\omega > 4\omega_n$, approximately.

Let us consider an example: A 40-hp centrifugal air-handling unit (AHU) is to be located in a ground-floor mechanical equipment room (MER) of an office building. The unit weighs 1000 lb and operates at 400 rev/min. What should the spring constant of each of four vibration isolators be for a transmissibility of 0.10?

The primary unbalance will be caused by an inertia force vector ($F = mr\omega^2$) rotating at fan speed. The equation of motion at steady state is

$$MX + KX = F \sin \omega t$$

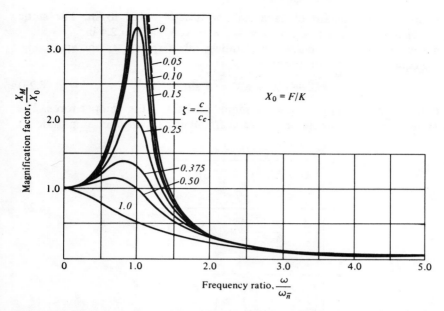

Figure 8.29 Steady-state response of spring-mass damper-system to harmonic excitation $F \sin \omega t$.

from which

$$\text{TR} = \left| \frac{KX_M}{F} \right| = \left| \frac{1}{1 - (\omega/\omega_n)^2} \right|$$

Thus

$$0.10 = \left| \frac{1}{1 - (\omega/\omega_n)^2} \right|$$

from which

$$\left| 1 - \left(\frac{\omega}{\omega_n} \right)^2 \right| = \frac{1}{0.10} = 10$$

Removing the absolute value signs:

$$\left(\frac{\omega}{\omega_n} \right)^2 - 1 = 10 \quad \text{and} \quad \left(\frac{\omega}{\omega_n} \right)^2 = 11$$

Since $\omega_n^2 = K/M = Kg/W$,

$$K = \frac{W\omega^2}{11g} = \frac{1000}{11 \times 386} \times \left(\frac{400 \times 2\pi^2}{60} \right) \quad \text{lb/in}$$

$$= 413 \quad \text{lb/in}$$

This is the equivalent spring constant. Since four isolators are to be used in parallel, the spring constant of each isolator is $K/4 = 103$ lb/in. The static deflection of the system is given by $\delta = W/K = 1000/413 = 2.4$ in.

If a viscous damper is placed in parallel with a spring, as shown in Fig. 8.28c, the equation of motion becomes

$$M\ddot{X} + C\dot{X} + KX = F \sin \omega t \tag{8.23}$$

where C is the coefficient of viscous damping and $C\dot{X}$ is the damper force. The steady-state response is simple harmonic at frequency ω_d, with an amplitude

$$\begin{aligned}
X_M &= \frac{F}{\left[(K - M\omega^2)^2 + (C\omega)^2\right]^{1/2}} \\
&= \frac{F/K}{\left[\left(\dfrac{1 - M\omega^2}{K}\right)^2 + \left(2\dfrac{C\omega}{K}\right)^2\right]^{1/2}} \tag{8.24} \\
&= \frac{F/K}{\left[\left(1 - \left(\dfrac{\omega}{\omega_n}\right)^2\right)^2 + \left(2\dfrac{C}{C_c}\dfrac{\omega}{\omega_n}\right)^2\right]^{1/2}}
\end{aligned}$$

where $\qquad \omega_d =$ damped natural frequency

$$= \omega_n\left[1 - \left(\frac{C}{C_c}\right)^2\right]^{1/2} \tag{8.25}$$

The term C/C_c is called the "damping factor"; it is the ratio of C to C_c, the "critical damping coefficient." This quantity is the smallest value of C which causes the system to return to its at-rest position without oscillation, after an initial displacement. If $C > C_c$, the system response is "overdamped"; if $C < C_c$, the response is "underdamped."

The transmitted-force amplitude is the vector sum of the spring-force (Kx) and damper-force ($C\dot{x}$) amplitudes; at frequencies $\omega > \sqrt{2}\,\omega_n$, the transmitted force with damping is greater than that with no damping. Transmissibilities for a spring-mass system with various levels of damping are shown in Fig. 8.30. If the supporting structure is resilient, the transmissibilities will be somewhat greater than those determined from Fig. 8.30.

Often a noise control engineer may wish to specify a desired level of vibration isolation, but the weight of the supported system is unknown. Fortunately, specification of the "static deflection" δ of the system achieves this objective. By definition,

$$\delta = \frac{W}{K} = \frac{Mg}{K} = \frac{g}{\omega_n^2} \tag{8.26}$$

where δ is deflection of the vibration isolators due to the weight of the supported

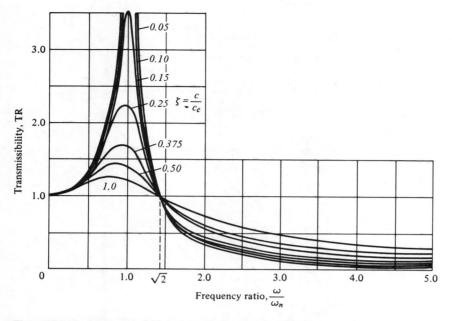

Figure 8.30 Force transmissibility of a spring-mass-damper system.

mass. Substitution of this equation in Eq. (8.22) yields

$$TR = \left| \frac{1}{1 - (\omega^2 \delta / g)} \right| \tag{8.27}$$

A plot of this equation (ω versus δ for various TR values) on log-log coordinates produces a family of straight lines, as shown in Fig. 8.31. Various regions are labeled according to the applications listed.

Typical ranges of static deflections for common isolators are

Helical springs	0.5–5.0 in
Rubber, neoprene, or glass-fiber pads in compression; rubber or neoprene in shear	0.1–0.4 in

In the case of springs, static deflections in excess of 5 in cause lateral and rocking instabilities that are unacceptable for most applications.* Rubber, neoprene, or glass-fiber isolators are typically 0.5 to 2 in thick; static deflections greater than 20 percent of the thickness can cause excessive creep or eventual failure in compression or shear.

---

* Alternate approaches include using inflatable air springs or supporting the equipment on an isolated foundation.

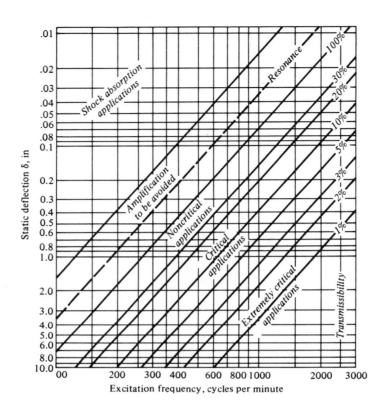

Excitation frequency, cycles per minute

Recommended minimum isolation efficiencies		
TYPE OF EQUIPMENT	CRITICAL AREAS: CHURCHES, RESTAURANTS, STORES, OFFICE BLDGS., SCHOOLS, HOSPITALS, BROADCASTING STUDIOS	NONCRITICAL AREAS: LAUNDRIES, FACTORIES, SUBBASEMENTS GARAGES, WAREHOUSES
Air-conditioners (self-contained)	90%	70%
Air handling units	80%	70%
Compressors (centrifugal)	99%	80%
Compressors (reciprocating) UP TO 10 hp 15 hp TO 50 hp 60 hp TO 150 hp	85% 90% 95%	70% 75% 80%
Heating and ventilating	80%	70%
Cooling towers	80%	70%
Condensers AIR COOLED EVAPORATIVE	80%	70%
Piping	90%	70%
Pumps UP TO 3 hp 5 hp OR OVER	80% 95%	70% 80%
Steam generators (packaged)	See selection guide	See selection guide

Figure 8.31 Recommended isolation efficiencies and static deflections for various applications. *From Vibration Mountings and Controls, Inc.*

The static-deflection data show that pads are effective only at relatively high excitation frequencies. Although springs are theoretically effective at both high and low frequencies, the spring mass (usually neglected) can reduce the transmission loss at elevated frequencies.* This phenomenon is caused by the lowest resonant response of the spring itself, given by

$$f_r = \frac{1}{2} \sqrt{Kg/m} \tag{8.28}$$

where m is the mass of the spring wire (active coils only). This response can become significant when the excitation frequency reaches or exceeds $f_r/15$. Two remedies are

- Selection of different springs with a higher resonant frequency.
- Placement of an isolation pad under each spring; the pad provides isolation at higher frequencies where the spring alone may be inadequate.

In certain critical applications, an "inertia base" may be required. This is a platform, usually concrete with a steel framework, upon which a machine (such as a reciprocating pump or large fan) is mounted. The inertia base is in turn supported by isolation springs; its weight is usually 1 to 2 times the machine weight. By referring to Eq. (8.21), the following characteristics of an inertia base can be verified:

- For a given TR, the spring constant is increased and the amplitude X_M is decreased. The first of these improves lateral and rocking stability, while the second simplifies the attachment of ductwork, electrical conduit, etc. to the machine.
- The moment of inertia of the system is increased, and oscillatory motion (produced by rotating unbalance) about the center of mass is reduced accordingly.
- The transmissibility of the system can be reduced without reducing stability.

The principal disadvantages of an inertia base are added cost and increased weight (which may be a critical factor on the upper floors of a building, for example).

REFERENCES

1. Beranek, L. L. (ed.), *Noise and Vibration Control*, McGraw-Hill, New York, 1971.
2. Beranek, L. L. (ed.), *Noise Reduction*, McGraw-Hill, New York, 1960.
3. Berendt, R., and G. Winzer, *Sound Insulation of Wall, Floor, and Door Constructions*, National Bureau of Standards, Washington, D.C.

---

* Remember that the shaking force may have significant components over a wide range of frequencies; the vibration isolator should be effective over the same range.

4. DeJong, R., and Eric Stusnick, "Scale Model Studies of the Effects of Wind on Acoustic Barrier Performance," *Noise Control Eng.*, May-June 1976.

5. Emme, J., "Composite Materials for Noise and Vibration Control," *Sound and Vibration*, July 1970.

6. Harris, C. M. (ed.), *Handbook of Noise Control*, McGraw-Hill, New York, 1957.

7. Hilliard, John K., "Practical Considerations in a Field Evaluation of Acoustically Effective Party Walls and Floors," *Noise Control Eng.*, May-June 1977.

8. Hirschorn, Martin, "The Aeroacoustic Rating of Silencers for 'Forward' and 'Reverse' Flow of Air and Sound," *Noise Control Eng.*, Winter 1974.

9. Ihde, W. M., "Tuning Stubs to Silence Large Air Handling Systems," *Noise Control Eng.*, November-December 1975.

10. Karnopp, D., et al., "Computer-aided Design of Acoustic Filters using Bond Graphs," *Noise Control Eng.*, May-June 1975.

11. McAuliffe, D., T. Agne, and J. Hammond, "Materials for Noise and Vibration Control," *Sound and Vibration*, July 1972.

12. Monograph 77, National Bureau of Standards, Washington, D.C., 1964. (Several related monographs also available.)

13. Moreland, J. B., and Ray S. Musa, "The Performance of Acoustic Barriers," *Noise Control Eng.*, Autumn 1973.

14. National Institute for Occupational Safety and Health, *Compendium of Materials for Noise Control*, Cincinnati, June 1975.

15. National Institute for Occupational Safety and Health, *Industrial Noise Control Manual*, Cincinnati, June 1975.

16. Nordby, K. S., "Measurement and Evaluation of the Insertion Loss of Panels," *Noise Control Eng.*, January-February 1978.

17. Sanders, Guy, "Silencers: Their Design and Application," *Sound and Vibration*, February 1968.

18. Soedel, W., "Designing Simple Low-Pass Filter Mufflers for Small Two-Cycle Engines," *Noise Control Eng.*, March-April 1978.

IMPORTANT TERMS AND FORMULAS

Dissipative material

Flow resistance

Porosity

Surface treatment

Dissipative silencer

Attentuation of lined duct: $A = 12.6 \dfrac{P}{S} \alpha^{1.4}$ dB/ft

Reactive silencer

Barrier material

Mass-controlled region

Random-incidence transmission loss: $TL \simeq TL_0 - 10 \log_{10} (0.23\, TL_0)$ dB

Field-incidence transmission loss: $TL_f = TL_0 - 5$ dB

Coincidence frequency: $f_c = \dfrac{c^2}{2\pi} \sqrt{\dfrac{\rho_s}{B}}$

Mechanical point loading

Composite structure

Pipe lagging

Partial barrier

Homogeneous damping

Constrained-layer damping

Loss factors: $\eta \cong \delta/\pi$ or $\eta \cong \Delta f/f$

Resonant flexural vibration of panel

Vibration isolation

Force transmissibility: $\text{TR} = \left| \dfrac{1}{1 - (\omega/\omega_n)^2} \right|$

Damping factor: C/C_c

Static deflection: δ

Inertia base

PROBLEMS

8.1 A large mine ventilation fan with a capacity of 9000 ft^3/s produces the following noise spectrum at 200 ft from a discharge duct that measures 12 ft square;

Octave-band center frequency, Hz	63	125	250	500	1000	2000	4000
Noise level, dB	70–74	76–80	70–74	70–72	63–65	54–56	46–47

Design a lined parallel-baffle silencer 12 ft wide and 12 ft high with a maximum of six baffles. The insertion loss is to be at least 30 dBA. Select appropriate structural and absorptive materials for the silencer. Prepare suitable drawings to illustrate your design.

8.2 An in-duct silencer, for a 25- by 36-in duct, is limited to a length of 9 ft.

    (a) Using 1-in duct liner and the Sabine approximation, design a silencer with a minimum number of baffles to provide an attenuation of at least 15 dBA for the input spectrum shown below.

    (b) Using 1-in duct liner and the design chart for 180° bends, design a silencer with a minimum L/D ratio to provide an attenuation of at least 15 dBA for this input spectrum:

Octave-band center frequency, Hz	63	125	250	500	1000	2000	4000
Input noise level, dB	82	82	79	75	70	66	58

8.3 A two-cylinder opposed four-stroke engine operates at 2000 r/min.

(a) Design a minimum-length expansion chamber to provide a maximum transmission loss of 20 dB at the firing frequency of the engine. The exhaust pipe has a diameter of 1 in.

(b) At what engine speed will the attentuation at the firing frequency be a minimum?

(c) Using the design of part (a), what will the maximum transmission loss be (i) for a 3/4-in-diameter exhaust pipe, (ii) for a 1 1/2-in-diameter exhaust pipe?

8.4 A steam vent produces a pure tone at 250 Hz that is a source of community annoyance. The discharge pipe has a diameter of 5 in. Design a Helmholtz resonator to correct this problem, with a 250-Hz resonant frequency and a transmission loss of 10 dB at 500 Hz.

8.5 A glass-fiber-reinforced plastic is 1/16 in thick, with a weight density of 0.042 lb/in^3 and a Young's modulus of 0.7×10^6 lb/in^2. Use Fig. 8.18 to construct an approximate transmission-loss curve for this material.

8.6 A 20-gauge steel plate measures 2 ft wide by 5 ft long and is simply supported at its edges.

(a) Calculate (i) the lowest forced-resonance frequency, f_r, and (ii) the critical frequency, f_c.

(b) Construct an approximate transmission-loss curve extending from f_r to $2 f_c$.

(c) Calculate the near-field sound power radiated from an attachment point that vibrates with a peak displacement of ± 0.04 in at a frequency of 200 Hz.

(d) Would a damping treatment of the panel surface be an effective noise control measure for the excitation described in part (c)? Explain.

8.7 An enclosure for a hydraulic pump is fabricated from welded steel plates that are 1/4 in thick. Noise levels measured inside the enclosure are shown below.

(a) Construct an approximate transmission-loss curve for the steel plate. Use this curve to estimate close-in noise levels outside the enclosure.

(b) What noise control measures would you recommend to reduce exterior noise levels by an additional 5 dBA? Justify your answer.

Octave-band center frequency, Hz	63	125	250	500	1000	2000	4000	8000
Noise level inside enclosure, dB	85	92	92	98	108	105	100	93

8.8 (a) Calculate the surface weight for the steel-stud wall described in Fig. 8.20a. Construct a theoretical transmission-loss curve for a homogeneous wall with this surface weight, for the 125- to 4000-Hz frequency range.

(b) On the same graph, plot the transmission-loss curve of Fig. 8.20a, for 3-in-thick insulation. Compare and discuss these two curves.

8.9 (a) Estimate the transmission loss of a 6-in-diameter steel pipe with a 3/8-in-thick wall.

(b) The same pipe is wrapped with a 1-in-thick glass-fiber blanket that is covered by an aluminum jacket 0.020 in thick. Calculate and plot the approximate insertion loss of the pipe wrap for the range from 125 to 4000 Hz.

8.10 A large transformer at a utility substation produces a pure-tone component at 125 Hz. The pure tone is generated at a point 6 ft above the ground and causes a 15-dB elevation of the ambient-noise level in the 125-Hz band at a residence 150 ft away. The tops of the bedroom windows at the residence are 10 ft above the ground. Investigate the feasibility of erecting a concrete-block wall 12 ft from the transformer to reduce noise levels at the residence by 15 dB. (Use trigonometric relationships to calculate distances A, B, and D in Fig. 8.24.)

8.11 A 20-ft-high concrete barrier is to be erected along an interstate highway to reduce the impact of traffic noise on nearby apartment buildings. The highway consists of four lanes, each 14 ft wide, and a 50-ft median. The barrier is to be erected at a distance of 20 ft from the nearest lane; the apartment buildings are 150 ft from the nearest lane. Calculate the maximum noise level at a second-story window 10 ft above the ground, with and without the barrier in place, from two sources:

- 120-Hz exhaust noise, produced by a 12-ft-high stack, at a level of 120 dB measured 2 ft from the exhaust pipe.
- 1000-Hz tire noise, produced at the road surface with a level of 105 dB measured at a distance of 2 ft.

(Assume that only direct sound is present, and that direct sound decreases 5 dB for each doubling of distance.)

8.12 A 40-hp air-handling unit (AHU) is located in a rooftop mechanical equipment room above an executive dining area. The AHU operates at 1200 r/min and is a suspected source of noise (in the 31.5-Hz octave band) in the dining area. The AHU weighs 900 lb and is supported by four helical springs, each with a spring constant of 200 lb/in.

(a) Determine whether the AHU is a probable source of noise in the dining room.

(b) What changes, if any, would you recommend in the isolation system? Justify your answer.

8.13 A reciprocating compressor weighs 400 lb and is supported on pad-type isolators with a static deflection of 0.3 in. The compressor operates at 1800 r/min.

(a) Calculate the transmissibility and isolation efficiency of the support pads.

(b) Redesign the isolation system for a transmissibility of 0.10, with the addition of an inertia base equal to the weight of the compressor. What is the static deflection? What type of isolator is required?

(c) Calculate the steady-state amplitude of the compressor, for parts (a) and (b).

PRINCIPLES OF NOISE CONTROL

Analysis and correction of noise problems, both elementary and complex, can be simplified by following a set of guidelines or principles. These principles are based upon information developed in previous chapters, specifically:

- Knowledge of the generation and propagation of noise
- Acoustical measurements
- Availability of suitable materials
- Common sense

The principles of noise control are:

1. Identify sources of noise and their relative importance.
2. List and evaluate possible noise control procedures as they apply to source, path, and receiver.
3. Identify relative contributions from direct and reflected sound.
4. Distinguish between absorption and attenuation of noise.
5. Identify and evaluate significance of flanking paths.
6. Identify and evaluate significance of structure-borne noise.

Each of these principles is described and discussed in the following sections.

9.1 PRINCIPLE 1: IDENTIFY SOURCES OF NOISE AND THEIR RELATIVE IMPORTANCE

Acoustic waves are produced by any disturbance that results in particle motion in an outward direction from the disturbance. Sound is generated when the

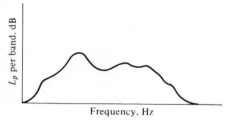

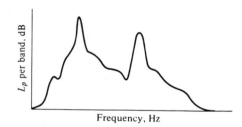

(*a*) Frequency spectrum of broadband source.

(*b*) Frequency spectrum of broadband source with pure tone components.

Figure 9.1 Representative frequency spectra.

frequencies of the disturbance fall within the "audio range" (20 to 20,000 Hz). Examples are:

- Vibrating surfaces, such as panels and piping
- Mechanical impact—e.g., from metal-forming operations
- Pulsating gas flows, such as exhaust gases from reciprocating engines
- Compression or rarefaction of the surrounding medium from meshing of gear teeth, or from a rotating blade passing a stationary object such as an inlet or discharge opening
- Flow of air around obstructions or over a surface, such as an air discharge grille or an aircraft wing

Methods for Identifying Sources of Noise

1. Obtain a frequency spectrum* of the noise; the bandwidth should be narrow enough to identify the character of the noise (wide for broadband sources, narrow for pure-tone components). Examples are shown in Fig. 9.1.
2. If possible, shut off individual noise sources one at a time and observe the changes in dominant portions of the frequency spectrum, as shown in Fig. 9.2.
3. Use one or more mufflers to reduce contributions from inlet and discharge openings (in an engine, air pump, fan, or compressor, for example). In this way, inlet and exhaust noise can be distinguished from noise radiated by an engine block or a machine housing.
4. Use a small probe microphone connected to a frequency analyzer (if available) for close-in measurements to identify locations of dominant noise sources. For example, the sources may be openings in an enclosure; the floor pan of an automobile near a spring hanger; or openings around an access door.

---

* In some cases, the A-weighted sound level of the noise may be sufficient (for example, to separate a high-frequency noise source from low-frequency ambient noise).

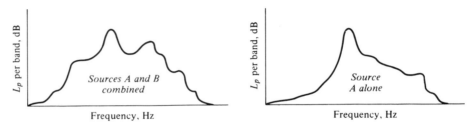

Figure 9.2 Individual and combined frequency spectra.

5. Measure the vibration spectrum from an accelerometer placed at various points on a vibrating surface such as an engine block, pump housing, machine enclosure, process piping, or vibrating hopper. Compare this spectrum with the existing noise spectrum, Fig. 9.3, to identify possible sources of acoustic radiation.
6. Compare peaks in the noise spectrum with possible noise-generating phenomena in gear boxes, machinery, fans, air pumps, etc. Examples are bending and torsional vibrations in rotating shafts; meshing of gear teeth; and passage frequencies of blades, impellers, or rolling elements in bearings.
7. Calculate the critical frequency and theoretical transmission loss of panels or other surfaces, as described in Sec. 8.4, to obtain estimates of the noise reduction they provide for airborne sound. In this way, an estimate of noise levels on the receiver side of a panel or housing can be obtained.
8. Compare the physical dimensions of possible noise sources. A source whose principal dimension (diameter, diagonal, or length, for example) is less than the wavelength corresponding to a particular frequency is usually a relatively inefficient radiator of sound at that frequency. (In order for such "acoustically small" sources to radiate significant sound power, the surface vibration must be large. Most sources cannot vibrate with amplitudes this large, so they do not radiate sound effectively.) In some cases an acoustically small source can transmit its vibratory energy to an element that is a much better radiator

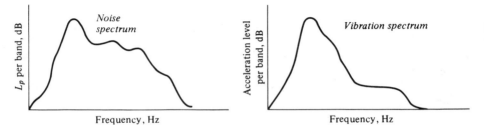

Figure 9.3 Noise spectrum and acceleration spectrum of vibrating surface.

of sound; radiated noise levels may be increased by as much as 10 to 20 dB. Energy is almost always transferred through a mechanical attachment point or other point of contact. As an example, if the discharge line from a refrigeration compressor contacts a panel, vibration from the line may be transferred to and effectively radiated from the sheet-metal surface.

Determining Priority Order for Implementing Noise Control Procedures

Assume that the A-weighted sound levels of individual noise sources have been identified, by means of one or more of the techniques just described. Most compliance-type criteria are specified in A-weighted decibels, so it is logical to measure and compare noise levels using the same units. However, a frequency analysis is usually required to isolate individual source contributions in various frequency bands; following this, the A-weighted noise level of each source can be calculated.

A typical situation is illustrated by Fig. 9.4. Obviously, the noise produced by source C should be reduced first, but by how much? This and similar questions can be answered by combining sources on an energy basis, using Fig. 1.6. For example, if source C is reduced by 6 dBA to the level of source E, the combined level of all sources is 73 dBA. If source C is then eliminated, the combined level decreases by only 3 dBA to 70 dBA. Obviously, this last measure is not only ineffective, but also impractical. The correct approach is to implement measures that will reduce C and E together; when their levels reach that of source B, the level of B should also be reduced.

The approach just described establishes a priority order for implementing a noise control program—one in which each successive step builds upon previous steps. In this way, the combined noise level from several sources can be reduced in an optimum manner. Furthermore, by evaluating the reduction achieved from each step, the program can be terminated at any stage that produces acceptable results.

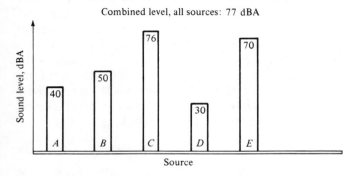

Figure 9.4 Contributions of individual noise sources.

9.2 PRINCIPLE 2: LIST AND EVALUATE POSSIBLE NOISE CONTROL PROCEDURES AS THEY APPLY TO SOURCE, PATH, AND RECEIVER

The three elements in any noise problem are the *source*, which generates the noise; the *path* (air, metal, plastic, glass, for example), which transmits the noise from source to receiver; and the *receiver*, who hears the noise. Each of these elements should be considered when a list of possible noise control procedures is being compiled.* In many cases the most effective, economical solution to a noise problem involves modifications of two or even all three of these elements, as shown in Fig. 9.5.

Consider, as a second example, an unacceptable level of transmission-gear whine in a vehicle interior:

Source	*Possible Noise Control Measures*
• Meshing of gear teeth	• Redesign gear teeth; change tolerances
• Vibration of gear teeth	• Change material
Path	
• Input/output shaft	• Change dimensions
• Transmission case	• Increase thickness, add damping
• Transmission support	• Modify design; change durometer of isolator
• Floor pan	• Increase thickness
	• Add damping
	• Add mass-backed carpet
Receiver	• Add absorption to headliner, floor mat, seats

By considering possible noise control measures related to the source, path, and receiver, the best single measure or combination of measures can be identified. In this case, the best solution may be modification of the transmission support and the addition of carpeting with a dense, limp backing (mass-backed carpet). It should be noted, however, that the ultimate solution is to eliminate the mechanism of noise generation (at the source): this obviates the need for additional measures. In general, the number of possible paths and receivers increases with distance from the source. For this reason, a noise control treatment should be located as close to the source as possible.

---

* Compilation of such a list usually requires a frequency spectrum of each noise source, because each procedure is more effective at some frequencies than others.

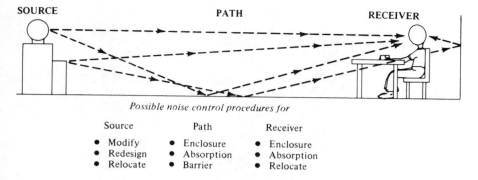

SOURCE   PATH   RECEIVER

Possible noise control procedures for

Source   Path   Receiver

- Modify   - Enclosure   - Enclosure
- Redesign   - Absorption   - Absorption
- Relocate   - Barrier   - Relocate

Figure 9.5 Noise control procedures as applied to source, path, receiver.

9.3 PRINCIPLE 3: IDENTIFY RELATIVE CONTRIBUTIONS FROM DIRECT AND REFLECTED SOUND

Unless a free field is present, both direct and reflected (reverberant) sound waves combine at each location (see Fig. 9.6) to produce observed or measured sound levels. (Direct sound travels by a straight-line path from source to receiver; reflected sound is the combination of sound waves arriving at the receiver after one or more reflections from surrounding surfaces.) The addition of absorption to a reverberant space, such as a van interior or a machine enclosure, will not be an effective noise control measure unless reverberant sound dominates direct sound. Remember that direct sound is unaffected by absorption because the sound waves do not impinge upon any surfaces before arriving at the receiver.

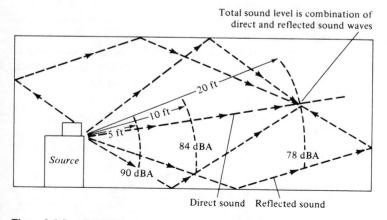

Total sound level is combination of direct and reflected sound waves

20 ft
10 ft
5 ft
84 dBA
78 dBA
Source
90 dBA

Direct sound   Reflected sound

Figure 9.6 Levels of direct and reverberant sound.

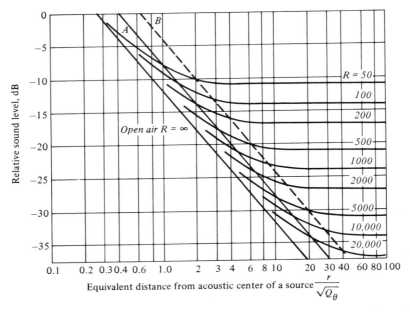

Figure 9.7 Variation of sound level with distance from a point source, for various values of R.

In a space with highly reflective surfaces (metal, glass, wood, plastic) reverberant sound is almost uniform everywhere; direct sound, on the other hand, decreases by 6 dB for each doubling of distance. In a typical situation, a vibrating surface or an opening serves as a source of sound in an enclosed space such as a vehicle interior. Figure 9.7 indicates the relative importance of direct and reverberant sound. The curves are plots of Eqs. (6.28) or (6.29) for various values of absorption (A) in a reverberant space. (Remember that absorption is the sum of $\alpha \times S$ values for each interior surface, for $\alpha \leq 0.2$; refer to Sec. 6.2.) The total sound level in each frequency band is obtained by combining the direct and reverberant contributions.

The effect of adding absorption is shown in Fig. 9.8. For each doubling of absorption, reverberant sound decreases by 3 dB. This means that the maximum practical decrease of reverberant sound in interior spaces is 7 to 9 dB.

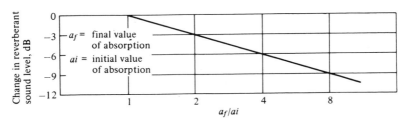

Figure 9.8 Variation in reverberant sound level with absorption.

We arrive at this conclusion by writing Eq. (4.38), with $Q_\theta/4\pi r^2 \ll 4/a$, for the initial and final values of absorption:

$$L_{p_1} = L_w + 10 \log_{10} \frac{4}{a_1}$$

$$L_{p_2} = L_w + 10 \log_{10} \frac{4}{a_2}$$

where a_1 = initial value of absorption
a_2 = final value of absorption
L_{p_1} = initial reverberant sound level
L_{p_2} = final reverberant sound level
L_w = sound-power level
Subtraction yields:

$$L_{p_2} - L_{p_1} = 10 \log_{10} \frac{4}{a_2} - 10 \log_{10} \frac{4}{a_1}$$

$$= 10 \log_{10} \frac{a_1}{a_2} \qquad (9.1)$$

If $a_2 = 2a_1$, the change in sound level ΔLp is given by

$$\Delta Lp = 10 \log_{10} \frac{1}{2}$$

$$= -3\text{dB}$$

As an example, consider a van interior measuring approximately 10 ft long by 5 1/2 ft wide by 5 ft high. The absorption coefficients (at a frequency of interest) of the glass, metal, and vinyl surfaces can be estimated from Table 8.4. Next, the absorption for each surface is calculated by multiplying each absorption coefficient by the appropriate surface area. The total absorption of the van interior is obtained by summing the absorption of individual surfaces. Now Fig. 9.4 can be used to determine the relative magnitudes of direct and reverberant sound. (Direct sound is negligible on the horizontal portion of each curve.) If reverberant sound dominates at the receiver's location, the effect of adding absorption (in the form of a new headliner, for example) can be estimated from Fig. 9.5. However, if direct sound is dominant, the new headliner will not reduce the noise level at the receiver's location.

Reduction of reverberant sound in a machinery enclosure, through addition of acoustical absorption to interior surfaces, is often an effective method for improving the insertion loss of the enclosure. Assuming that the enclosure meets the requirements for a reverberant sound field in the lowest octave band of interest (volume greater than $4/3 \lambda^3$), Fig. 9.8 can be used to estimate the reduction in reverberant sound produced by the addition of absorption. Then the effective transmission loss of the enclosure (TL of enclosure material, adjusted for openings, access doors, viewing panels, etc.—see Sec. 9.5) can be used to predict the insertion loss of the enclosure in the far field. In essence, this

Table 9.1 Insertion loss of a plywood enclosure with various interior absorption treatments

Construction type	Octave-band center frequencies, Hz					
	125	250	500	1000	2000	4000
Plywood enclosure, 1/2 in, unlined	13*	11	12	12	13	>15
Plywood enclosure, 1/2 in, lined with 1-in OCF 703 board†	18	17	23	30	38	>40
Plywood enclosure, 1/2 in, lined with 2-in OCF 703 board	18	23	30	37	45	>50
Plywood enclosure, 1/2 in, lined with 4-in OCF 703 board	19	29	38	47	58	>60
Plywood cnclosure, 1/2 in, lined with 3 5/8-in R-13 full wall‡	17	25	29	36	41	>45

* Insertion-loss data based on enclosure with exterior dimensions of $3 \times 4 \times 5$ ft.
† 3 lb/ft³ density.
‡ Building insulation.

procedure simply replaces the actual noise source with one that radiates less sound power (specifically, the surfaces of the enclosure). Representative data for a plywood enclosure are given in Table 9.1.

9.4 PRINCIPLE 4: DISTINGUISH BETWEEN ABSORPTION AND ATTENUATION OF NOISE

The ability of a material or structure to absorb or attenuate noise is the principal measure of its acoustical performance. *Absorption* (measured by absorption coefficient) is desirable for reducing noise within a space. An absorptive material must have a porous structure into which sound waves can propagate, thereby losing some of their energy. Such materials are usually relatively lightweight and often lack structural properties. *Attenuation* (measured by transmission loss) is desirable for preventing the escape of sound waves from a space. An attenuating material is nonporous, dense, and relatively heavy, and usually it has structural properties.

Frequently, the functions of absorption and attenuation are misunderstood, and an unsatisfactory solution to a noise problem results. Consider the following example (Fig. 9.9a): A sound wave with energy E_1 strikes the surface of an absorbing material. One-tenth of the arriving energy is reflected, one-tenth is transmitted, and eight-tenths is absorbed within the material. Thus:

$$\alpha = 0.8$$

$$\text{TL} = 10 \log_{10} \frac{1.0}{0.1} = 10 \log_{10} 10$$

$$= 10 \text{ dB}$$

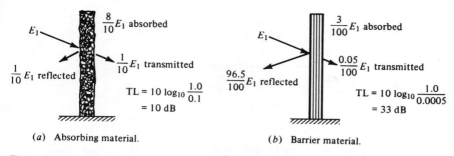

(a) Absorbing material. (b) Barrier material.

Figure 9.9 Absorption and transmission-loss characteristics of absorbers and barriers.

Although the absorption coefficient is relatively high, the transmission loss is unacceptably low for most situations. Therefore, an acoustical absorber is, by itself, a poor attenuator or barrier. Conversely, a good attenuator (Fig. 9.9b) is usually a good reflector of acoustic energy and has a low absorption coefficient at all frequencies. Of course, a combination of materials (urethane foam bonded to loaded vinyl, for example) can provide both good absorption and good attenuation. Proper selection of materials for a given application requires a knowledge of acoustic properties, as we have seen, as well as the correct identification of major noise sources and transmission paths.

9.5 PRINCIPLE 5: IDENTIFY AND EVALUATE SIGNIFICANCE OF FLANKING PATHS

A flanking path is any route by which sound travels from one side of a barrier to the other, excluding the barrier material itself. Flanking paths can be airborne or structure-borne. Examples of the first category are holes; cracks; and clearance around wires, cables, and tubing. The second category includes glass or plastic panels; access doors; rubber grommets; and HVAC ducts.

The ability of flanking paths to transmit sound more readily than the barrier material is easily appreciated. However, the effect of flanking paths on overall performance of a barrier is neither as obvious nor as well understood. The simplest way to evaluate flanking paths is to consider each such path, and the barrier itself, as a source of sound. The total sound power transmitted is obtained by summing the contributions from the flanking paths and from the barrier. Three representative cases are shown in Fig. 9.10. In a given frequency band, the incident sound level is 90 dB; the barrier attenuates this level by 30 dB and creates a 60-dB sound level on the receiver side. The total power transmitted by flanking paths produces sound levels of 50, 60, or 70 dB. Combining transmitted sound levels on an energy basis yields 60.4, 63, and 70.4 dB, respectively. In the first case, overall performance is controlled by the barrier itself; in the second case, both the barrier and flanking paths contribute equally; in the third case, performance is controlled by flanking-path contributions.

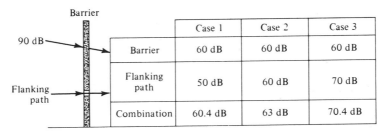

		Case 1	Case 2	Case 3
Barrier → 90 dB → Flanking → path	Barrier	60 dB	60 dB	60 dB
	Flanking path	50 dB	60 dB	70 dB
	Combination	60.4 dB	63 dB	70.4 dB

Figure 9.10 Effects of flanking-path contributions on barrier performance.

(Note that overall performance in the third case will not be affected by improvements in the barrier material.)

The effect of an opening, viewing panel, or other flanking path on the performance of a barrier material can be estimated from the transmission coefficients (τ_i) and surface area (S_i) of each element. For example, assume that a panel with a TL of 40 dB and a surface area of 10 ft^2 has a 2-ft^2 viewing panel with a TL of 20 dB and openings equal to 3 in^2. By definition TL = $10 \log_{10} (1/\tau)$, where τ is the fraction of randomly incident acoustic intensity that is transmitted by a given element. The transmission coefficient τ_{eq} of a uniform structure that is equivalent to the actual panel is obtained by equating the transmitted sound power for each, leading to the equation:

$$\tau_{eq} S = \sum_i \tau_i S_i \qquad (9.2)$$

where S = total surface area of panel. For our example:

$$\tau_{eq} \times 10 = 10^{-4}(8) + 10^{-2}(2) + 1.0(0.02)$$
$$\tau_{eq} = 0.00408 \qquad (9.3)$$

where the transmission coefficient for openings is assumed to be unity. The corresponding transmission loss is obtained from

$$TL = 10 \log_{10} \frac{1}{\tau_{eq}}$$
$$= 24 \text{ dB}$$

Inspection of Eq. (9.3) shows that the viewing panel and openings contribute equally to degradation of the panel performance to 24 dB from 40 dB.

Figure 9.11 demonstrates the small percentage of open area (in the form of airborne sound paths) that is required to seriously degrade the performance of a barrier. From the graph, it is also apparent that a barrier with a low transmission loss will be less affected by a given percentage of open area than a barrier with a high transmission loss. This behavior can be understood by combining sound-power contributions, as was done in the previous example.

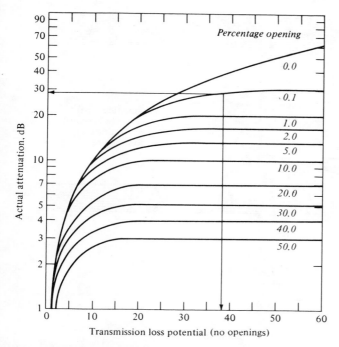

Figure 9.11 Effect of openings on transmission loss. *From the National Institute for Occupational Safety and Health,* Industrial Noise Control Manual, *Cincinnati, Ohio, 1975.*

9.6 PRINCIPLE 6: IDENTIFY AND EVALUATE SIGNIFICANCE OF STRUCTURE-BORNE NOISE

One of the the first requirements for solving a noise problem is to identify correctly the dominant noise sources. In particular, energy that is delivered to a structure by mechanical excitation and then radiated as airborne sound through resonant vibrations of the structure must be distinguished from airborne-sound excitation. One method for doing this is to compare noise and vibration spectra (both amplitude and frequency content), as discussed earlier.

Noise generated by structural vibration can be a difficult problem to correct because the vibrations may travel relatively long distances from the point of excitation before they appear as airborne sound. This characteristic can make the point of excitation difficult to locate. In many cases, the most desirable and effective method for reduction of structure-borne noise is isolation of the exciting force from the structure itself. This procedure, called *vibration isolation*, was discussed in Chap. 8. The purpose of vibration isolation is to reduce the transmission of force into a structure by decoupling the input from the structure. Springs, grommets, and rubber or elastomer pads are commonly used for this purpose, as illustrated in Fig. 9.12.

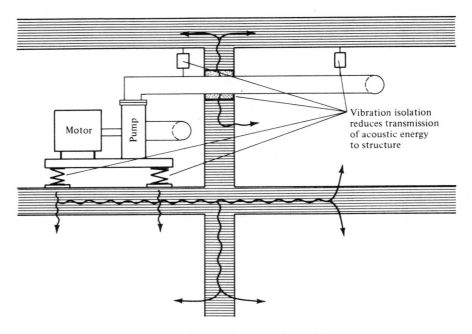

Vibration isolation reduces transmission of acoustic energy to structure

Figure 9.12 Vibration isolators for reduction of structure-borne noise.

The excitation may be from impact, such as that delivered by an automotive suspension to a frame or unitized body. Rubber bushings are used at mounting points to reduce the transmission of forces (which often cover a wide frequency range—from a few Hertz to several hundred Hertz) into the frame or body. Because they are relatively stiff, rubber isolators are not very effective for isolating force components at the lower end of this range. On the other hand, frequencies above 50 Hz are primary contributors to ride harshness and structure-borne noise.

Another type of structural excitation is produced by unbalance in rotating machines such as compressors, pumps, and fans. In these cases, the primary excitation frequency occurs at the operating speed of the machine; this speed is usually less than 3600 rev/min (60 Hz), so the range of frequencies is much narrower than that for impact excitations. Rubber or elastomer mounts are often used to isolate forces produced by rotating unbalance. (Whenever possible, however, a better solution is to reduce the magnitude of the unbalanced force by improved quality control or on-line balancing.)

The effectiveness of vibration isolation can be reduced or nullified by rigid connections to the supported equipment. In Fig. 9.12, for example, the use of rigid pipe supports or inflexible caulking where the discharge pipe penetrates the wall would "short circuit" the spring and pad isolators beneath the motor and pump. (A widely used guideline states that pipe supports should be resilient for at least 100 pipe diameters from the pump.) Other common "short circuits" are rigid electrical conduit and inflexible couplings between air-handling units and connecting ductwork.

REFERENCES

1. Baade, P. K., "A Sound Strategy for Developing Quiet Products," *Noise Control Eng.*, November–December 1974.
2. Ingard, K. and G. Maling, "Physical Principles of Noise Reduction," *Noise Control Eng.*, Spring 1974.
3. Miller, T. D., "Industrial Noise Control: Putting It All Together," *Noise Control Eng.*, July–August 1977.
4. Moreland, J. B., "Controlling Industrial Noise by Means of Room Boundary Absorption," *Noise Control Eng.*, November–December 1976.
5. Peterson, A. P., and Ervin E. Gross, *Handbook of Noise Measurement*, 7th ed., General Radio Company, Concord, Mass., 1974.
6. Shiner, Allen, "Acoustical Flanking in Structures," *Noise Control Eng.*, September–October 1974.

IMPORTANT TERMS AND FORMULAS

Noise source identification

Frequency spectrum

Probe microphone

Vibration spectrum

Acoustically small source

Priority order

Source, path, and receiver

Direct- and reflected-sound contributions

Reverberant-sound reduction: $\quad L_{p_2} - L_{p_1} = 10 \log_{10} \dfrac{a_1}{a_2}$

Absorption and attenuation of noise

Flanking path

Structure-borne noise

PROBLEMS

9.1 Excessive noise levels occurring in a penthouse apartment result from the operation of HVAC equipment. Octave-band levels measured in the apartment are shown below (in decibels).

(*a*) Estimate the octave-band levels for (i) the cooling-tower pump alone, (ii) the rooftop ventilation fans alone, (iii) the apartment air conditioner alone.

(*b*) Calculate the corresponding A-weighted value for each source and for the combination of all sources.

(*c*) Estimate the minimum dBA reduction required for each source in order to reduce the combined level (with all sources operating) to 35 dBA. In what order would you reduce the noise level produced by each source?

(*d*) What are the NC values for all sources operating? All sources off?

	Octave-band center frequency, Hz							
	31.5	63	125	250	500	1000	2000	4000
All HVAC sources operating	75	63	62	57	47	38	30	29
Cooling-tower pump off	69	57	56	53	43	34	26	23
Cooling-tower pump and ventilation fans off	63	53	54	51	43	34	26	23
All HVAC sources off	61	50	52	50	43	34	26	23

9.2 Refer to Fig. 9.7. Calculate values for $R = 10$ and $R = 25$ at equivalent distances of 1, 2, 4, 8, 16, and 32 ft: plot the curves on Fig. 9.7.

9.3 A manufacturing area has a concrete floor and roof, unpainted concrete-block walls, and dimensions of 100 ft by 60 ft by 20 ft high.

(*a*) Calculate the amount of additional absorption required to reduce reverberant-sound levels in the 500-Hz octave band by 3 dB: 6 dB; 9 dB.

(*b*) If 1-in-thick glass-fiber board is used to provide additional absorption, calculate (i) the number of square feet of glass-fiber board required for a 9-dB reduction (assume a no. 4 mounting) and (ii) the total surface area (walls and ceiling) available for placement of added absorption.

9.4 Typical sound levels in a food-packaging area are listed below. These levels result from many sources within the area and are uniform everywhere within ±2 dB. The space is 150 ft long by 90 ft wide by 20 ft high; all surfaces are poured concrete. Design an absorbing treatment, consisting of hanging baffles on 4-ft centers, to reduce the noise level by 7 dBA. Show locations of baffles on a plan view of the area.

Octave-band center frequency, Hz	31.5	63	125	250	500	1000	2000
Sound level, dB	84–89	82–86	84–86	83	86	85	82

9.5 An enclosure measures 15 ft long, 6 ft wide, and 5 ft high. All surfaces are 1/16 -in-thick steel; the interior absorption coefficient averages 0.2 in the frequency band of interest. At an attachment point on one side, the peak velocity is 0.150 in/s, at a frequency of 400 Hz.

(*a*) Verify that the enclosure is reverberant at 400 Hz.

(*b*) Calculate the critical frequency of the enclosure material.

(*c*) Calculate the sound power radiated into the enclosure.

(*d*) Determine the reverberant-sound level inside the enclosure.

9.6 The curve in Fig. 9.11 for 20 percent leaks shows no change in realized noise attenuation for a transmission-loss potential ranging from 20 to 60 dB. However, the curve for 0.1 percent leaks shows no change only over the 40- to 60-dB range.

(*a*) Give a thorough and clear written explanation of this behavior.

(*b*) For a given percentage of open area, what is the minimum transmission-loss potential that will provide acceptable performance?

9.7 A wall is constructed from 2 1/2-in studs with 1/2-in-thick gypsum board on each side and 2-in-thick insulation in the cavities. The wall is 20 ft long by 8 ft high and contains a gasketed 3- by

7-ft steel door and a 5- by 3-ft glass viewing panel, 1/4 in thick. Calculate the effective transmission loss of the composite structure at the octave-band frequencies from 125 to 4000 Hz. (Use data from Figs. 8.18, 8.20, and 8.23 and from Table 8.11.)

9.8 A wall consists of 4-in-thick dense concrete. The wall measures 40 ft long by 10 ft high and contains a 1 1/2-in-thick wooden door, 12 ft wide by 8 ft high. An air gap at the perimeter of the door averages 1/4 in wide.

(a) Calculate the transmission loss of the concrete wall alone.

(b) Calculate the effective transmission loss of the actual wall structure.

(c) Calculate the effective transmission loss if the wall thickness is increased to 8 in.

(d) Calculate the effective transmission loss for a 4-in-thick wall and a door with edges completely sealed.

9.9 A machine produces the following octave-band sound levels in the reverberant field:

Frequency, Hz	125	250	500	1000	2000	4000
Level, dB	95	90	90	87	88	83

An enclosure is placed over the machine. Its dimensions are 5 ft long, 4 ft wide, and 5 ft high; 2 percent of the enclosure surface is open area. Calculate the insertion loss of the enclosure in octave bands and in dBA for the following cases: (i) enclosure is 3/4-in plywood, (ii) enclosure is 3/4-in plywood lined with 1-in-thick glass-fiber board. Proceed as follows:

(a) Verify that the sound field within the enclosure is reverberant, or approximately so.

(b) For each case, estimate the reverberant sound pressure and the effective transmission coefficient for each octave band.

(c) Compute the transmitted sound pressure and the corresponding sound-pressure level for each octave band.

(d) For each case, compare the transmitted octave-band levels and the corresponding dBA value with the levels without an enclosure.

9.10 A 40-hp chilled-water pump is located in a rooftop mechanical equipment room. The pump operates at 1800 r/min and produces a noise level of 90 dB in the 31.5-Hz octave band. Four helical springs, each with a static deflection of 1/2 in, support the pump-motor assembly. The noise level in the space immediately below the mechanical equipment room is 80 dB in the 31.5-Hz octave band. The floor-to-ceiling structure is 4-in-thick dense concrete with a suspended acoustical ceiling.

(a) Evaluate whether the 80-dB noise level results primarily from airborne-sound or mechanical excitation.

(b) What steps would you take to reduce the 80-dB noise level to 70 dB? Justify your answer.

TEN

CASE STUDIES IN NOISE CONTROL

In this chapter we will apply the principles of Chap. 9, as well as the concepts and relationships developed in earlier chapters, to a variety of practical problems. From these case studies the reader should develop an appreciation that noise control is neither a black art nor an exact science. Rather, it is an approach that utilizes physical principles (often in simplified form), engineering judgment, and knowledge of available technology. In the sections that follow, a variety of noise control problems and the methods employed to solve them are described.

10.1 REDUCTION OF NOISE LEVELS IN A FOOD-PACKAGING AREA

Description An area used for packaging cereals and dry prepared mixes occupies an entire floor of a large building. The area measures about 180 ft long by 120 ft wide by 20 ft high; all surfaces are poured concrete. Three packaging lines, each with similar equipment, are set up on the floor. In each line, the major noise sources are a paper shear, a box former, and a wrapping/sealing machine. The machines are old but well maintained. Some employees are stationed at specific locations, while others circulate among the major pieces of machinery.

Noise measurements A survey of the packaging area showed that A-weighted noise levels varied from 88 to 91 dBA at employee locations. Table 10.1 compares sound levels measured at a typical employee location, with the nearest box former operating and shut off. The similarity between levels indicates that

Table 10.1 Noise levels at 10 ft from box-forming machine, in dBA

		Octave-band center frequency, Hz						
		31.5	63	125	250	500	1000	2000
Former on, dBA	89	84–89	82–86	84–86	83	86	85	82
Former off, dBA	88	85–89	82–84	83–85	82	84	84	82

other contributions are almost as significant as those from the box former, a nearby major source. Because of the surroundings (poured concrete), and the fact that no other major sources were nearby, it was concluded that reverberant sound was a significant contributor. This conclusion was reinforced by the uniformity of noise levels throughout the packing area.

Analysis Addition of acoustical absorption to the packaging area, in the form of film-covered hanging baffles, was recommended for several reasons:

• No one type of source was dominant; noise levels were produced by operation of many sources.
• The space was highly reverberant, so that a reasonable amount of additional absorption could reduce noise levels by a significant amount.
• A reduction in noise level of about 7 dBA would satisfy present and proposed OSHA regulations and was attainable by use of absorption.
• Hanging baffles covered with a thin Mylar film would not interfere with lighting, the sprinkler system, or production. In addition, they could resist vermin infestation and withstand a periodic 130°F soak temperature, as required by health regulations.
• The only other alternative, enclosure of dominant sources, would interfere with production and be of only limited value for reducing noise levels.

In the octave bands of greatest interest for reduction of A-weighted sound levels (500, 1000, and 2000 Hz), the average absorption coefficient was estimated to be 0.04. The existing absorption was estimated by calculating $S\bar{\alpha}_{SAB}$.

Design The amount of additional absorption required to produce a 7-dB reduction in the 500-, 1000-, and 2000-Hz bands was calculated from Eq. (4.39):

$$\Delta L_p = -10 \log_{10} \frac{a_f}{a_i}$$

where a_f = final value of absorption and a_i = initial value of absorption, both in sabins. (The 500-, 1000-, and 2000-Hz band levels were dominant and approximately equal; therefore, a 7-dB reduction in each band would provide an overall reduction of about 7 dBA.) From these calculations, it was determined that 800 hanging baffles of the type described in Table 8.6 would be needed. Twenty-five rows of baffles hung from cables stretched on 4-ft centers, with 32 baffles in each row, were recommended.

Evaluation Only a partial coverage of the packaging area was completed initially. Baffles were concentrated over the noisiest areas of two lines. In these areas, a reduction of about 6 dBA was measured; this decrease was very noticeable to employees.

Note that the existing absorption must be estimated with some care, either by use of published values or by the measurement of reverberation times. For example, if $\bar{\alpha}_{SAB}$ had been estimated at 0.05 instead of 0.04, a total of 1100 baffles would have been required.

10.2 REDUCTION OF ENGINE-GENERATOR COOLING-FAN NOISE

Description Three diesel-powered emergency engine-generator units are located on the ground floor of a three-story brick building, in a room with an outside wall. The wall is penetrated by five louvered openings, each approximately 3 ft square. Two of the openings are used for induction of cooling air into the room; each of the remaining openings is connected by a 3-ft section of ductwork to a radiator which serves one engine-generator unit. An engine-driven multibladed fan forces cool air through the radiator and discharges it through the ductwork to an alleyway outside the building. During operation of the engine-generator units (about 3 h per week), fan noise is objectionable to residents located about 250 ft away.

Noise measurements Table 10.2 lists sound-pressure levels (overall, A-weighted, and in octave bands) corresponding to operation of all three units, and typical daytime ambient noise.

Analysis The noise produced by the engine-generator units was broadband in nature, without distinct pure-tone components. Engine exhaust passed through silencers and into a vertical discharge stack that terminated above the third-floor roof. Exhaust noise at the discharge was negligible; the cooling fans were clearly the dominant sources of noise.

Table 10.2 Outdoor noise levels near engine-generator units, in dBA

		Octave-band center frequencies, Hz							
		31.5	63	125	250	500	1000	2000	4000
Alleyway, 15 ft from louvers, dBA	82	77	81	87	79	78	78	75	66
Nearest residence, dBA	61	57	61	67	59	58	58	53	42
Daytime ambient-noise level, dBA	49	56	55	56	45	46	40	35	39

The exterior wall of the engine-generator room was masonry faced with brick; transmission of noise by the wall was insignificant. Modification of the cooling fans was not feasible, and insufficient space was available in the discharge ducts to permit installation of silencers. Therefore, a decision was made to design exterior silencers for each of the five openings. The possibility of a concrete-block plenum was discussed with the building architect. However, since footings would be required, this proposal was rejected in favor of custom-fabricated silencers designed for attachment to the outside wall of the building.

Design Each of the five silencers consisted of a 1 1/2-in welded steel angle framework to which 3/8-in-thick cement asbestos board was attached with screws (Fig. 10.1). This material was selected because of its relatively high surface weight, its relatively low cost, and its resistance to weather. Each silencer contained parallel baffles, lined on all sides with 1-in-thick commercial duct liner, and a lined 180° bend. Baffles were spaced 6 in apart because of the relatively high frequency content of the noise. The outlet of each silencer faced downward to prevent entry of rain or snow; however, individual designs were modified so that cooling-air discharge and inlet-air openings were separated by as great a distance as possible.

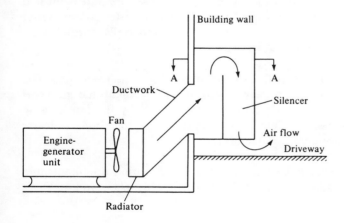

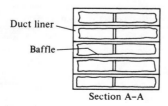

Section A–A

Figure 10.1 Schematic of typical silencer.

Removal of the existing louvers before installation of the silencers maintained about the same flow resistance; however, the two inlet-air openings in the building wall were undersized, so that a negative pressure existed in the engine-generator room during operation of the units. This problem was largely eliminated by locating a centrifugal fan in the room, with its suction connected to one of the inlet-air openings.

Evaluation After completion of the installation, operation of the units was inaudible at the nearest residence and caused no measurable increase in ambient-noise levels. An estimated noise reduction of 25 dBA was obtained by use of the silencers.

It should be noted that although this project was highly successful, the necessity for custom fabrication of the silencers resulted in a cost of several thousand dollars.

10.3 REDUCTION OF NOISE FROM A MINE VENTILATION FAN

Description A large (6000 ft^3/s) vaneaxial fan provides ventilation air for a coal mine in a rural area. The discharge duct measures 12 ft square and is located approximately 300 ft from the nearest residence. The fan operates continuously; residents have complained about excessive noise levels, especially during nighttime hours, and have threatened legal action.

Noise measurements Noise levels at the residence are shown in Table 10.3. The A-weighted sound level is approximately 35 dB above the nighttime ambient-noise level. A comparison of close-in noise levels radiated by the fan housing and discharge duct with those radiated from the duct opening showed clearly that the opening was the dominant source of noise.

Analysis The noise spectrum of the fan was broadband, with a dominant pure tone at 360 Hz; energy was concentrated in the 125-, 250-, 500-, and 1000-Hz

Table 10.3 Measured sound levels and estimated insertion loss at nearest residence, in dBA

	Octave-band center frequency, Hz						
	31.5	63	125	250	500	1000	2000
Sound level at residence, no silencer, dBa	68–70	62–66	64–68	70–74	68–72	64–68	57–61	48–51
Estimated insertion loss of silencer, dBa	35	15	25	35	40	40	30	20

octave bands. Two possible noise control methods were considered:

• Addition of a 45° bend to the existing discharge duct. The bend would direct sound waves away from the residence and provide some noise reduction, particularly at frequencies above 250 Hz. However, the effects of wind could reduce the insertion loss of the bend to an unacceptable value at the residence.
• Addition of a lined parallel-baffle silencer to the discharge-duct termination. This option was recommended because it would provide a predictable attenuation of fan noise in a reasonable length, with a minimum increase in static pressure.

Design A plan view of the silencer is shown in Fig. 10.2. The floor is a poured-concrete slab, exterior walls are cement asbestos board attached to 6-in steel studs, and the roof is corrugated cement asbestos sheet. The transmission loss of the walls and roof was selected to exceed the insertion loss of the silencer in each frequency band. Each of the interior wall surfaces and the five internal

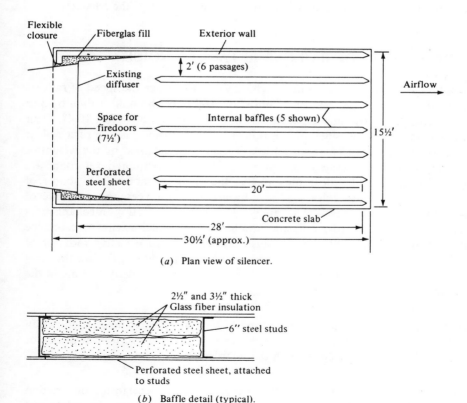

(a) Plan view of silencer.

(b) Baffle detail (typical).

Figure 10.2 Details of lined parallel-baffle silencer.

baffles is fabricated from 6-in steel studs covered by 30 percent open perforated-steel sheet. Cavities within the walls are filled with 3-lb/ft³ glass-fiber insulation. This construction is adequate to protect the glass fiber from erosion by flow; the flow velocity is about 60 ft/s. The cross section of the silencer is larger than the duct opening, to minimize the additional increase in static pressure. Glass-fiber fill is used in the transition duct to provide additional attenuation.

The estimated attenuation of the silencer is shown in Table 10.3. The reduction in A-weighted sound level at the residence was estimated to be 35 dBA; this reduction would make the fan barely audible, even at night.

Evaluation Although the silencer was designed to minimize construction costs, the only bid received was excessive. Two contributing factors were the remoteness of the area and the requirement that the fan remain in operation during construction. As a result, the coal company decided to purchase the residence (no other residences were affected by the fan noise). The cost of the residence was about $7000 less than the estimated construction cost of the silencer.

10.4 REDUCTION OF RAILCAR RETARDER NOISE

Description Retarders are used in switching yards to reduce the speed of railcars on individual spurs. Most retarders consist of steel bars about 30 ft long by 3 in wide, located just above and on each side of a section of track (Fig. 10.4). Their purpose is to clamp the sides of the railcar wheels during passage of a railcar through the retarder. The clamping force is usually determined by the weight of the railcar, through a system of springs and levers. Although retarders are effective for control of railcar movements, the clamping action is a source of high-intensity pure-tone noise that is a hazard to employees and a source of annoyance in nearby residential areas. The noise-generating mechanism is friction between the retarder rails and a railcar wheel, which excites a resonance in the wheel at about 2000 Hz. Because the wheel is an effective radiator of acoustic energy at this frequency, a piercing noise is produced. In fact the level can exceed 130 dBA at a distance of 20 ft, and the noise is clearly audible in the surrounding area.

Noise measurements A characteristic time history of retarder noise is shown in Fig. 10.3 (upper trace). Typically, each railcar will produce two to four peaks (or "squeals") during its passage through the retarder.

Design The purpose of this study was to evaluate a new design for the friction surfaces, as shown in Fig. 10.4. Instead of a continuous steel bar, the redesigned surface consisted of a series of cast-iron pads welded to a backing strip with random spacing.

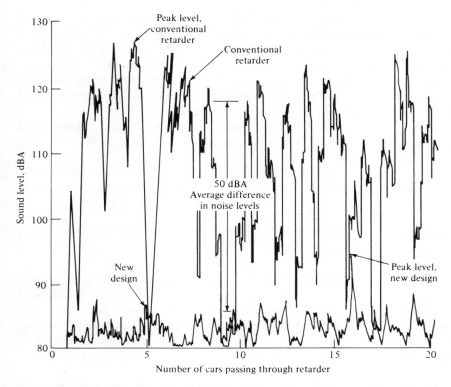

Figure 10.3 Representative sound levels for conventional and modified retarders, measured at a distance of 20 ft.

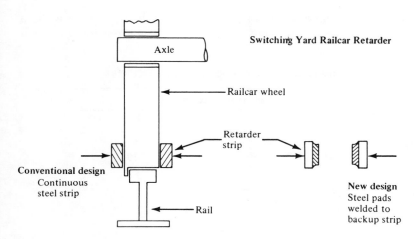

Figure 10.4 Details of conventional and modified retarder designs.

Analysis and evaluation The new design produced a dramatic reduction in sound level, as shown by the lower trace of Fig. 10.3. Not only was the average level reduced (almost to the yard ambient level), but the character of the noise changed from repeated high-intensity squeals to a low-frequency "grinding" sound punctuated with occasional squeals of reduced intensity. Apparently the random spacing of the pads prevents reinforcement of vibrations at the resonant frequency, so that much less acoustic power is produced.

Although the wear rate of the new design is somewhat greater, the increased maintenance is not excessive. The new design is currently being manufactured and marketed by at least one firm.

Note that the new retarder design is an example of noise reduction at the source, which—when feasible—is the most desirable approach to noise control.

10.5 REDUCTION OF MECHANICAL EQUIPMENT NOISE IN A PENTHOUSE APARTMENT

Description A mechanical equipment room, containing two boilers, a chiller, a 40-hp supply pump for a cooling tower, and several smaller pumps, adjoins a penthouse apartment. The common wall is 8-in cement block, finished on one side with gypsum board. In addition to the equipment mentioned, several ventilation fans (for kitchens and bathrooms), are mounted on curbs installed on the roof. The apartment tenant had moved out because of high noise levels.

Noise measurements Noise levels were measured in the apartment with all equipment operating and with individual sources shut off (Table 10.4). From these measurements, the contribution from each source could be identified.

Analysis Comparison of band levels shows that the cooling-tower pump is a major noise source, followed by the rooftop ventilation fans. Contributions from

Table 10.4 Noise levels with various sources operating, in decibels

	Octave-band center frequency, Hz							
	31.5	63	125	250	500	1000	2000	4000
All HVAC sources operating	75	63	62	57	47	38	30	29
Cooling -tower pump off	69	57	56	53	43	34	26	23
Cooling-tower pump and ventilation fans off	63	53	54	51	43	34	26	23
All HVAC sources off	61	50	52	50	43	34	26	23

the apartment air-conditioning unit were relatively minor. Levels with all sources off resulted from daytime traffic; nighttime levels would be significantly less.

The common-wall transmission loss was adequate, except for an opening where it joined the building exterior wall.

Inspection of the cooling-tower pump showed that its vibration isolators were effectively short-circuited by a pipe support (Fig. 10.5). The rooftop fans were rigidly attached to the roof and to the supply and return ductwork.

Design The following steps were recommended, in priority order:

1. Paint the common cement-block wall with two coats of bridging paint; seal all openings with resilient caulk.
2. Remove the rigid discharge-pipe supports; support the pipe with resilient pipe hangers; install a flexible rubber coupling in the discharge pipe near the pump to reduce the load carried by the vibration isolators.
3. Measure the noise reduction obtained in steps 1 and 2. If inadequate, proceed to step 4.
4. Mount the rooftop ventilation fans on spring isolators; install flexible vinyl duct connectors between each fan and the supply and return ductwork.

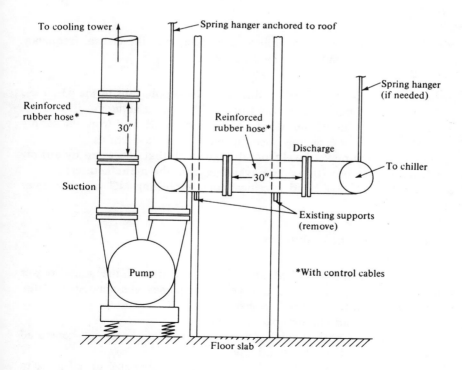

Figure 10.5 Schematic of pump, showing existing and recommended pipe supports.

Evaluation The owner and the architect could not agree on how the costs for the noise control program should be shared. None of the steps were implemented, and the apartment remained vacant.

10.6 GUIDELINES FOR CONTROL OF AIRBORNE DUCT NOISE IN AN HVAC SYSTEM

Description A mechanical equipment room is located above three retail floors in a department store that is being designed by an architect. Supply fans (two 40-hp tubeaxial, in parallel) and return-air fans (two 20-hp tubeaxial, in parallel) provide heated and/or cooled air through an unlined double-duct system. The ducts supply a large number of mixing boxes located in the ceiling plenum above each floor. Cooled or heated air is delivered by each mixing box to several supply diffusers through rectangular ductwork lined with 1-in-thick duct liner. The architect has requested a set of guidelines that will ensure ambient-noise levels in sales and office areas of NC 40 or less. An additional requirement is that only the ductwork between the mixing boxes and the diffusers can be modified.

Analysis The following steps were followed to determine the critical frequency band, for which design guidelines could be formulated.

1. Estimate the sound-power level produced by the supply fans in the 63-, 125-, and 250-Hz octave bands (available from the fan manufacturer).
2. Estimate the attenuation from heating and cooling coils, and from the supply ductwork to the nearest mixing boxes, in the same octave bands.
3. Combine the sound-power level from the fans with that generated by airflow within each mixing box (these data available from the manufacturer).
4. Determine which octave band is critical for establishing NC values in sales and office areas.

Results obtained from the analysis were:

1. The critical band was centered at 125 Hz, because of the sound-power spectrum of the fans, the attenuation versus frequency characteristics of the lined ductwork and bends, and the shape of the NC curves
2. For the flow rates and mixing boxes specified:
   - Fan noise at the nearest mixing boxes predominates over self-generated noise in the 125-Hz octave band.
   - Fan noise at the nearest mixing box is approximately equal to self-noise in the 250-Hz octave band.

Design Guidelines were established from the following data (for the 125-Hz octave band)

• Fan sound-power level	104 dB
• Attenuation of:	
Heating/cooling coil	8 dB
90° bend,	
Unlined	0 dB
Lined	2–3 dB
Duct,	
Unlined	0.10 dB/ft
Lined	0.25 dB/ft
Two-way split in ductwork	3 dB per branch
Split at mixing box	4 dB
Diffuser end loss (from	
reflection of sound waves)	4 dB
Room effect (difference between	
L_w at diffuser and L_p at	
listener's ear)	10 dB

Based on these data, the design guidelines were

1. All ductwork between mixing boxes and diffusers is to be lined with 1-in-thick duct liner. (In addition, all return-air ductwork is to be lined with 1-in duct liner, to reduce noise from return fans to an acceptable value.)
2. Minimum requirements from mixing box to nearest diffuser:
   (a) 8 ft of lined duct, one branch, and one 90° bend, or
   (b) 16 ft of lined duct and one branch, or
   (c) 12 ft of lined duct and two 90° bends, or
   (d) 20 ft of lined duct and one 90° bend, or
   (e) 25 ft of lined duct, or
   (f) Three-way branch and 90° bend, or three-way branch and 8 ft of lined duct.
   (g) For mixing boxes 5 in and smaller, the minimum requirement is 6 ft of lined duct and one 90° bend, or 16 ft of lined duct.
3. Mixing boxes 8 in and larger should not be located above offices or similar areas.
4. Minimum requirements for common supply ducts between adjoining offices or other areas where speech privacy is desired:
   (a) 20 ft of lined duct, or
   (b) 15 ft of lined duct and one 90° bend, or
   (c) 12 ft of lined duct separating two 90° bends.

Evaluation The architect found the guidelines useful; a number of changes were made in the supply ductwork as a result. Ambient-noise levels in the retail and office areas were highly acceptable to the building owner.

10.7 REDUCTION OF MATERIAL-HANDLING IMPACT NOISE [4]

Description

When ore rock, forgings, metal parts, castings, etc., are handled in metal chutes, shaker tables, tumbling machines, and metal bins; substantial noise levels can be generated by impacting of parts and by abrasive sliding action which occurs during these processes. Consider, for example, the inspection area in a forging plant where there are six parts-inspection benches having large metal supply hoppers situated above and in front of each inspection table, as shown in Figure 10.6. Small forgings are loaded into the metal hoppers by means of a fork lift truck prior to the inspection process. A worker must stand in front of the hopper being loaded and hold a retaining board over the bin slot to prevent forgings from spilling out onto the inspection table.

Noise Measurements

Noise levels measured at the workers' ear position during the loading operation show peak levels of 120–123 dBA_f, which may be sustained for several seconds, with a total loading time of 8–10 seconds. The equivalent continuous level for the loading period is approximately 115 dBA. Although the frequency with which the hoppers are loaded during the day is such that the workers' total noise exposure is within acceptable limits specified in the OSHA Noise Regulations, the maximum levels exceed the allowed 115 dBA limit level. In addition, workers complain about excessive noise occurring during the loading operation.

Analysis

Three basic noise source elements exist in any impacting process. The first element is a *falling or moving mass*. Noise is generated by impacting and abrasive sliding action of this mass interacting with other objects. In the particular case being considered, the mass impacts panels of the hopper during initial filling, and then impacts other forgings as the hopper becomes filled. The second element is a *structural path* whereby kinetic energy from the source is transmitted to other surface elements which radiate sound. The path generally begins with the contact area between the falling mass and the impacted surface, and may extend to other structural elements not in direct contact with the falling mass. The *radiating surfaces* comprise the third basic element, and are usually composed of relatively large structural panels connected to the system, and surfaces of the impacting mass itself.

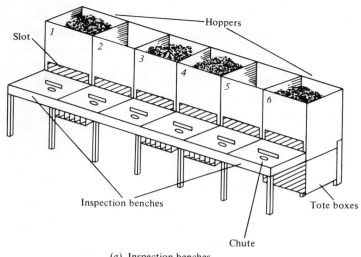

(a) Inspection benches.

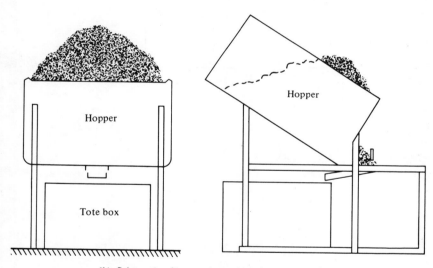

(b) Schematic of hopper into which forgings are dumped.

Figure 10.6 Inspection stations for small forging operations.

With a single impact there is an initial peak sound level generated due to forced acceleration of the struck surface by the impacting force. This sound will be followed by ringing associated with resonance vibrations of the surface, which decays slowly. Since the initial impacting force is impulsive it will usually excite all resonance frequencies of the struck panel. If the impact is repeated many times per second, as occurs when loading forgings into a hopper, then the panel vibrations (and noise) will be sustained continuously over the entire loading interval.

Noise control methods for impact noise must be directed toward: (1) reducing the energy of the moving mass, (2) isolating the structural path, and/or (3) damping the motion of the radiating surfaces. Reduction of the kinetic energy of the impacting mass can often be achieved by reducing the distance through which the object must fall, by breaking the fall with one or more intermediate obstructions, or by providing a continuous chute for the part to slide along (see Fig. 10.7).

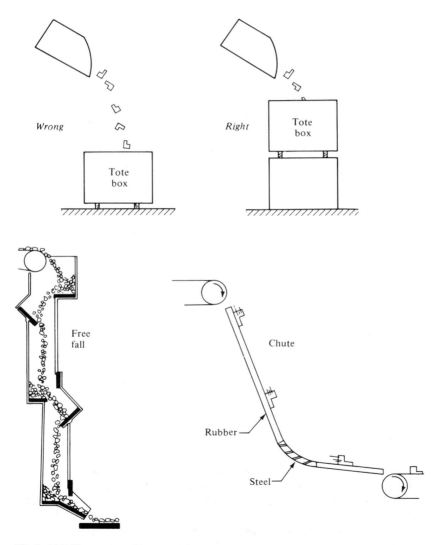

Figure 10.7 Treatments of impact noise sources.

If it is impractical to reduce the energy of the source, then control of noise must be achieved solely by treatment of the path and the radiating surfaces. In such cases rubber can be very effectively used as: (1) *an isolator* to reduce the rate of energy transfer at impact and (2) a *vicoelastic damper* to reduce the resonance vibration occurring after impact (see Fig. 10.8). Very little special equipment or training is needed for application of rubber materials in the field. The major suppliers of the material should have brochures giving detailed instructions for application of their products. Although rubber linings can provide relief from many abrasion and noise problems, they are not a cureall for every problem. From a cost standpoint, it is important that the correct rubber linings for a specific application be selected. When selecting a rubber lining the engineer must have in mind whether it is to be used to treat the source, the structural path, or the radiating surfaces as described in the preceding paragraphs. The engineer should seek the manufacturer's recommendation for the type, gauge, and hardness of rubber lining to be used for each particular application. A rubber must then be selected which has properties suited for the particular treatment and which will ensure continuation of production with a minimum of wear and maintenance on the materials-handling equipment.

Regardless of whether a material is being selected primarily for abatement of noise or wear resistance, performance as a protector against abrasion and wear must be considered first. The wear rate of rubber lining is a function of the angle of impact of parts striking the lining. Figure 10.9 shows, for incline angles of 0 to 5 degrees and angles of 70 to 90 degrees, that an abrasive-resistant rubber lining will actually outwear steel [5]. For maximum wear the angle of impact should be 90 degrees.

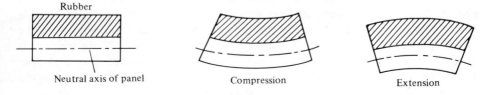

(*a*) Rubber layer as an isolation and/or extensional damper.

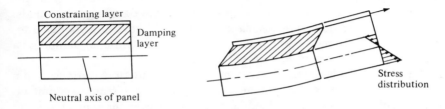

(*b*) Rubber layer as a constrained layer damper.

Figure 10.8 Use of rubber to reduce sound radiation of panels.

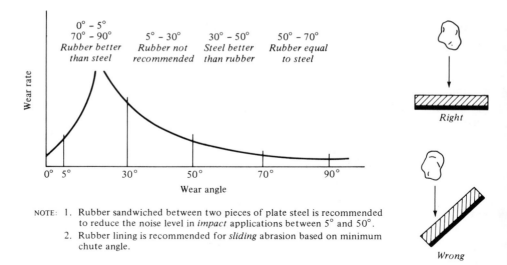

NOTE: 1. Rubber sandwiched between two pieces of plate steel is recommended to reduce the noise level in *impact* applications between 5° and 50°.
2. Rubber lining is recommended for *sliding* abrasion based on minimum chute angle.

Figure 10.9 Wear rate of rubber versus steel.

Application of rubber linings as an isolator to reduce impact force is most effective if the angle of impact is 90 degrees and the rubber lining is relatively thick and has a low modulus. In cases where abrasive wear is critical and the angle of impact cannot be controlled, it may be possible to cement a small metal plate to the surface of the rubber lining at the point of impact. The metal will provide the wear resistance, and yet sink into the rubber at impact to provide the desired isolation. If the parts strike over a large area at impact, then the rubber lining can be applied to the back of the metal panel being treated. It must be kept in mind, however, that now the rubber sheet is acting as a damper rather than as an isolator. Accordingly, the properties of the rubber lining would be chosen to give maximum damping without regard to wear characteristics.

A rule of thumb to use when selecting rubber linings for extensional damping purposes only is that the lining should be as thick as the metal panel being treated. For surfaces of complex shape there are rubber compounds available which can be troweled or brushed on. These are damping compounds best suited for reducing ringing or resonance, and should have a depth equal to the thickness of the material to which they are applied. Extensional damping is best suited for large surfaces of thin cross section.

Constrained layer damping is recommended for radiating surfaces with relatively thick cross sections, or for any case where a significant amount of damping is required. If the constrained layer is placed over the impact area, it can also provide a wear-resistant metal surface upon which falling parts will land.

Design

An engineering study was performed to evaluate several different applications of rubber to reduce noise levels produced by the hopper loading operation. The four interior hoppers (2 through 5, in Fig. 10.6) were treated with sheet rubber. The treatments were applied in three steps, as indicated in Table 10.5, so that various combinations of treatment could be evaluated. The individual hopper panels are shown and identified in Fig. 10.10.

10.5 Test Outline for An Engineering Study of Hopper Impact Noise

Hopper number	Test panel	Treatment			
		I	II	I + II	III
2	1	X AI (E)	—	X AI (E)	Cushion*
	2	—	X AI (I)	X AI (I)	—
	3	—	X AI (I)	X AI (I)	—
	4	X AI (I)	—	X AI (I)	—
	5	0.25"N	—	N	—
3	1	CL DB (I)	—	CL DB (I)	Cushion*
	2	—	0.125"N (I)	0.125"N (I)	—
	3	—	0.125"N (I)	0.125"N (I)	—
	4	0.25"N (I)	—	0.25"N (I)	—
	5	0.25"N (I)	—	0.25"N (I)	—
4	1	CL AI (I)	—	CL AI (I)	Cushion*
	2	—	CL AI (I)	CL AI (I)	—
	3	—	CL AI (I)	CL AI (I)	—
	4	—	0.125"N (I)	0.125N (I)	—
	5	—	—	—	—
5	1	X DB (E)	—	X DB (E)	Cushion*
	2	—	X DB (I)	X DB (I)	—
	3	—	X DB (I)	X DB (I)	—
	4	X DB (I)	—	X DB (I)	—
	5	—	—	—	—
6	1	—	—	—	Cushion*

LEGEND (I) – Inside.
(E) – Exterior.
X – Extensional damping (0.125" rubber).
CL – Constrained layer damping (0.06" rubber with 0.125" steel septum).
DB – Deadbeat.
N – Novitane.
AI – Experimental damping material.
* – 1" foam rubber cushion sandwiched between 0.125" Novitane on one side and 0.125" AI plus 0.125" steel on other side. Portable panel which could be placed in bottom of any hopper.

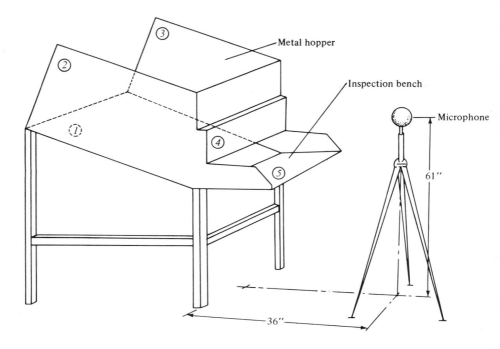

Figure 10.10 Schematic identifying test panels and microphone positions.

Four types of rubber sheets were used in these treatments: (1) Novitane, an 85 durometer polyurethane sheet with high abrasion resistance, moderate isolation properties, and moderately high damping effectiveness; (2) Deadbeat, a 90 durometer cured rubber with high modulus and high damping effectiveness; (3) an experimental damping material (AI) with properties similar to that of Deadbeat; and (4) a 1-in layer of very soft foam rubber sheet. The foam rubber was used in a composite sandwich structure designed as an isolator to reduce impact forces from reaching the hopper panels. The other treatments used were extensional damping with some isolation, and constrained layer damping.

A standard impact test was developed for testing the effect of treating hopper panels. The test used a mass-pendulum device to provide equal impacts to each panel of the empty hoppers. Sound levels were recorded at the operator's position of the hopper during the impact tests. Pendulum-impact tests were made on each hopper for each noise control treatment. The results of these tests were used to evaluate the effectiveness of each type of treatment in reducing the noise caused by impacts on individual hopper panels. Finally, sound levels were measured during filling operations to determine the overall effect of the hopper treatment in reducing noise generated when loading forgings into the treated hoppers. Maximum A-weighted sound levels, $L_p$max, were recorded during panel impact tests. The A-weighted sound level was recorded continuously during the hopper filling operation, and the equivalent continuous sound level, L_{eq}, was determined by numerically integrating the sound level history over the time T required to load the hopper, using Eq. (7.3).

Evaluation

The results shown in Table 10.6 give noise reduction at the operator's position when impacting individual hopper panels for various types of panel treatments. In reviewing these results it must be kept in mind that all hopper panels are interconnected. Hence, an impact force on one panel will cause all other panels to radiate, even though most of the original impact energy is going into the panel being struck.

The effect of each type of treatment is best seen by looking at noise reductions associated with impacting panel number 1, since it is the largest and should be the most efficient sound radiator. Noise reductions when impacting that panel (on hoppers 2 and 4) are about 6 dBA greater for constrained layer damping than for extensional damping treatments. Therefore, the intensity of the peak acoustical energy radiated by the constrained layer panel is only about one-fourth of that radiated by the panel with extensional damping.

In all cases for treatment I there is a reduction in noise levels from panels 2 and 3 of about 3 dBA or greater, even though these panels were not treated. This was due to treatment of panel 1 and shows that damping of resonating panels can be effective without covering the entire radiating surface.

Comparing the results of the impact tests on panels 2 and 3 with those of panel 1 (for hoppers 2 and 5) shows the effect of placing extensional damping on the impact side of the test panel. The $\frac{1}{8}$-in rubber sheets on the side panels serve as isolators as well as dampers, while that on the bottom panel acts only as a damper. There is also increased noise reduction from the side panels.

The $\frac{1}{4}$-in Novitane sheet applied to panel 5 of hoppers 2 and 3 yields even greater noise reductions of 14–15 dBA. The increased thickness and lower modulus improve the effectiveness of the sheet as an isolator.

In all the above impact tests, vibrating panels of the hoppers were the major noise sources. However, in testing for the overall effect of treatment during filling of the hoppers, ringing of forgings falling into the hoppers became one of the major noise sources. Consequently, the simple impact test alone could not be used to predict the effect of treatment.

Table 10.6 shows noise levels measured during filling of the treated hoppers.* If we look at the maximum A-weighted sound levels, L_p, recorded during the filling operation on a given day, we see that there is no substantial

---

* In reviewing these results, it should also be kept in mind that these data were obtained under normal shop operating conditions. Tests were taken on four different days. Three different sized forgings were used in the tests; tote boxes used for dumping forgings were not always filled to the same level, and different drivers operated the fork-lift used to dump the forgings.

Table 10.6 Noise Data from Engineering Study of Hopper Impact Noise

Hopper number	Test panel	Panel noise reduction, ΔdBA maximum			A-weighted noise levels during filling operation							
					None		I		I + II		I + II + III	
		I	I + II	I + III	L_p	L_{eq}	L_p	L_{eq}	L_p	L_{eq}	L_p	L_{eq}
2	1	7–9	7–9	—	—	—						
	2	3–5	9–11	—								
	3	4–6	9–11	—			122	114	121.5	113	—	—
	4	6–7	9–10	—								
	5	14–15	14	—								
3	1	16	14	—								
	2	5	10	—								
	3	5–6	9–10	—	122	114.3	120	112	120	112.7	119.5	111.6
	4	3	2	—								
	5	13–15	13	—								
4	1	15–17	15	—								
	2	2–4	10–12	—								
	3	4	14	—	122	114	122.5	114.5	122	112.7	120	112.8
	4	3–4	7–8	—								
	5	0	0	—								
5	1	4–6	6–8	17								
	2	2–3	7–8	—								
	3	3–5	9–11	—	—	—	120	114.5	125	116.8	120	113.4
	4	5–6	5–6	—								
	5	2	1	—								
1					120	116.8	—	—	—	—	—	—
6					126	119	—	—	—	—	—	—

change in these levels with different treatments. However, there was a reduction in the equivalent level at the operator position, which is related to hearing-damage risk caused by long-term noise exposure. A 3–5 dBA reduction in equivalent levels occurred for the fully treated hoppers. Reductions in the equivalent sound level were also obtained by placing the "cushion" in three different hoppers. A reduction of 4.8 dBA was measured when this panel was placed in the untreated hopper, number 1. Also, additional reductions were measured of 1.1 dBA with hopper 3 and 3.4 dBA with hopper 5, above that obtained with the combined treatment I and II. There was practically no change in the equivalent level observed with hopper number 4. However, in this test 25 to 30 percent more material was dumped into the cushioned hopper. Hence, the additional acoustical energy associated with the increased load size was absorbed by the "cushion" panel placed in the bottom of the hopper.

The overall test results show less noise reduction for hopper loading than expected from single panel impact tests. This is because impact and ringing noise of the parts became a major source as the hoppers filled up, and was affected very little by structural damping and isolation applied to hopper panels. The 3 to 5 dBA reduction in equivalent levels indicates that hopper radiation and part ringing were the two major noise sources and that they were roughly equivalent in level.

Thus to obtain significant additional reduction, it would be necessary to treat the airborne path of sound coming from the ringing parts. Hence, noise reductions of 8 to 10 dBA or greater for these hoppers would require treatments using both structural damping and isolation and airborne path barriers.

Some general conclusions drawn from the results of study on impact noise are listed below:

1. Constrained layer damping is much more effective than extensional damping in reducing noise levels caused by resonance vibration of panels.
2. Substantial noise reduction of resonating panels can be achieved by partial treatment of the panels.
3. Additional noise reduction can be achieved when using extensional damping if the rubber sheet is applied on the impacting side of the panel. However, in this case wear resistance of the sheet must be taken into account in the design.
4. The effect of isolation of a rubber sheet is increased with increased thickness of the sheet.
5. The overall effect of rubber sheet used to reduce impact noise cannot, in general, be determined from data obtained from simple panel impact tests alone. A substantial reduction in equivalent noise level generated during an impact operation can be achieved, even though this would not be detected by the usual method of measuring maximum sound pressure levels. A better measure of the overall effectiveness is obtained if both maximum and equivalent noise levels are measured.

10.8 NOISE REDUCTION OF AIR EXHAUST AND JET THRUST DEVICES

Description

A common source of noise found in many industries is that of air jet noise associated with: (1) air exhaust from pneumatic valves, and (2) jets used for parts ejectors, scale and grit blowers, or as cooling devices. Air exhaust noise is usually intermittent and impulsive in nature, but may cause very high noise levels. Air jets used as thrust or cooling devices can be either intermittent or continuous and often produce excessive noise levels. Several practical cases are considered in this study to demonstrate noise control methods for both types of jets. However, prior to looking at particular methods of noise control, we will give a general description of the mechanism of industrial jet noise generation and its control.

Analysis

Noise generated by jets is caused by turbulence due to mixing of gases having widely different velocities. Shearing action occurring in the mixing region results in "quadrupole" type sound radiation, where the intensity of the sound is proportional to the eighth power of the speed of jet flow [6, 7].

The structure of the jet flow can be divided into three regions, as indicated in Fig. 10.11. The jet may reach sonic velocities (speed of sound) in the region of its *orifice* for line pressures commonly used in industrial applications. High-speed laminar flow exists in the *core region*. The magnitude of the core flow velocity is the same as at the orifice. As the high-velocity jet flows into relatively still air, there will exist a *turbulent mixing region* between the still air and the laminar flow of the core.

Fluctuating pressures due to eddies formed in the turbulent mixture region are the main source of noise. The small eddies at the beginning of the mixing region cause mainly high-frequency noise, while the lower frequencies are generated downstream by the larger eddies, as indicated in Fig. 10.11. The bulk of the noise generated by a free jet occurs in the turbulent mixing region along the first 10 diameters of the jet [8].

Since the jet sound intensity is proportional to the eighth power of the jet velocity, *the most effective way to control jet noise is by reducing its velocity*. This technique is incorporated in most commercially available pneumatic silencers (see Fig. 10.12).

Silencing of jets from air or steam exhausts will be considered first. Since the thrust from exhaust jets performs no useful work, the main concerns in controlling the exhaust noise are the effect on back pressure and the time required to discharge the gas. Two basic methods of noise control are used extensively in commercially available silencing devices for exhaust jets, with substantial noise reductions being achieved. Although both of these methods are often incorpo-

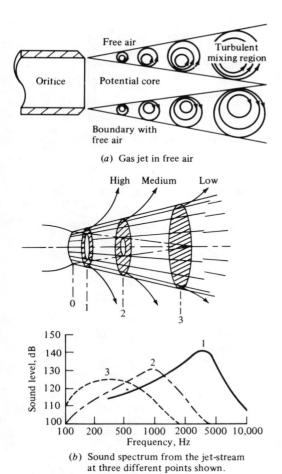

(a) Gas jet in free air

(b) Sound spectrum from the jet-stream
at three different points shown.

Figure 10.11 Schematic of jet flow and
noise generation.

rated in a single unit in silencer design, the two methods are listed separately
below in order to describe the basic concepts associated with each method of
control:

The diffuser silencer encloses a high-velocity jet and distributes the flow over
many small areas at a reduced velocity. A sketch showing the basic configuration of the diffuser is given in Fig. 10.12a. In practice, the diffusion
mechanism is achieved by using a porous product such as sintered metal or
plastic, open slots, wire mesh or screens, compacted metal nodules, etc. The
restricted flow of the diffuser silencer causes a back pressure in the flow
stream and reduces velocities in the characteristic jet core and high-shear
mixing regions. In cases where large back pressure and time of discharge can
be tolerated, very large reductions in noise level—up to 30 dBA—are possible
by increasing the flow resistance of the silencer.

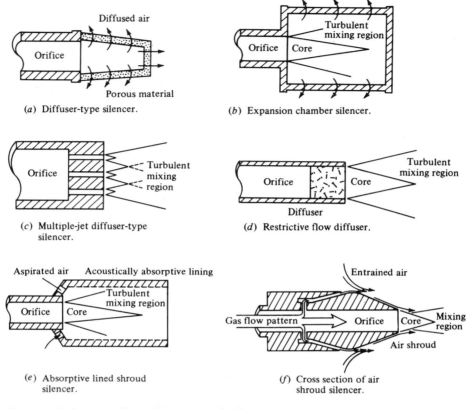

Figure 10.12 Commercially available pneumatic silencers.

Expansion chamber silencers are used where little back pressure can be tolerated. The principle of noise control is that the silencer encloses the jet and lets the high-flow discharge gas expand into a large chamber. The gas is then discharged through many small holes (diffusers) at a greatly reduced velocity. Figure 10.12*b* shows a sketch of an expansion chamber silencer. If the chamber is large enough, the jet may be fully developed with turbulent noise generation. However, most of the acoustical energy is contained within the walls of the chamber, or reflected back into the orifice.

The second system to be considered is that of jets used for parts ejection and scale or grit blowing. These are called *functional jets*, since the jet thrust is used to perform a useful task. In this case any noise control measures employed which reduce the jet flow velocity will also reduce the thrust and, hence, the effectiveness of the functional jet. Four methods of control of functional jets are commonly found in commercial silencers. In any practical application, a combination of two or more of these methods may be used. A brief description of each method follows:

Multiple-jet diffuser silencers replace a single large orifice by several smaller parallel orifices as shown in Fig. 10.12c. The three regions of flow mentioned earlier exist for each small jet considered separately. Since the orifice diameter of the multiple-jets is smaller, the eddies are also smaller. Hence, there is a shift in the frequency content of the noise to higher frequencies which are more easily controlled by other noise control methods. Less noise is generated because of the reduction in size of the core and turbulent mixing region. Moreover, the inner jets flow into air which has a high-velocity component in the direction of the jet velocity, thus reducing the noise generated by shearing action. Finally, there is a reduction in thrust since the smaller total exit area reduces the weight flow rate of the gas.

Restrictive flow diffuser. The restrictive flow diffuser makes use of a screen or mesh placed in the nozzle orifice to reduce the flow velocity of the jet. A sketch of a restrictive flow diffuser-type silencer is shown in Fig. 10.12d. Since noise generated by the jet is proportional to the eighth power of the jet velocity, a large decrease in sound-pressure level is achieved using this method. However, the noise reduction is achieved at the expense of jet thrust, which is proportional to the weight flow rate.

Absorptive lined shroud. A schematic showing the essential elements of an absorptive lined shroud used to quiet jet noise is shown in Fig. 10.12e. The principle of noise control employed with this method is that the lining will absorb the acoustic energy generated in the mixing region through multiple reflections in the shroud. This type of silencer will be most effective in reducing the higher frequency components of the jet noise. The thrust effectiveness of the jet can be improved by placing openings at the base of the shroud. The aspirated air increases the weight flow rate of the nozzle and, hence, its thrust. Although this type of silencer provides noise reduction with limited effect on jet thrust, it has found little application in silencers available on the market—probably because of size limitations.

Air shroud. A shroud of moving air enveloping the jet can reduce the difference in velocity between the jet and the medium into which it flows. Hence, there is a reduction in the intensity of the shearing action in the turbulent mixing region, which results in a reduction in the intensity of sound generated. An example of a means of creating an air shroud silencer is demonstrated in Fig. 10.12f. An added benefit gained from this design is that ambient air is entrained in the air shroud. The increase in weight flow rate due to ambient air entrainment causes an increase in the jet thrust [9].

The commercially available pneumatic silencers described above are designed to reduce noise from the jet. However, in an industrial jet thrust system, other aerodynamic noise sources may be as important as the jet noise itself. A schematic identifying the main sources of noise in a practical jet thrust system is shown in Fig. 10.13. The three sources of noise identified are: (1) in-line noise due to turbulence caused by valves and other flow obstructions, (2) jet noise,

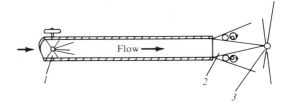

Figure 10.13 Schematic of practical jet thrust system.

and (3) turbulent mixing of the free jet impinging on surfaces [10]. Since all three sources are caused by turbulence, the only effective way to control the noise is to reduce the flow velocity of all three sources.

It is important in the design of jet thrust devices to recognize that the sound generated by an in-line noise source propagates down the line with very little attenuation. Consequently, the noise generated by the turbulence of a valve, inserted in the line to reduce the noise generated at positions 1 and 2 in a jet system, can offset any noise reductions made downstream. Guidelines for controlling noise from continuous jet thrust systems are given in Ref. [11].

CASE STUDY A: AIR-ACTIVATED CLUTCH ON AJAX FORGING PRESS [11]

Noise levels from the air exhaust ports of a 6000-ton Ajax Press clutch mechanism were measured at a position approximately 8 ft from the exhaust side of the press and at the press operator's position. There were two peaks in sound pressure level noted with each cycle of the press: one peak when the pneumatic clutch engaged, followed by another, higher peak when the clutch disengaged. The following A-weighted levels, fast meter response, were

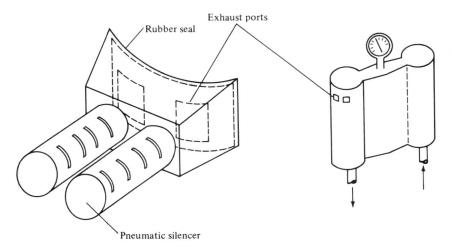

Figure 10.14 Clutch exhaust manifold (enlarged) and silencers.

Table 10.7 Clutch noise

Operating condition	Maximum A-weighted levels	
	Engage	Disengage
Without silencer	116	122
	113	122
	114	122
With silencer	99	107
	100	107
	100	107

recorded:

$$\text{Operator's position} \quad 103-107 \text{ dBA}_f$$
$$\text{8 ft from exhaust} \quad 113-122 \text{ dBA}_f$$

Although the noise levels measured were impulsive in nature and did not violate the upper limit specified by OSHA for impulsive noise, they were considered annoying.

A sketch of the clutch exhaust system is shown in Fig. 10.14. There were dual exhaust ports on each exhaust cylinder which were not designed to accept standard threaded pneumatic silencers. Therefore, a manifold was designed and fabricated for each exhaust chamber to fit over the two exhaust ports. Two holes were cut in the manifold and threaded to accept standard screw-in–type pneumatic silencers. The manifolds (see Fig. 10.14) were attached to the two exhaust chambers with bolts, and had rubber seals to prevent leaks between the manifold and the exhaust chamber. Two commercial pneumatic silencers ($1\frac{1}{2}$ NPT) were then installed in each manifold.

A test was run to evaluate the effectiveness of the silencers. The press was operated without actually forging parts. Sound pressure levels were measured at a fixed position on the exhaust side of the press, with and without the silencers attached. The maximum A-weighted levels (fast meter response) were recorded at engagement and disengagement of the clutch. The results of these tests are given in Table 10.7. An average insertion loss of 15 dBA$_f$ was determined for the control treatment applied. Measurements taken at the operator's position showed that exhaust noise from the clutch was no longer the dominant source of noise during press operation.

CASE STUDY B: AIR VALVE EXHAUST NOISE ON BALANCING MACHINES

Twenty air valve exhausts were used on the balancing machine of a large manufacturer of forged crankshafts. The exhausts were associated with pneumatic clamping devices used for holding crankshafts during an automated balancing operation. Impulsive noise levels of 95 dBA, due to air exhausts, were measured at the operator's position. The background level during normal shop operation was about 88 dBA. A noise survey was made using personal noise dosimeters to determine worker noise exposure. Results of the dosimeter survey indicated that no worker was exposed to more than 70 percent of the noise level allowed by OSHA regulations. Nevertheless the manufacturer decided to apply easily installed, inexpensive pneumatic silencers to improve the noise environment.

The air lines on the balancing machines were supplied with in-line oilers. Therefore, it was necessary to select silencers which would not cause too much back pressure and would not clog from the oil. A restrictive diffuser silencer, slot-type with wire mesh insert, was selected. Ten commercially available $\frac{1}{4}$ in NPT and ten $\frac{3}{8}$ in NPT silencers were installed.

A noise survey made with a hand-held sound level meter after the silencers were installed indicated that the impulsive peaks of air exhaust noise had been reduced below background levels.

CASE STUDY C: AUTOMATED STEAM SCALE BLOWER STUDY

An automated scale blower system on a 6000-ton forging press, consisting of a row of 15 steam jets on each side of the lower die of the press, was used to blow scale from the dies during the forging process. The steam jets were activated for a period of approximately 8 s per cycle, maintaining peak sound levels of 115–119 dBA at a typical worker position for about 6 s. The sound pressure level history recorded for several cycles of operation is shown in Fig. 10.15. There were approximately 80 cycles per hour for the type of forging being manufactured, with actual forging production occurring approximately 7 hours per workshift. Not only did the maximum levels of sound exceed OSHA standards, but the daily noise dose computed from the sound level history shown, using Eqs. (7.10) and (7.11), predicted a daily noise dose equal to 566 percent of the allowed exposure!

The most effective way to abate aerodynamic noise sources of the scale blowing system would be to reduce the flow velocity. However, a reduction in flow velocity would also reduce the scale blower thrust which is related to flow and nozzle diameter according to the equation [10]

$$T = K\rho D^2 U^2 \tag{10.12}$$

where
K = constant
ρ = mass density of the medium
D = jet nozzle diameter
U = jet exit velocity

Thus, the jet thrust can be maintained at a reduced flow rate providing the jet nozzle diameter is increased in proportion to the decrease in jet velocity.

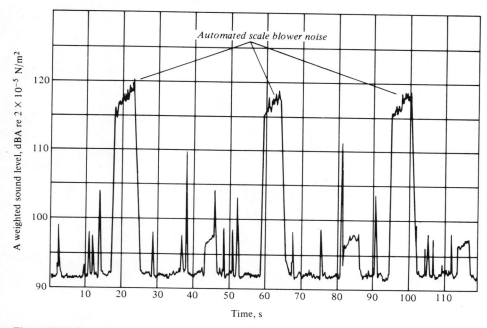

Figure 10.15 Sound pressure time-history of scale blower noise recorded for several scale blowing cycles.

A schematic of the scale blower system is shown in Fig. 10.16. The original banks of steam jet nozzles were made from $\frac{1}{4}$-in pipe, welded to 1-in pipe manifolds as shown in Fig. 10.16a. Each manifold was connected by a 1-in hose and pipe section to a 2-in steam supply line which, in turn, was connected to a larger 3-in pipe section. The automated scale blowing system is controlled by an air-activated ball-valve having a $2\frac{1}{2}$-in port. Steam flow in the system was established by the pressure in the main steam line and the size of the exit area of the jet nozzles, with some pipe losses in the 1-in manifold section. A modified system shown in Fig. 10.16b, was installed, which used $\frac{1}{2}$-in pipes for the jet nozzles, welded to 2-in manifolds to reduce pipe losses. A 3-in gate valve was also installed to control the steam flow in the modified system. This valve could be adjusted to give the same thrust at a reduced jet velocity.

Tests were made to evaluate the effectiveness of the modified scale blowing system. Jet thrust and noise levels were first measured under standard operating conditions with the original system. The modified scale blowing section was then installed in the system, and the rate of steam flow reduced by means of the 3-in ball-valve until the modified system produced the same thrust as the original system. The noise level generated by the modified system was then measured and compared with earlier levels determined for the original scale blower. The results of these tests are given in Fig. 10.17, showing a 10-dBA reduction in the

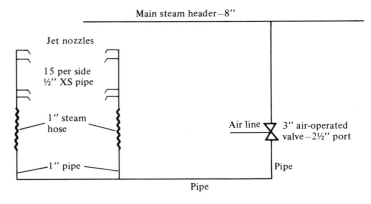

(*a*) Original steam scale blower system.

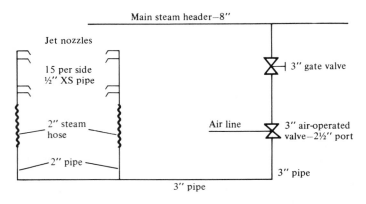

(*b*) Modified steam scale blower system.

Figure 10.16 Automated steam scale blower system.

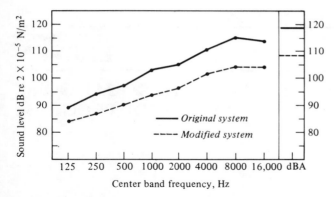

Figure 10.17 Scale blower noise spectrum and A-level.

peak levels of scale blower noise. The worker daily noise dose computed for the modified system was 141 percent of the allowed dose, which represents a 400 percent reduction in noise exposure.

REFERENCES

1. Faulkner, L. L., *Handbook of Industrial Noise Control*, Industrial Press, New York, 1976.
2. National Institute for Occupational Safety and Health, *Industrial Noise Control Manual*, Cincinnati, June 1975.
3. Peterson, A., and E. Gross, *Handbook of Noise Measurement*, 7th ed., General Radio Company, Concord, Mass., 1974.
4. Lord, H. W., H. Canada, S. J. Caprette, and H. Jacobs, "Use of Sheet Rubber in Treatment of Material Handling Impact Noise," Proceedings of the National Noise and Vibration Control Conferences, NOISEXPO 76, Chicago (1976).
5. Kesig, W. E., "Rubber Linings—Abate Abrasion and Noise," *Pit and Quary*, June 1971.
6. Lighthill, M. J., "On Sound Generated Aerodynamically II: General Theory," Proc. R. Soc. A211, 1952.
7. Lighthill, M. J., "On Sound Generated Aerodynamically II: Turbulence as a Source of Sound," Proc. R. Soc. A222, 1954.
8. Bowen, A. J., J. H. Dunmore, and D. C. Stevens, "An Investigation of the Noise Produced Near a Half-Inch Diameter Stream Jet," J. Sound Vib., vol. 5, no. 1, 1967.
9. Frochaux, A., "High Thrust, Low Noise Level Nozzle," Proceedings of NOISEXPO, 1975.
10. Lord, H. W., "Design Parameters for Quiet Jet Thrust Devices," Proceedings of the National Noise and Vibration Control Conference, NOISEXPO 78, Chicago (1978).
11. *Engineering Guidelines to Forging Noise Control*, volumes I and II, Forging Industry Educational and Research Foundation, 55 Public Square, Cleveland (1977).

ESTABLISHING AN INDUSTRIAL NOISE CONTROL PROGRAM

11.1 INTRODUCTION

Establishing an industrial noise control program will draw on the knowledge and experience of the noise control engineer in a very broad sense. In this chapter a step-by-step procedure for establishing an effective noise control program is developed, with the assumption that protection of employee hearing is the purpose of the program and that standards set down by the OSHA noise regulations are used to determine its effectiveness. It is possible in some industries that employee hearing impairment would not be of primary concern, in which case the program would be based on other appropriate criteria and standards, such as those relating to speech interference or annoyance. Nevertheless, the essential ingredients outlined in the procedures below should ultimately be incorporated in most industrial noise abatement programs.

The seven steps suggested for setting up an effective noise control program are listed below, then expanded in the body of the text:

1. Identify unacceptable noise areas and work environments.
2. Identify major producers of noise and determine their contribution to worker noise exposure.

The material presented in this chapter is drawn from *Engineering Guidelines to Forging Noise Control*, vol. 2, Cleveland, Ohio, 1977. Used by permission of the Forging Industry Educational and Research Foundation.

3. Determine noise control methods available for treating the noise sources, and assess the economic feasibility of implementing such controls.
4. Estimate expected reduction in worker noise exposure if available methods of control were implemented, and determine whether the reductions would bring any workplace into compliance.
5. Establish a review procedure for periodic examination of the progress being made and for updating of the written noise abatement plan.
6. Enforce use of personal hearing protection in all potentially hazardous noise areas.
7. Establish an audiometric testing program to perform base-line and yearly examinations of all personnel exposed to excessive noise environments, with proper record keeping, instrument maintenance, and analysis of results.

At least one person within the plant, who will be responsible for implementing or directing the noise control program, should have knowledge of or obtain special training in the fundamentals of sound, acoustical measurements, and noise control. In the absence of a very basic understanding of the subject by the person directing the program, much time and money can be needlessly spent, even though an experienced noise control engineer has been called in to help set up the program. This basic understanding can be obtained through short courses on noise control which are designed for this purpose, or through self-study.

Finally, it is essential when embarking on a noise control program that plant management be committed to the program. A person should be assigned responsibility for setting up the plan, and a budgetary allotment should be designated for initiating the program.

11.2 IDENTIFYING UNACCEPTABLE NOISE AREAS AND WORK ENVIRONMENTS—INITIAL NOISE SURVEY

The first step in setting up a noise control program is to establish the nature and extent of the noise problem. In this text we assume the problem to be the risk of employee hearing impairment as a result of prolonged exposure to excessive levels of sound. The extent of the noise problem will be determined by means of an initial noise survey covering the entire plant in order to identify potentially hazardous noise areas. "Hazardous areas" will be defined as noise environments having levels in excess of limiting levels deemed acceptable by OSHA noise regulation standards for an 8-h daily exposure, which were discussed in Sec. 7.3. If community annoyance is the main issue, the extent of the noise problem will be determined by neighborhood noise surveys evaluated in accordance with local or state ordinances dealing with community noise.

To aid in an initial plant survey, a plant layout should be obtained which shows the floor plan and location of major pieces of equipment in the plant. It is often helpful to precede the plant noise survey by a walk-through inspection to determine the location of workers relative to obviously noisy sources of sound and to identify areas of potential noise problems. The inspection should be followed by a plantwide survey made with a portable sound-level meter conforming (as a minimum) to the requirements of a Type 2 general-purpose meter. The sound-level meter should be calibrated at the beginning and end of the survey, and periodically in between if the survey lasts several hours. An acoustical calibrator accurate within ±1 dB should be used. Noise-level measurements should be taken in each of the various work areas at positions which approximate the head positions of employees during normal plant operation. All measured values obtained during the initial survey should be recorded on the plant layout at positions representing their locations in the plant. A-weighted slow-response measurements should be obtained in all areas where continuous noise is predominant. If the difference between minimum and maximum noise levels at any position is 5 dBA or less, the average between these extremes should be recorded. If the difference is 6 dBA or greater, the range of levels at that position should be recorded. A Type 1 sound-level meter capable of measuring true-peak level should be used to measure impact noise. However, in the absence of a Type 1 meter, the Type 2 meter can be used to measure impulsive or impact noise by setting the meter on the 130-dB range, C weighting scale, and fast meter response.* The range of maximum levels should be recorded.

The results of the plant survey should be evaluated in terms of the OSHA criteria outlined below. Work areas in the plant having noise levels which exceed these criteria will be designated *hazardous noise areas*:

1. Continuous noise with levels above 90 dBA
2. Short intermittent levels above 115 dBA
3. Impact noise with peak levels in excess of 140 dBp*

These hazardous areas should be clearly marked on the plant layout and designated for further investigation.

11.3 IDENTIFYING MAJOR SOURCES OF WORKER NOISE EXPOSURE—COMPLIANCE NOISE SURVEY

A follow-up compliance survey should be made in each of the plant areas initially designated as hazardous. The objectives of the second survey are (1) *worker exposure*—to determine which work stations have noise levels which result in excessive worker noise exposure as specified by OSHA regulations, and

---

* Special sound-level meters capable of measuring true-peak level, or oscilloscopes, should be used for evaluating impact noise against the OSHA 140-dB peak standard. However, for impulses in the 5- to 30-ms range, the C-weighted fast response of an ordinary sound-level meter can be used to estimate whether the 140-dB peak level may have been exceeded. Readings of 125 dBC_f or greater, with the meter set on its 130-dB range and fast response, indicate that true-peak levels of 140 dB may have been exceeded and that more precise measurements are needed in order to evaluate the noise environment.

(2) *diagnostic measurements*—to identify sources of noise amenable to noise control treatment. The first objective can be achieved by determining the noise exposure of all employees engaged in activity in hazardous noise areas; the second requires diagnostic measurements to locate specific noise sources and to determine the amount of reduction needed. Methods for determining worker exposure and taking diagnostic measurements are discussed later.

A detailed noise survey should be made of each hazardous noise area. A Type 1 sound-level meter with true-peak capability and an octave-band filter set is recommended for the task, although a skillfully used Type 2 meter will suffice. It is recommended that all information from these surveys be recorded on standard data forms to ensure that all pertinent data are recorded and that permanent, uniform, and meaningful records are kept. If many surveys are to be made, the time saved by drawing up a single standard form can be considerable. A standard form should be developed, then updated and improved as experience dictates. The following list of important items should be included on this form:

1. Identification of all instruments and measuring equipment
2. Description of measurement area and location
3. Detailed description of source being measured, including size, speed, power, location, kind of operation, etc.
4. Description of secondary or nearby sources
5. Location of workers during measurements
6. Measurement positions, including microphone orientation relative to the source.
7. Barometric pressure, temperature, wind velocity, and humidity, if appropriate
8. Calibration times and levels
9. Date and time of measurements
10. Meter weighting and response mode (fast or slow), and measured levels
11. Any observations made during the survey
12. Recommendations (should be summarized on the data sheet, even if formulated later)

A form incorporating many of these items is shown in Fig. 11.1. All impressions and ideas should be written down immediately so that they can be evaluated later, in the quiet of your office or work area. The basic aim of this documentation should be to record as clear an understanding of the noise sources as possible for detailed analysis later.

Worker Exposure

The proposed OSHA noise regulations (*Federal Register*, October 24, 1974) are recommended for hearing-damage-risk criteria to be used for evaluating worker noise exposure. Any employee exposed to an 8-h time-weighted average of 85 dBA or above should be identified and his or her exposure measured and recorded.

FACILITY NOISE SURVEY   Sheet _____ of _____

CLIENT_____ SLM_____ SN _____

PROJECT _____ CALIBRATOR_____ SN _____

OBSERVERS_____ MICROPHONE_____SN _____

DATE/TIME_____ FILTER _____SN _____

Cable?_____ Windscreen? _____ Random Incidence Corrector? _____

Signal Monitored?_____ How Monitored?_____

Calibration Level_____ Calibration Times_____

Location_____

No. Exposed Personnel_____ Ear Protection?_____

NOTES & COMMENTS   DIAGRAM:
(Show measuring
location with
an X)

Position or symbol (see sketch)	Sound Level, dB Re 20 μN/m^2						Operating and Measuring Conditions	Estimated Exposure Time, h
	A (slow)		A (fast)		true peak			
	Max.	Min.	Max.	Min.	A	Lin.		

Figure 11.1 Sample noise survey form.

328

1. Steady-state noise—one or more levels When the noise levels at the work site are known to change very little during the day, and when the time spent by the worker at each work site is clearly defined, simple sound-level-meter readings will suffice to establish employee exposure. The microphone of the meter should be located at the ear position of each worker, but with the worker at least 3 ft away. For a general standing position, the preferred microphone height is 1.5 m (about 5 ft); for a seated worker, 1.1 m (about 3.5 ft). A-weighted levels should be measured with slow meter response.

Employee exposure to continuous noise at one or more levels should be computed in terms of *daily noise dose D* defined by the equation

$$D = \frac{C_1}{T_1} + \frac{C_2}{T_2} + \cdots + \frac{C_n}{T_n} = \sum_{L=1}^{n} \frac{C_i}{T_i} \qquad (7.10)$$

where L_i = workplace sound level measured in dBA, slow
$\qquad C_i$ = actual exposure (in hours) at level L_i
$\qquad T_i$ = allowed exposure at level L_i

and
$$T_i = \frac{16}{2^{[0.2(L_i - 85)]}} \qquad (7.11)$$

Alternatively, T_i can be obtained from Fig. 11.2. The daily noise dose should be computed for each worker, or workplace, in each of the hazardous noise areas, using Eq. (7.11).

Compliance with both the current and proposed OSHA noise regulations requires that a worker's daily noise dose be less than unity,* i.e.,

$$D \leqslant 1 \qquad \text{for compliance} \qquad (11.1)$$

A value of $D = 1$ corresponds to an 8-h time-weighted average of 90 dBA, while a value of $D = 0.5$ corresponds to an 85-dBA 8-h time-weighted average. The 1970 OSHA noise regulation states that feasible engineering and administrative controls shall be used to reduce the noise exposures of employees to within permissible levels ($D \leqslant 1$). The proposed regulation recommends that an audiometric testing program be initiated for all employees exposed to an 8-h time-weighted average of 85 dBA or greater ($D \geqslant 0.5$).*

If the noise levels fluctuate widely and rapidly, or if the worker moves frequently, measuring the noise levels and determining exposure times at each level and location can be extremely difficult. In such cases a personal noise dosimeter with a lapel- or ear-mounted microphone can be invaluable. Such a device travels with the worker wherever he or she goes and continuously monitors the changing noise levels. Most dosimeters read out the percentage of allowed daily noise dose, $100 \times D$. Hence, a readout value of 75 corresponds to a value of $D = 0.75$. If the work pattern is repetitive, it may be convenient to monitor the worker for only a fraction of the workshift, $1/n$. In this case, the

---

* By periodically monitoring worker hearing acuity it is possible to identify those who are more suseptible to hearing damage and thus to transfer them to jobs in quieter environments before irreparable hearing damage has occurred.

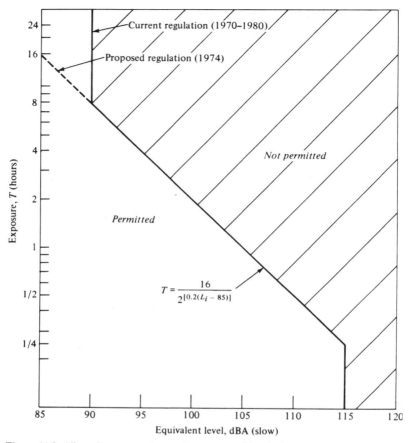

Figure 11.2 Allowed exposure for continuous sound level (OSHA).

value of D determined from the dosimeter readout must be multiplied by n to correspond to a full shift.

The American National Standard on noise dosimeters, ANSI S1.25–1978, provides tolerances for the instrument. Several precautions should be taken when using dosimeters. Calibration is essential, and the manufacturer's instructions should be carefully followed. A newly purchased dosimeter should be left on continuously for at least 8 h and calibrated periodically to determine whether there are any shifts in calibration readings. Some observations of the employee being monitored may be necessary to attest to normal activity. The employee can influence the reading by deliberately favoring positions with high or low noise levels. In addition the readout should not be available to the employee directly from the instrument, lest he or she be encouraged to alter the true reading.

2. Maximum steady-state noise level Exposures to continuous noise should not exceed 115 dBA, regardless of any value computed in (1) above. Any work site with continuous levels exceeding 115 dBA should be identified.

3. Impulse or impact noise The current OSHA noise regulation states simply that "exposures to impulse or impact noise *should* not exceed a peak sound-pressure level of 140 dB." measured on the linear scale. Impulse or impact noise is defined as a sound with a rise time of not more than 35 ms to peak intensity and a duration of not more than 500 ms (1/2 s) to the time when the level is 20 dB below peak. If the impulses recur at intervals of less than 1 s, they are considered to be continuous sound.

The current noise regulation cannot adequately treat impact noise since it does not allow for the cumulative effect of exposure to a large number of impacts, nor does it take into account the diminishing effect of decreasing peak levels. For example, the regulation indicates that there should not be *any* exposure to peak noise levels above 140 dB, while putting *no limit* on the number of impact sounds one can be exposed to at peak levels of 139 dB! The new proposed OSHA noise regulation would prohibit exposures to impulse or impact noise at peak sound-pressure levels above 140 dB with linear weighting, but in addition it would limit the number of impacts allowed at or below peak levels of 140 dB (see Sec. 7.3).

The proposed regulation states that exposure to impulses of 140 dB shall not exceed 100 such impulses per day. Moreover, for each decrease of 10 dB in the peak sound-pressure level of the impulse, the number of impulses to which employees are exposed may be increased by a factor of 10. Hence, the number N of *impacts* allowed at a peak level L can be determined by the equation

$$N = \frac{10^2}{10^{[0.1(L-140)]}} \tag{11.2}$$

Alternatively, N can be obtained graphically from Fig. 11.3.

The limits specified by the proposed OSHA noise regulation for the number of impulses permitted at a given peak sound-pressure level provide the basis for defining an allowable noise dose for impact noise which is similar to that defined for continuous sound. We introduce here a quantity D_I, defined as the daily noise dose for impact noise:*

$$D_I = \frac{n_1}{N_2} + \frac{n_2}{N_2} + \cdots + \frac{n_k}{N_R} = \sum_{i=1}^{k} \frac{n_i}{N_i} \tag{11.3}$$

---

* The impact-noise dose D_I defined in this section is a quantity introduced by the authors to evaluate worker exposure to impact-noise environments. We recommend that the method of using D_I developed here for evaluating such environments be used until a standard is established.

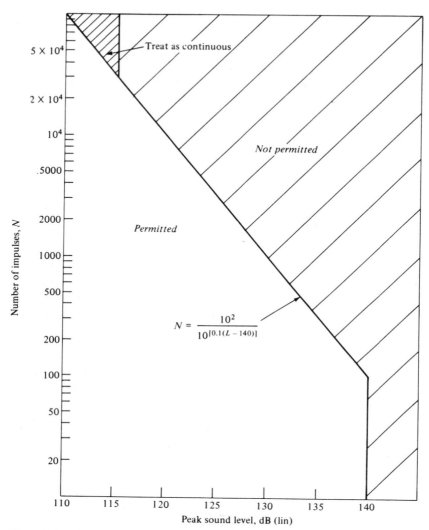

Figure 11.3 Allowed number of impacts (OSHA).

where L_i = peak sound-pressure level of impact noise
n_i = actual number of impacts at level L_i
N_i = allowed number of impacts at level L_i

The value for N_i can be obtained from Fig. 11.3 or computed using Eq. (11.2).

Thus, when the noise field at the work site is made up of impact noise occurring at intervals greater than 1 s, the peak levels should be measured at the worker's ear position and the daily noise dose for impact noise computed for each worker, using Eq. (11.3). For compliance with the proposed OSHA noise regulation, D_I should be less than unity, i.e.,

$$D_I \leqslant 1 \qquad \text{for compliance} \qquad (11.4)$$

If the impacts occur at intervals of less than 1 s (less than 1/2 s for the proposed OSHA noise regulation), the noise should be treated as continuous and the A-weighted slow response of the meter used to determine worker exposure in accordance with Eq. (11.1) above.

A Type 1 sound-level meter with peak-hold capability can be used to measure impact noise if the peaks are separated sufficiently to allow time to record the measured values. In cases where the peaks are more closely spaced, such as a series of forge-hammer blows, it may be necessary to use additional instrumentation in order to capture the peak level of each impact. One method which can be employed is to use the sound-level meter as a microphone/amplifier system, with the "ac" output from the meter fed into an oscilloscope. The system can be calibrated by placing the sound-level meter calibrator over the microphone and reading the peak value of the calibration signal on the oscilloscope. Since the output voltage of the meter is proportional to the sound pressure, that is, $v \propto p$, then

$$\frac{p_{peak}}{p_{cal}} = \frac{v_{peak}}{v_{cal}} \qquad (11.5)$$

where p_{cal} = peak value of calibration pressure
p_{peak} = peak pressure being monitored
v_{cal} = peak voltage of calibration signal
v_{peak} = peak voltage of signal monitored

Taking the logarithm of both sides of Eq. (11.5) and rearranging terms, one obtains

$$L_{peak} = L_{cal} + 20 \log \frac{v_{peak}}{v_{cal}} \qquad (11.6)$$

where L_{peak} is the peak sound-pressure level and L_{cal} is the peak level of the calibration sound. One should note in applying Eq. (11.6) that the calibration level listed with a calibrator is usually specified in terms of p_{rms}. Since we are interested in the peak level at calibration, 3 dB must be added to the specified calibration level:

$$L_{cal} = L_{cal}(\text{rms}) + 3 \text{ dB} \qquad (11.7)$$

Care must also be taken in selecting the scale on the sound-level meter when monitoring impact noise; overloading of the meter amplifier could result in "clipping" of the peaks.

4. Mixed continuous and impact noise In cases where impact noise is clearly superimposed on a continuous background noise, e.g., when the peak levels due to impact are at least 15 dB higher than the A-weighted (slow meter response) background levels,* worker exposure can be determined by computing the daily noise dose for the two noise fields separately. The total daily noise dose is given by

$$D_{\text{total}} = D + D_I \leqslant 1 \qquad \text{for compliance} \tag{11.8}$$

where D and D_I are determined using Eqs. (7.10) and (11.3), respectively.

11.4 DIAGNOSTIC MEASUREMENTS

Having established the noise exposures of all employees working in hazardous noise areas, the next step of the compliance noise survey requires diagnostic measurements to locate specific noise sources and to determine the amount of noise reduction needed at each work site to bring it into compliance. Diagnostic measurements are, in a very real sense, a type of detective activity in which clues must be properly read, hunches followed up, and data cross-checked. The success of the diagnostic measurements will depend to a great extent on the experience of the person making the measurements. The National Institute of Occupational Safety and Health (NIOSH) has published an *Industrial Noise Control Manual*, which has an excellent section (pp. 19–32) on diagnostic measurements [2]. Much of the material presented in this section is based on the NIOSH publication. The reader should also review Chap. 9 and Lab. 6 for more information on diagnostic measurements.

The basic tool for diagnostic measurements is the Type 1 or Type 2 sound-level meter with A, B, and C weighting and "fast" and "slow" settings. Although additional instruments can add significantly to the diagnostic capability of the investigator, this basic instrument can be used to solve many problems regarding noise sources for which specific data based on frequency analysis are not required. The treatment needed to reduce A-weighted noise levels can be selected in part by a knowledge of the frequency region which contributes most to the A level. When the C-level measurement of a noise field is greater than the A level, there are strong low-frequency components of acoustic energy; but when the A level is approximately the same as the C level, the energy is mainly in the high-frequency bands.

Special attachments which are often available with a sound-level meter include:

- Extension cable for microphone
- Tripod
- Windscreen
- Earphone coupler
- Vibration pickup and adapter

* If the difference in levels is less than 15 dB, the impact noise will not cause large fluctuations in readings at the slow meter setting. In this case the sound should be treated as fluctuation continuous sound and measured with the sound-level meter set on A weighting and slow response.

The *extension cable* for the microphone is used for making noise measurements close to a source. With this extension it is possible to probe with the microphone near those portions of the machine at which candidate noise sources are located. The *tripod* can be used as an extension arm to place the microphone in locations otherwise difficult to reach. The *windscreen* allows sound-level measurements to be made in moving airstreams, such as in the vicinity of cooler fans, for airspeeds up to 22 ft/s (15 mi/h). The windscreen also acts as a protective cover to shield the microphone from dirt and accidental bumping against objects while probing for noise sources. By monitoring the sound-level meter with an *earphone coupler* while probing with a microphone it is possible to detect noise sources which would otherwise be difficult to distinguish from competing sources. Finally, the *vibration pickup and adapter* allows the sound-level meter to be used to measure the motion of vibrating surfaces and to determine which surfaces of a machine vibrate at the highest levels. It is sometimes possible to verify the connection between received sound and its source by using C and A weighting to determine which frequencies contain most of the vibrational energy. This technique is enhanced if the sound-level meter being used has a 1/1- or 1/3-octave-band filter attachment. Locations with thin machine panels and guards are prime candidates for vibration-induced sound sources.

Trained ears, eyes, and hands can also play an important role in diagnostic measurements. The investigator must listen critically to detect any unusual noise event which may influence measurements being made and must observe the complex motion of machinery in order to determine how that motion may relate to the noise levels measured. One's ears can often help to determine the direction of a source (particularly of a high-frequency noise source) and to serve as a frequency analyzer. For example, a hiss or a ping would indicate that much of the acoustic energy is contained in the higher frequencies, while a rumble or a thud would indicate low-frequency content. The fingertips, or fingernails, can be used to detect vibrating surfaces.

An important adjunct to the sound-level meter is a set of octave-band filters. This package may be an attachment to the sound-level meter. It measures the sound-pressure level in each octave band, normally at center-band frequencies from 31.5 to 16,000 Hz. It is possible in this way to identify the band in which a maximum noise level occurs. This information can aid in determining the source of that noise—for example, in verifying that the blade passage frequency of a fan, or the gear tooth mesh-frequency of a press flywheel, is in the band with maximum sound level. Octave-band data are also useful in the selection of materials for noise control treatments, since sound absorption and transmission properties of materials are frequency-dependent. For example, enclosures and barriers are often designed to suit particular noise sources by using the calculations for required noise reductions in each frequency band. Narrow-band frequency analyzers are also available and are particularly useful for source analysis and machine redesign for noise abatement. However, the octave-band analyzer will serve most needs for the design of barriers, enclosures, isolators, damping treatments, and room absorbers to reduce noise produced by existing equipment.

Table 11.1 Chart for converting to A-weighted band levels

Octave-band center frequency, Hz	Change in measured band level, dB
31.5	− 30.5
63	− 26
125	− 16
250	− 8.5
500	− 3.0
1000	− 0.0
2000	+ 1.0
4000	+ 1.0
8000	− 1.0
16,000	− 6.5

Several diagnostic techniques are available which make use of A-weighted octave-band levels. The A-weighted band levels can be obtained by altering the measured band levels as indicated in Table 11.1. The character of the measured sound can be diagnosed by observing the difference between the A level and the maximum A-weighted octave-band level. The greater the difference, the more likely it is that several A-weighted octave bands of approximately the same level are contributing to the total A level. If the difference is small, it is possible that pure tones are causing the level in one A-weighted octave band to be much greater than that in other bands. Having identified the A-weighted band that contributes most to the A level, one can then set the octave-band analyzer at the center frequency of this maximum band and probe with the microphone to locate the area on the machine giving the maximum contribution in this band.

In most industrial plants there may be several noise sources contributing to the noise level at any one work station, and it is often difficult to separate the contribution of the various noise sources. One very effective way of isolating and identifying noise sources is to enter the work area when there is no activity, such as at night or on weekends, so that one source at a time can be operated. The machine in question may then be put through several operating modes: idling, at full production, or with some functions selectively turned off. The different modes of operation aid in identification of machine noise sources that may be close together or may have noise sources nearly identical. This may not always be possible, however, since some sources must always operate simultaneously.

As an example of the method described above, we consider a typical forging-hammer work site in which there are frequently four major sources of noise: (1) forge-hammer impact noise, (2) cooling fans, (3) slot furnaces for heating, and (4) air or steam jets for blowing scale from dies. The slot furnaces can be run individually, first with the burners on and then with the burners turned off, to determine the individual contribution of combustion and burner blower noise. The cooling fans can be run individually and in groups to determine their contribution at each work site. The descaler nozzles can also be run separately. During normal forge-hammering operation the furnaces and descalers will also be operating, so it is not possible to measure the hammer impact noise alone. However, in this case the hammer impact noise levels are usually significantly higher than the background levels, so that they can be measured even with the other noise sources operating.

Ideally, only the machine in question should be operating when making diagnostic measurements in order to avoid interference from other noise sources. However, this ideal arrangement is often impossible, and measurements must be made during normal production operations. If the background noise is relatively continuous and does not contain audible tones, it may still be possible to calculate the sound level due to the machine alone. The only requirement is that at some time during the measurements the machine in question can be shut down. This may occur naturally, because of change in work piece or tooling, or at a rest break. The noise levels should be measured with all machines operating and with the machine under study shut off. If there are small changes in the two levels measured, it is possible to infer the noise level (in each octave band) produced by the machine alone. The scheme for determining the levels works best when the differences of the two sets of readings are over 2 dB. The machine's noise level can be determined mathematically by using the equation

$$L_M = L_B + 10 \log(10^k - 1) \qquad (11.11)$$

where $k = (L_C - L_B)/10$
L_B = background level with machine shut down
L_C = combined level, background plus machine
L_M = machine sound level
Alternatively, the machine levels can be determined using Table 11.2. Let Δ_L be

Table 11.2

Δ_L, dB	Reduction in level, dB	Δ_L, dB	Reduction in level, dB
0.5	9.6	6.5	1.1
1.0	6.9	7.0	1.0
1.5	5.3	7.5	0.9
2.0	4.3	8.0	0.7
2.5	3.6	8.5	0.7
3.0	3.0	9.0	0.6
3.5	2.6	9.5	0.5
4.0	2.2	10.0	0.5
4.5	1.9	10.5	0.4
5.0	1.7	11.0	0.4
5.5	1.5	11.5	0.3
6.0	1.3	12.0	0.3

the decibel decrease recorded when the machine under study is shut down. Table 11.2 lists, for a given Δ_L, the number of decibels which must be subtracted from the combined level (all machines operating) in order to obtain the contribution of the machine under study. Final levels obtained using either method should be rounded off to the nearest decibel.

11.5 DOCUMENTATION FOR THE NOISE SURVEY

It is very important that all results of the exposure and diagnostic surveys be carefully documented and recorded, for these are the data upon which decisions will be made regarding control of the various noise sources. The data obtained from the exposure survey should be sufficient to define the daily noise dose for all employees exposed to hazardous noise areas, and the document should indicate those employees whose noise dose is in excess of the OSHA standard.

The data from the diagnostic measurements should be in sufficient detail to be clearly understood by others and to serve as reminders of the problem details for final corrective recommendations. Some or all of the following data may be required, depending on the noise source and methods of treatment contemplated [1].

1. Sound-pressure levels, A and C, at operator's position for compliance, plus peak level.
2. Octave-band levels measured 1 ft from the source, or at any distance for which noise from that source predominates.
3. Octave-band levels made on an imaginary surface that encloses the source 1 m away from actual source. Use in sound-power calculations.*
4. A and C levels at the critical distance where the source and background noise contribute equally; the source will dominate at positions closer to it than this distance. The critical distance is established by a 3-dB increase above the background level while approaching the source from a remote position (with only that source operating).
5. Background-noise levels: A, C, and octave-band.
6. Noise-source probe readings, comparing fast and slow readings related to machine operation if possible. Use in diagnostic analysis of sources.
7. Sketch of area, machine, noise source, and operator location. Augment with photographs if required for later analysis.
8. Vibration measurements to determine acceleration levels of vibrating surfaces (in some cases velocity and displacement) plus description of vibrating region. For vibration-isolation requirements, obtain weight on footings and lowest forcing frequency (revolutions per minute of motor, drive, and other vibration contributors).

---

* For large machines the 1-m envelope may be in the near field of the source. In this case additional measurements will be needed when computing the sound power of the machine. See, for example, Diehl's two-surface method for sound-power calculation [3].

The basic aim of this documentation will be to give as clear and complete a description of the noise sources as possible for detailed analysis later. In addition, whenever an effort is made to control a noise source, a follow-up sound survey should be made to establish the effects of the treatment. A brief report giving the basic details of changes made, and the before and after levels, should be added to the previous documentation, even if the new levels are the same or higher after the changes.

11.6 DETERMINING NOISE CONTROL METHODS— ASSESSING FEASIBILITY

Once the individual noise sources have been identified and their relative contribution to the worker's noise exposure evaluated, methods of reducing the noise produced by the dominant noise sources must be considered. Several sources of information deal with the control of particular noise sources or present new techniques for noise abatement, and the engineer should be aware of them. One of the first to be considered is the manufacturer who produces the noisy equipment. In some cases the manufacturer will already have developed a noise control method for the product, or may be aware of customers who have. Use of this information as a basis for abating the noise source could cost much less than developing a method independently.

The technical literature is another source of information. Four technical journals which treat the practical aspects of noise abatement problems are:

American Industrial Hygiene Association Journal
Applied Acoustics
Noise Control Engineering
Sound and Vibration

The *Proceedings* of three national and international noise conferences held each year—INTERNOISE, NOISECON, and NOISEXPO—also provide a wealth of information on noise control technology. When using information from the technical literature, one must take care to assess the exact conditions under which the reported control methods were employed. For example, in one article a 20-dB reduction in punch-press noise reportedly was obtained by applying a partial enclosure around the die area of the punch. Close inspection of the data presented revealed that the noise was predominantly high-frequency air-nozzle noise, which can be easily attenuated by other methods. Partial enclosures applied to other punches where impact noise is the predominant source of noise would not be nearly as effective.

Suppliers of noise control equipment and materials are another source of information. Each year *Sound and Vibration* devotes two entire issues to this topic, one focusing on systems and the other on materials for noise and vibration control. These issues give a current list of suppliers and their addresses.

A letter sent to each of these sources requesting information on products and their applications will result in a flood of information. Although much of this material will be of a commercial nature, a significant amount of design information and technical knowledge about particular noise control applications can be obtained from these commercial brochures or from discussions with company sales engineers.

Before final selection of engineering control methods is made, administrative control should be given serious consideration, since in some cases they have the potential for being the least costly and easiest to initiate. Two basic methods of administrative control available for reducing worker exposure to noise are (1) job rotation and (2) production scheduling. An example of the first method would be to use two operators, each working only 4 hours, on a job that has a time-weighted average exposure of 95 dBA. Each operator would run the job for 4 hours and then work in a location where the noise level is less than 90 dBA (less than 85 dBA for the new proposed OSHA noise regulation) for the other 4 hours. An example of the second administrative method on the same job would be to run the operation only 4 hours per day, or per shift. This method is applicable only when less than full-time production of a noisy machine is needed. If administrative controls are found to be impossible or less desirable than available engineering controls, the latter must be considered.

Once the available engineering control methods are determined, the most suitable ones must be selected and their cost and effectiveness estimated. For some of the simpler noise sources this process will be straightforward and precise. For example, control of cooling-fan noise can be achieved either by replacing the noisy fan with a new one of quiet design or by modifying the existing fan. With either approach an accurate assessment can be made of expected cost and noise reduction. On the other hand, for situations where the machine or operation to be quieted is complex, and when there are many noise sources present, it may be very difficult to predict the cost and amount of noise reduction expected. Very often the approach taken will be to treat the dominant noise source first, then to treat whichever new source emerges as dominant, as described in Sec. 9.2. This process is continued until the desired overall noise reduction is achieved, or until the remaining dominant source cannot be reduced further by known techniques. It is very often difficult to predict accurately the reduction in noise that may be expected at each step. Moreover, it may be necessary to measure the effect of changes at each step and to use the new data as a guide in taking subsequent steps. Consequently, it may not be possible to forecast what the full treatment will be or what cost and degree of success can be expected. Nevertheless, even though the selection and cost of engineering controls is at best an estimate, it must be done in order to determine feasibility and establish priorities in any viable noise reduction program.

In cases where a plant has many similar machines or operations, it may be necessary to *initiate engineering studies* in order to determine (1) the amount of noise abatement possible for a typical operation and (2) the cost per machine to implement noise control measures. The results of these studies are used to determine the best noise control methods available and to assess the feasibility of implementing such controls on a plantwide basis.

If insufficient information is available to establish noise control methods for control of a particular problem, or if expenditure of a significant amount of money is anticipated to abate a particularly complex noise problem, it may be wise to work with a consultant who is a noise control expert.

If there are any doubts regarding the method of noise control needed, an *independent* consultant, free from ties to a particular line of products, should be called in. On the other hand, if it has been ascertained that the best solution to a particular noise problem can be achieved by using a certain type of product, a *special-interest consultant* who is associated with the manufacture or sale of that product may be best suited to offer assistance. In the latter case there is usually no fee paid for the consultant, who will supply the client with design and installation information; the client pays only for the product. The use of a competent consultant could save considerable time and money, which might otherwise be spent on incorrect approaches. On the other hand, if noise control means have been installed that do not work, it may be necessary to use a consultant to remedy the situation. Since there is no legal bar to an individual's offering his or her services as an acoustical consultant, care should be taken to select someone fully qualified by training and experience. Guidelines for selecting and using a consultant are given in the NIOSH *Industrial Noise Control Manual* [1].

Assessment of the feasibility of noise control methods must consider not only the question of whether the controls are technically possible, but also the economical practicability of the methods. These latter considerations must determine whether the noise control treatments can be accomplished at an affordable cost and whether they will result in benefits considered worthy of the money being expended. The costs include (1) investigative, developmental, and operative expenditures; (2) lowered productivity (if there is a loss); and (3) potential maintenance and safety problems. The benefits can include improvement in health and safety aspects of the work environment and increased productivity (if there is a gain). The cost/budget determinations must be applied to specific situations by the company involved. A noise control treatment considered satisfactory for one company might be found unacceptable by another. Other factors which may enter into the situation are likelihood of worker acceptance, likelihood of success, ease and speed of implementation, down time involved, future plans for plant expansion, etc.

11.7 WRITTEN NOISE ABATEMENT PLAN—
ESTABLISHING PRIORITIES

Rarely will sufficient funds, personnel, or time be available to undertake a comprehensive noise abatement program aimed at the simultaneous reduction of all noise sources in a plant. Instead, it will be necessary to establish a set of priorities to determine which noise sources should receive immediate attention and which should await more funds or development of new technology. When setting priorities one should consider the overall health and safety program of the plant, recognizing that noise hazards represent only one aspect of that program. Once the priorities have been determined, a written formal plan for implementing noise controls should be established. There are several reasons why the plan should be written:

1. A written plan provides a document which can be used by plant management as a planning document.
2. A plan listing each noise control step and its projected completion date provides a guide for the plant engineer in implementing the program.
3. A written plan is essential for periodic evaluation of the program's progress.
4. A formal written plan provides a document which can be used to demonstrate to OSHA, or other groups concerned with worker health and safety, that an effective noise control program is in progress.

Since there is always only a finite amount of time and resources available in industry which can be diverted to abate health hazards, priorities must be established. Moreover, the ultimate goal in setting up a noise control program is to reduce hearing-damage risk for as many employees as possible by eliminating unnecessary noise exposure. Therefore, considerable weight should be given to the number of employees exposed to a particular noise source in determining its place on the priority list. The order in which noise control measures should be implemented must be decided on a problem-by-problem basis, keeping in mind that the company should receive the greatest possible employee protection for each dollar spent.

Consider the example of a typical forge-hammer work site which has four major sources of noise: (1) cooling fans, (2) slot furnace, (3) descaler nozzles, and (4) drop hammer. Table 11.3 lists average exposure times and levels for a forging operation, which typically operates for a total of 5 h during an 8-h shift.

Table 11.3 Hammer exposure times and levels

Source	Sound level	Exposure	Total equivalent exposure	Allowed exposure (OSHA)
Cooling fan	97 dBA	5 h	5 h at 100 dBA	2 h
Slot furnace	97 dBA	5 h		
Descaler	115 dBA	1/2 h	1/2 h at 115 dBA	1/4
Drop hammer	130 dB$_p$	300 impacts/h	1500 impacts	1000 impacts
Drop hammer	125 dB$_p$	600 impacts/h	3000 impacts	3200 impacts
Drop hammer	120 dB$_p$	600 impacts/h	3000 impacts	10,000 impacts

The impact noise of hammer blows is estimated at three different peak levels, with the finishing blow giving the highest level. When combining the effects of the slot furnace and cooling fans, the rule for combining sound levels is used to obtain an equivalent continuous level of 100 dBA. It is also assumed for the purpose of this example that the workers are in a relatively quiet environment when the hammer is not operating. Hence, the workers' daily noise dose can be computed using Eq. (11.1) for continuous noise:

$$D = D_{100} + D_{115} = \frac{5}{2} + \frac{1/2}{1/4} = 2.5 + 2.0 = 4.5$$

The value of $D = 4.5$ corresponds to an exposure equal to 450 percent of the allowed daily exposure. Of this exposure, 250 percent is the result of the combined effect of the slot furnace and cooling fans, and 200 percent comes from the descaler nozzle. A similar calculation for impact noise, using Eq. (11.5), gives

$$D_I = D_{130} + D_{125} + D_{120} = 1.5 + 0.94 + 0.30y = 2.74$$

where $D_I = 2.74$ indicates a daily exposure to impacts equal to 274 percent of that allowed under the proposed OSHA regulation. Of this, 150 percent is from the finishing blows of the hammer.

In order to establish priorities it is necessary to consider noise control measures available, their costs, the expected reduction in sound level, the number of people exposed, and the estimated reduction in workers' daily noise dose. Table 11.4 summarizes the information needed to make a cost-benefit analysis for the example being considered. In the analysis which follows it is assumed that there is no feasible method for controlling the hammer noise. Moreover, it is assumed that for each control method taken there would be three employees affected by the noise at the hammer work site. With each of the proposed controls there is no loss in productivity after installation, and the estimated cost includes down time and other installation expenditures. With these simplifying assumptions it is necessary to consider only the estimated costs

Table 11.4 Summary of proposed noise control measures

Source	Proposed control	Estimated cost	Expected source reduction	Number exposed
Cooling fans	Replace	$1800.00	15 dBA	3
Slot furnace	Intake silencer	$1200.00	5 dBA	3
Descaler	Pneumatic silencer	$ 6.00	5 dBA	3
Drop hammer	None available	–	none	3

and reduction in worker exposure when making cost-benefit analyses. The following four options would have to be considered when setting priorities:

1. Control descaler noise only

Source	Level, dBA	Exposure, h	Equivalent exposure, h	Allowed exposure, h
Cooling fan	97	5 ⎫	5 at 100 dBA	2
Furnace	97	5 ⎬		
Descaler	110	0.5	0.5 at 110 dBA	0.5

$$\text{Daily noise dose, } D = \frac{5}{2} + \frac{0.5}{0.5} = 3.5$$

Reduction in noise dose = 22 percent   Cost = $6.00

2. Control descaler plus fan noise

Source	Level, dBA	Exposure, h	Equivalent exposure, h	Allowed exposure, h
Cooling fan	82	5 ⎫	5 at 97 dBA	3.5
Furnace	97	5 ⎬		
Descaler	110	0.5	0.5 at 110 dBA	0.5

$$\text{Daily noise dose, } D = \frac{5}{3.5} + \frac{0.5}{0.5} = 2.43$$

Reduction in noise dose = 46 percent   Cost = $1806.00

3. Control descaler plus furnace noise

Source	Level, dBA	Exposure, h	Equivalent exposure, h	Allowed exposure, h
Cooling fan	97	5 ⎫	5 at 97.8 dBA	2.7
Furnace	90	5 ⎬		
Descaler	110	0.5	0.5 at 110 dBA	0.5

$$\text{Daily noise dose, } D = \frac{5}{2.7} + \frac{0.5}{0.5} = 2.85$$

Reduction in noise dose = 37 percent   Cost = $1206.00

4. Control descaler, fans, and furnace noise

Source	Level, dBA	Exposure, h	Equivalent exposure, h	Allowed exposure, h
Cooling fan	82	5 ⎫		
Furnace	90	5 ⎬	5 at 90.7 dBA	7.5
Descaler	110	0.5	0.5 at 110 dBA	0.5

$$\text{Daily noise dose, } D = \frac{5}{7.5} + \frac{0.5}{0.5} = 1.67$$

Reduction in noise dose = 63 percent   Cost = \$3006.00

Several observations can be made immediately when studying the four options presented above. First, we see that a 22 percent reduction in noise exposure can be achieved simply by installing a \$6.00 pneumatic silencer on the descaler nozzle. The expected noise reduction would be realized immediately with a simple installation at very low cost. Consequently, option 1 would be given high priority. On the other hand, if funds are limited so that implementation of the remaining controls must be spread out over an extended period, the order of implementation of options 2 and 3 would be determined by particular circumstances within the plant; for we see that although the costs to implement option 3 are less than for 2, so also are the benefits achieved. Finally we see that even after all three sources of noise are treated, the expected noise environment at the hammer work site would not comply with OSHA limits. However, the intent of the OSHA regulation is that all feasible engineering controls will be implemented, even if compliance cannot be achieved.* If no other feasible engineering controls were available for the above example, the final treatment, 4, plus the use of personal hearing protectors, would be deemed as meeting the requirements of the OSHA noise regulation.

The example given above was simplified in order to separate certain important aspects of setting priorities. The process will in general be much more complicated since it will be necessary to consider all hazardous noise areas in

---

* OSHA's stand on these matters has been challenged in the courts. We give as an example the decision issued by the Occupational Safety and Health Commission in the case of *Secretary (of Labor) v. Continental Can Company, Inc.*, BNA 4 OSHC 1541, CCH para. 21,009 (docket numbers 3973 et al., 1976). The Commission agreed that "feasible" as employed in the noise regulations incorporated economical as well as technical factors, and that the burden of establishing feasibility remained with the Secretary. The ruling of the Commission in this case established that in order for the Secretary to successfully cite a company for violation of the noise standard, he must provide evidence to demonstrate two things: (1) that economically as well as technically, feasible administrative and/or engineering controls exist which are not already implemented by the company; and (2) that such controls, if implemented, would bring the company into compliance with citation, either by reducing noise levels to those specified in the noise regulation or by accomplishing "significant" reductions.

the plant when doing the cost-benefit analysis. Once this analysis is completed and priorities are set, a formal written plan for implementing the controls should be undertaken. The plan should list each noise control step and its planned completion date. The written plan should *not* be considered an inflexible document which allows no changes or deviations. As the program progresses, continuing noise measurements will be needed to assess the degree of noise reduction obtained. During this period conditions in the plant may change, or new technology may become available for control of certain noise sources, making it necessary to adjust priorities and update the written plan as the program progresses. Thus, the written plan should be considered a flexible set of *guidelines* upon which the progress and success of the noise control program can be judged.

11.8 ESTABLISHING A REVIEW PROCEDURE

A review procedure should be established to periodically examine progress being made on the noise control program and to update the written noise abatement plan. The review should attempt to make an assessment of the effects of the noise abatement program, looking at the total expenditures of time and money spent to implement the program; this would include any reduction in production rates brought about by noise control measures. The benefits accrued from these expenditures should also be summarized, indicating any reduction in the perimeters of hazardous noise areas, reduction in worker noise exposures, and improvements in production output.

The review process should cover alterations that have occurred within the plant, such as addition of new machines, changes in production processes, changes in types or number of products being manufactured, or changes in the number of workers assigned to areas of excessive noise. Moreover, any anticipated plant expansion or purchase of new machines should be evaluated in terms of expected effects of these changes on the noise environment.

Finally, a periodic review should be made of new technology available for reduction of noise sources within the plant. All effects of changes, or anticipated changes, on the noise environment and on worker noise exposures should be summarized in a report as part of the review process.

11.9 PERSONAL HEARING PROTECTION—
EDUCATIONAL PROGRAM

A successful noise control program requires not only a sincere effort by plant management and supervision, but also the enthusiastic cooperation of employees. For this reason an educational program is often needed to explain the goals of the noise control program and to indicate its benefits for individuals in the plant. This is particularly true in the area of personal hearing protection.

Selling the idea of the use of ear protectors to employees and supervisors will usually require that an educational program precede the required use of ear protection. Information and materials necessary for such an educational program are available from federal and state departments of labor, insurance companies, and manufacturers of ear protectors.

The Department of Labor's Bulletin 334, "Guidelines to Occupational Noise Standards" [4], and the National Institute of Occupational Safety and Health (NIOSH) publication, "Criteria Document: Recommendations for an Occupational Exposure Standard for Noise" [5], are examples of information available from federal agencies. These brochures cover the following major points regarding the use of hearing protective equipment:

1. The use of personal protective equipment is considered by the Department to be an interim measure while engineering and administrative controls are being perfected. There will be very few cases in which the use of this equipment will be acceptable as a permanent solution to noise problems.
2. Only approved ear protectors that have been tested in accordance with ANSI Standard Z24.22-1957 should be used.
3. Any ear protector used by an employee should reduce the effective noise level to which he or she is exposed so that the noise exposure is within authorized limits. Furthermore, 5 dB less than the stated attenuation of ear protectors should be allowed, because test data were obtained under ideal conditions that are not normal in day-to-day operation.
4. Earmuffs and earplugs should be fitted and supplied through a properly trained person who can educate the workers in the use and maintenance of the muffs and plugs.
5. Wax-impregnated cotton and fine glass wool are acceptable, but dry cotton stuffed in the ears has very little value and is not acceptable.
6. Inspection procedures to ensure proper issuance, maintenance, and use of personal protective equipment should be established by the employer. A method to be used for determining the A-weighted noise reduction for ear protectors is given in the NIOSH document

The purpose of personal hearing protectors is to reduce the hearing-damage risk of the employee in working areas where the noise cannot be reduced to a suitable level. *It is the employer's responsibility* to see that the hearing protectors are used. This is the view not only of OSHA, but also of the courts regarding decisions awarding compensation for employees who have suffered noise-induced hearing loss while on the job. A successful hearing-conservation program will have a compassionate but *firm* policy regarding the use of hearing protectors. Several types of protectors should be provided, so that the workers can choose the one they prefer. On the other hand, failure on the employee's part to use the hearing protection provided should be grounds for dismissal, as is the case with enforcement of other health and safety rules in many plants.

11.10 ESTABLISHING AN AUDIOMETRIC TESTING PROGRAM

The upper limit of an 8-h time-weighted average of 90 dBA in the OSHA regulations was chosen to protect the majority (80 to 85 percent) of employees exposed to such noise levels. However, some individuals who are more susceptible to hearing damage will suffer losses in hearing acuity even at a reduced level of 85 dBA. For this reason, a medically supervised hearing-testing program should be established for preemployment examination and periodic follow-up checks of all employees who work in hazardous noise areas, including those who wear hearing-protective devices. The audiometric records provide reference data which include initial hearing-threshold levels and a continuing history of each employee's hearing acuity. These records serve to protect both employee and employer. Noticeable changes in an employee's threshold levels can be an indication of susceptibility to hearing loss due to excessive noise levels, or of other otological disorders. On the other hand, a preemployment record and continued history of the employee's hearing acuity protects the employer from blame for hearing damage that accrued prior to employment with that firm. A schedule for an audiometric test program recommended by NIOSH is outlined below to serve as a guide for minimum requirements.

A baseline audiogram should be obtained for all employees initially assigned or reassigned to work in noise environments where (1) they are exposed to noise limits in excess of those described in Fig. 11.2, (2) their daily noise dose is greater than unity, or (3) they are required to wear hearing-protective devices. A baseline audiogram is obtained from an examination that is preceded by a period of at least 14 h of quiet, preferably at the beginning of a work shift. The baseline audiogram should be obtained within 30 days of assignment to such employment, in the sixth year of such employment, and once every sixth year thereafter. In addition, an audiogram, not necessarily baseline, should be obtained every 2 years for each employee exposed to hazardous noise environments. (Note that these are *minimum* requirements; in many industries yearly audiograms of all employees are required.)

Each audiogram should contain the following information: (1) employee's name or identification, (2) employee's job location, (3) significant aural medical history of the employee, (4) examiner's name and signature, (5) date and time of test, (6) serial number of audiometer, and (7) last exposure to high level of noise. Number of hours since exposure, type of exposure, and noise level should be included if known.

Each employee's audiogram should be examined by a properly trained person to determine whether it indicates a significant threshold shift (higher threshold) compared with the employee's most recent baseline audiogram and with his or her initial baseline audiogram, corrected for age. If either comparison indicates a significant shift, the following action should be taken:

1. The employee should be referred for appropriate medical evaluation.

2. If an employee needs personal protective equipment or devices, ensure that he or she is issued the proper equipment and receives the proper training in use and care of the equipment.
3. If the last audiogram was not a baseline audiogram, take a baseline audiogram within 60 days to be used for future comparisons.

Calibration of the audiometric facility should occur on a regular basis in order to safeguard the investment in collection of data. Reliable firms exist which provide full or partial audiometric service for companies that cannot afford to maintain their own audiometric facilities. The employer should maintain records of all audiometric data for each· employee for the duration of his or her employment, plus five years.

PROBLEMS

11.1 Compute the daily noise dose for the following noise exposures:

	Exposure level	Period of exposure
(a)	90 dBA	4 h
	93 dBA	three 1.5-h intervals
(b)	95 dBA	seven 15-min intervals
	102 dBA	thirty-five 1-min intervals
(c)	102 dBA	15 min
	132 dBp	200 impacts per shift

Answer: (a) 3.96; (b) 0.82; (c) 0.48

11.2 Two machines operate in a room. Machine A operating alone causes a continuous level of 93 dBA at the worker location; while machine B operating alone causes a continuous level of 102 dBA at the worker location. Assuming machine A operates for 4 h continuously during a workshift, determine how long machine B can operate under OSHA noise limits: (a) if the machines operate at separate times; (b) if machine B is in operation during the same time period as machine A.
Answer: (a) 22 min; (b) 20.6 min

11.3 Discuss the differences between the 1970 OSHA noise limits on impact noise and those in the proposed regulations of 1974.

11.4 List the important features of an industrial hearing conservation program.

11.5 Briefly discuss the differences between administrative and engineering controls for reducing worker noise exposure. Give several examples of each.

11.6 Outline the steps necessary to carry out an industrial plant noise survey for the purpose of:
(a) Identifying potentially hazardous work environments
(b) Identifying work stations for which the worker's daily noise dose exceeds limits established by OSHA Noise Standards
(c) Identifying dominant noise sources and determining noise source contributions to worker daily noise dose

11.7 Discuss briefly the most important factors which must be addressed in determining the feasibility of engineering noise controls.

11.8 List the basic features necessary in an effective audiometric testing program.

11.9 A worker is exposed to noise according to the following schedule:

Exposure level, dBA	Period of exposure, h
89	3
95	2
97	2
103	1

Compute the daily noise dose in percentage of allowed exposure.

Answer: 192 percent

REFERENCES

1. *Engineering Guidelines to Forging Noise Control,* vol. 2, Forging Industry Educational and Research Foundation, 55 Public Square, Cleveland, Ohio, 1977.
2. Salmon, V., J. S. Mills, and A. C. Petersen, *Industrial Noise Control Manual,* HEW Publication No. (NIOSH) 75-183, National Institute for Occupational Safety and Health, Cincinnati, June 1975.
3. Diehl, G. M., *Machinery Acoustics,* Wiley, New York, 1973.
4. *Guidelines to the Department of Labor's Occupational Noise Standards,* Bulletin 334, U.S. Department of Labor, Occupational Safety and Health Administration, 1971.
5. *Criteria for a Recommended Standard—Occupational Exposure to Noise,* Document HE 20.2811.N69, U.S. Department of Health, Education, and Welfare, National Institute for Occupational Safety and Health, 1972.

THREE

LABORATORY AND FIELD
EXPERIMENTS

INTRODUCTION TO THE LABORATORY EXERCISES

The laboratory exercises presented in this section have three objectives: (1) to familiarize the reader with the operation of some basic instrumentation used in noise control; (2) to assist the development of the reader's ability to apply this instrumentation to a variety of vibration and noise problems; and (3) to guide the reader through some practical applications of the instrumentation. When the exercises are used as part of a course, we recommend that emphasis be placed on these three objectives rather than on striving to obtain exact numbers and firm conclusions often implicit in "classroom" experiments. We would even recommend that these exercises be **ungraded** in a classroom situation, so that students can concentrate on understanding the equipment and its function. The instruments used in noise control are sufficiently rugged electronically that students need not worry about ruining them if they follow common-sense guidelines. They will discover that they can learn more by remaining flexible in executing these laboratory exercises, and they should not hesitate to try out a few ideas of their own.

The laboratory experiences should be conducted as informally as practical. The introduction to the instruments should be brief, concentrating on the controls and their *functions* rather than on details of operation. Familiarization should consist of exercising the controls to see their effects on the instruments' functioning. Carry out the suggested experiments, and any other related exercises which seem appropriate, then finish with a debriefing session during which specific problems and results can be discussed. We suggest that no specific time limits be imposed during the early laboratories, since they can readily be extended into follow-up sessions if desired.

A record should be kept of the measuring conditions and the data obtained in each laboratory exercise. During debriefing, the data should be used to substantiate conclusions or to initiate follow-up measurements. Deficiencies in data-taking technique can be identified and corrected immediately during the debriefing.

In an informal laboratory exercise, it is possible for a participant to stand by and become a passive observer of his or her lab mates' efforts, or to assume that the "essence" of the laboratory exercise can be absorbed by merely reading the material. These passive observers may feel that they perfectly understand all that takes place, but it has been our experience that they will generally perform very poorly when their turn for action finally arrives. All students should strive to be active members of their lab group right from the beginning. If necessary, they should *demand* their right to operate the instruments! A reader performing these exercises on a self-study basis should read through the laboratory exercise carefully, select a convenient room or noise environment in which to perform the experiment, and then carefully work through the experiment making full use of the suggested instruments and instrument manuals.

The practice of noise control is so closely interrelated with the instrumentation that it is virtually impossible to become competent in noise control without hands-on instrumentation experience.

LAB 1 MEASUREMENT OF SOUND

L1.1 The Sound-Level Meter

The sound-level meter is the heart of any noise control program. Its value is derived from its ability to provide a *numerical* measure of the sound environment. Although the unaided ear is excellent for detecting noise problems, it can at best assign subjective evaluations such as "loud," "soft," "irritating," "noisy," or "pleasant" to an acoustic environment. It is only with repeatable numerical descriptors of a sound field that the sound field can be evaluated in a consistent manner and a basis can be established for selecting and evaluating control measures or for supporting contentions made in a court of law.

The sound-level meter is actually a measurement *system*, consisting of four to five distinct components: (1) a microphone, (2) a preamplifier, (3) a weighting network, (4) an output amplifier, and (5) an rms voltmeter. The operation of the meter can be better understood if these components are considered by their *functions* rather than as wiring diagrams. Using this "black box" approach, the engineer can focus on features essential to the operation (but not repair!) of the sound-level meter, while ignoring internal details. A schematic of the sound-level meter is shown in Fig. 1.11. The behavior of the meter is fairly simply described: sound waves strike the diaphragm of the microphone, causing the diaphragm to deflect or to strain with the pressure fluctuations. The pressure fluctuations are converted by the microphone into corresponding voltage fluctuations, which are then amplified and conditioned by the preamplifier for further analysis. The amplified signal is passed through a weighting network, which usually modifies the electrical signal to correspond to some feature of human response such as

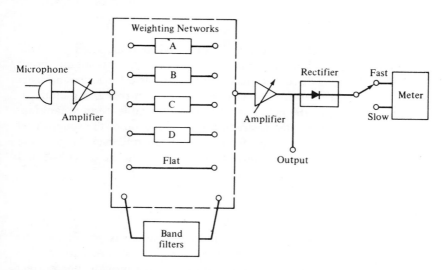

Figure 1.11 Block diagram of a sound-level meter.

loudness, annoyance, or hearing damage. The modified signal is then amplified again, if necessary, for detection in the rms voltmeter. The voltmeter, laid out on a logarithmic rather than linear scale, provides a numerical measure of the sound level in decibels. A more detailed visualization of the sound-pressure history can be obtained by oscilloscope monitoring of the signal from the output amplifier of the sound-level meter, before the signal is fed into the rms voltmeter.

L1.2 Components

The operation of the sound-level meter becomes straightforward once the *functions* of the components are understood.

1. Since the sound-pressure signal must be conditioned for analysis by the weighting network or for measurement by the rms voltmeter, a *gain control* must be provided to adjust that boost. This gain control is usually connected mechanically to the meter so that meter scaling is also changed as the gain control is manipulated.
2. Since several characteristics of the sound field may need to be measured, *a weighting selector* is provided to permit selection of weighting networks (typically A, B, C, D, or "flat").
3. The *meter* provides a display of the sound level in decibels. The responsiveness of the meter to changes in level is adjusted through the *meter speed control*. The "fast" response permits the meter to follow rapid changes in level, while the "slow" response smooths out the fluctuations so that the meter can be conveniently read. Neither setting affects the signal itself; "fast" and "slow" refer only to the speed with which the meter can respond to changes in the sound level.

These controls should be the first to be identified when familiarizing oneself with the instrument. Other functions may be added by the manufacturer to enhance versatility, but the three described above are basic for all sound-level meters used in noise control. With knowledge of these controls and a study of the manual, the operation of the meter should be quite simple. Many manufacturers provide detailed, step-by-step instructions on operation of the sound-level meter—detailed to the point of being tedious. With an understanding of the *functions* of the controls, it should be possible to cut through the checklists and begin using the meter almost immediately.

L1.3 Calibration

The most direct way to calibrate the sound-level meter is to expose the microphone to a known sound-pressure level, then adjust the gain of the amplifier (usually by means of a set screw) until the meter provides the correct reading. This known sound-pressure level is usually obtained using a controlled source provided by the manufacturer. The source, or calibrator, is normally placed over the microphone and the sound produced by a battery-powered oscillator driving either a piston or a miniature loudspeaker. Each manufacturer provides full details on the (weighted) level produced by its calibrators when used with specific microphones. Since microphone shapes and volumes vary, the calibration level produced by a calibrator may differ when used on different microphones. Be certain that the calibrator and microphone are matched according to the manufacturer's specifications. Since some calibrators must be corrected for barometric pressure, the reader should study the manufacturer's instructions to obtain the proper corrections to the readings.

No sound-level reading should be accepted unless it is taken between two satisfactory calibrations. When measurements are to be made over a period of hours, the calibration should be checked periodically, not only to ensure that the instrument is functioning properly but also to validate blocks of measurements. If calibration is found to change between, say, the fourth and fifth calibration checks, all readings made since the fourth calibration check should be repeated, if possible. The longer the period between calibration checks, the higher the risk of having to repeat a large block of data. In any event, *the first and last readings in any important test sequence should be valid calibration checks.*

L1.4 Experiment

A sound-level meter will be used to obtain numerical measures of several different sound fields. The object of this experiment is familiarization, not data collection.

L1.4.1 Familiarization with instrumentation

1. Locate the important controls on the sound-level meter, using the manual as a guide to finding the *gain*, *weighting*, and *meter response* controls.
2. Calibrate the sound-level meter, taking care that the proper weighting network is used when measuring the calibration signal.
3. Check manufacturer's recommendation for positioning the sound-level meter and orienting the microphone. In general, the microphone should be kept as far from the body (including the hands!) as possible, and the body should not be placed along the line between the obvious sound source and the microphone. The optimum orientation of the microphone is specified by the manufacturer and should be ascertained before use.

L1.4.2 Sound sources
Several different sound sources should be employed, preferably individually at their normal settings. A source with some low-frequency components, such as a portable tool driven by universal motor, should provide the desired range of signals.

L1.4.3 Background sound-pressure levels With selected sources not operating, the ambient or background level should be evaluated first.

1. dBA, dBB, dBC, dB (lin): Why would these levels be different?
2. "Fast" and "slow" meter response: Note the speed with which the needle responds when impulsive or rapidly fluctuating sound levels are produced (by tapping, for example).
3. Are readings affected by microphone position in the room or by orientation?
4. Can the readings be affected by holding the microphone near the body?
5. Are levels affected when readings are made near walls and other reflective surfaces?

The answers to questions 3 to 5 are all in the *affirmative*.

L1.4.4 Sound-pressure levels with source(s) operating

1–5. Same as above.
6. Compare levels (same weighting) when two sources operate first individually, then simultaneously. Compare combined level with that predicted from individual readings.
7. How are individual and combined readings affected by position in a room?
8. Take readings at 1, 2, 4, 8, 16 ft (or m) from a small sound source. To what extent is the 6-dB doubling rule satisfied? Does the choice of weighting network affect the *differences* between successive readings?

LAB 2 EVALUATION OF NOISE ENVIRONMENTS

L2.1 The Sound-Level Meter as an Evaluation Tool

The purpose of this exercise is to provide further experience with the sound-level meter, emphasizing its use in the *evaluation* of the sound environment. Although the sound-level meter is a valuable tool for obtaining numerical measures of the sound, it alone does not evaluate a sound environment. Any evaluation must be based upon a criterion: an *experimentally determined* relationship between some numerical measure of the sound environment and the subjective response being estimated. Only through derived empirical relationships can the user translate the readings of the sound-level meter into appropriate indices of loudness, hearing-damage potential, speech interference, or annoyance. For example, the equal-loudness contours provide ample experimental evidence that the sound-pressure level alone is not an index of subjective loudness. Two sounds with identical sound-pressure levels can have different perceived loudnesses because of differences in frequency content. A user wishing to determine loudness must first find an appropriate loudness criterion such as the Stevens Mark VI, then collect his or her sound-level readings with filtering or weighting appropriate to that criterion. It is emphasized that no single measure of the noise environment has yet been shown to simultaneously evaluate loudness, annoyance, speech interference, and potential hearing damage. The user must select the criterion he or she feels most appropriate, then collect readings to implement that criterion.

L2.2 Combined Octave-Band Levels

Whenever two or more sources operate independently and simultaneously, the sound-pressure level at any point is estimated after adding the intensities produced by each source at that point. The combined sound pressure $L_{p_{\text{total}}}$ is then equal to the combined sound-intensity level $L_{I_{\text{total}}}$ that is:

$$L_{p_{\text{total}}} = L_{I_{\text{total}}} = 10 \log_{10} \left[\frac{\overline{p_1^2} + \overline{p_2^2} + \cdots + \overline{p_n^2}}{\overline{p_{\text{ref}}^2}} \right]$$

where $\overline{p_i^2}$ is the mean square pressure associated with the ith source. Since the calculation of the combined level can be very tedious, an equivalent graphic procedure using Fig. 1.6 is normally employed.

In determining octave-band levels the basic sound-level meter diagrammed in Fig. 1.11 is slightly altered, replacing the weighting network with a filter set consisting of eleven contiguous octave-band filters. By switching each filter in turn into the circuit, eleven corresponding sound-level readings are obtained which make up the octave-band spectrum of the sound.

Octave-band levels can be combined in exactly the same manner that independent source levels are combined. Imagine that the signal passed through each octave filter were fed into its own amplifier and loudspeaker and the

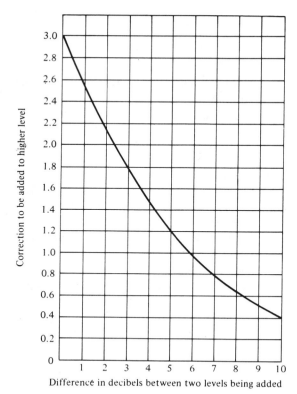

Figure 1.6 Adding levels.

corresponding band level were produced at the listener's position. If all eleven filtered signals were reproduced simultaneously, the sound at the listener's position would be identical to that received at the microphone. To the listener, there would appear to be eleven nearly uncorrelated sources acting simultaneously, and the overall sound-pressure level could be determined by combining the eleven levels. Table L2.1 illustrates a straightforward procedure using nine

Table L2.1 Combination of octave-band readings by successive pairs

	Center frequency, Hz								
	31.5	63	125	250	500	1000	2000	4000	8000
Band level	60	60	76	76	80	80	60	60	73
Step 1	63		79		83		63		73
Step 2	63			84.5				73.4	
Step 3	63				84.8				
Combined	84.8 $\doteq$ 85 dB								

Table L2.2 Combination of octave-band readings using expedient method

	Center frequency, Hz								
	31.5	63	125	250	500	1000	2000	4000	8000
Band level	60	60	76	76	80	80	60	60	73
Step 1	Ignore			79		83	Ignore		73
Combined				84.5 =	84 1/2 dB				Ignore

octave-band levels. Pairs are successively combined, using Fig. 1.11 and considering each succeeding combined level as a new independent source. Any combination sequence can be used; in this example the combinations 60–60, 76–76, 80–80, 60–60, and 73 produced five combined levels 63, 79, 83, 63, and 73 dB, respectively. These five levels are again combined in pairs 63, 79–83, and 63–73 dB to produce 63, 84.5, and 73.4 dB respectively. This routine continues until the overall level 84.8 ($\sim$ 85) dB is obtained.

The estimation time can be considerably reduced by first combining all the *higher* readings, then ignoring levels more than 10 dB below these combined levels. This expedient always yields underestimates, which are usually close enough for field data. As Table L2.2 illustrates, this procedure produces an estimate within 1/2 dB of the estimate obtained by considering all the levels.

Readers with hand calculators may wish to compute the combined level using the formula:

$$L_{p_{\text{total}}} = 10 \log_{10}\left(\frac{\overline{p_1^2} + \overline{p_2^2} + \cdots + \overline{p_n^2}}{p_{\text{ref}}^2} \right)$$

$$= 10 \log_{10}\left[10^{0.1L_1} + 10^{0.1L_2} + \cdots + 10^{0.1L_n} \right]$$

Storing the number $10^{0.1} = 1.258925$, raising it successively to the powers L_1, $L_2, \ldots, L_n$ and accumulating the sum, easily provides the sum in the square brackets. When using the calculator, the reader should still round the answer to the nearest 1/2 dB to remain consistent with the precision of the measured levels $L_1, L_2, \ldots, L_n$.

L2.3 Weighted Levels from Octave-Band Levels

The A, B, and C weighting networks, whose frequency characteristics are shown in Fig. L2.1, were earlier attempts to obtain loudness indices directly from the sound-level meter. These networks were designed to behave in the same way as the ear at 40-, 70-, and 100-phon loudness levels, respectively, in the hope that sound levels measured through these networks would provide reliable measures

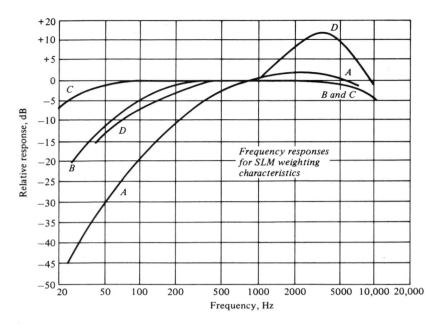

Figure L2.1

of moderate, loud, and intense sounds. Despite their derivation from experimental data, the numbers obtained through them do not correlate well with subjective evaluations of loudness. As a result, none of the three networks is used for loudness evaluations. However, in what appears to be a fortunate accident, the A-weighted sound level was later found to correlate reasonably well with hearing damage, speech interference, and annoyance, and it has since been used extensively as an expedient measure for estimating these responses- to a sound environment.

The weighted levels (A, B, C, D) can also be estimated from octave-band levels after applying appropriate tabulated corrections. For example, an A-weighted sound level can be derived from octave-band levels in a two-step procedure: (1) add the corrections shown in Table L2.3* to the appropriate octave-band reading, then (2) combine the adjusted levels in the manner described in Sec. L2.2. This procedure is illustrated by an example in Table L2.4. Note that in this example the corrections have rendered all but three of the octave-band levels insignificant, implying that only the 500- and 1000-Hz octave bands contribute significantly to the A-weighted level. If specific sources could be linked with these two octave bands, a priority of noise control measures could be established.

---

* The corrections shown in Table L2.3 are based on the A-weighting contour described in Fig. L2.1.

Table L2.3 Corrections for A-weighted analysis, using octave-band levels

Octave-band center frequency, Hz	Correction to be added, dB
31.5	− 39.4
63	− 26.2
125	− 16.1
250	− 8.6
500	− 3.2
1000	0.
2000	+ 1.2
4000	+ 1.0
8000	− 1.1

In this example, the combined A-weighted level, 82 dBA, is only slightly lower than the overall level determined earlier, because of the absence of significant components in the high- and low- frequency ranges. If significant components occurred in the 31.5- and 63-Hz octave bands, the difference between the A-weighted and overall levels would be greater. In many field situations, both A-weighted and overall (or "C") readings are taken, with large differences between the two being interpreted as evidence of significant low-frequency components.

L2.4 Evaluating Environments from Octave-Band Levels

Evaluation of environments will be illustrated using loudness and speech-interference criteria applied to octave-band levels.

Table L2.4 Determination of A-weighted level from octave-band readings

	Center frequency, Hz								
	31.5	63	125	250	500	1000	2000	4000	8000
Band level	60	60	76	76	80	80	60	60	73
"A" correction	− 39.4	− 26.2	− 16.1	− 8.6	− 3.2	0	+ 1.2	+ 1.0	− 1.1
Adjusted band level	20.5	34	60	67.5	77	80	61	61	72
Step 1	Ignore	Ignore	Ignore	Ignore	81.8		Ignore		72
Combined					82.2 ≐ 82 dBA				

Evaluation of loudness The most reliable measure of loudness is obtained by dividing the sound spectrum into frequency bands, evaluating the subjective loudness of each band level, then determining the total loudness by an appropriate combination of these individual values. This procedure accounts for the fact that the ear's loudness response is frequency-dependent, while utilizing the simplicity of the sound-level meter. The Stevens Mark VI method, summarized in Chap. 2, is the currently accepted procedure for evaluating loudness. In this procedure, the spectrum is divided into either octave or 1/3-octave divisions. The octave-band breakdown is most useful for field work because of the small number of measurements required, while the 1/3-octave breakdown is more precise for laboratory work. It is questionable whether the added precision of the latter would be warranted for field data. The octave-band breakdown will be used in this exercise because of the relative ease of its application.

In determining the loudness, nine octave-band levels (31.5- to 8000-Hz center frequencies) are measured at the listener's position. Table 2.1 in Chap. 2 is used to determine the loudness index S_i for each band level. The total loudness S is then determined from the empirical summation

$$S = 0.7 \, S_{\max} + 0.3 \, S_{\text{total}} \qquad \text{sones}$$

where $S_{\max}$ is the highest of the loudness indices and S_{total} is the sum of all the loudness indices, in sones.

Table L2.5a illustrates this procedure for a set of nine octave-band readings. The sound being considered has a *subjective loudness* of 37 sones: it is 37 times louder than a reference 1000-Hz tone at 40 dB. Table 2.1 also shows that this corresponds to a *loudness level* of 92 phons, meaning that it is as loud as a 1000-Hz octave-band noise at 92 dB.

After the Mark VI method has been applied, it is possible to arrange the octave bands in descending order of loudness and, with some knowledge of the noise sources in the sound environment, to determine which sources should be treated first to reduce loudness. The effects of successful treatment can then be estimated by assuming considerable reduction of loudness index in the treated octave bands and recalculating the projected loudness.

Comparing loudness indices in Table L2.5a, it is evident that sources associated with the 8000-, 1000-, and 500-Hz octave bands should be treated first, in that order, if loudness is to be reduced. If we assume that the source associated with the 8000-Hz octave band is successfully treated, while the other octave-band levels remain unaffected, an estimate of the resulting loudness can be made by ignoring the loudness index (18.7) associated with the 8000-Hz octave band, forming the new sum ($S_{\text{total}} = 61.4$), and determining the next dominant octave band (16.5, in the 1000-Hz band). The projected loudness $S = 29.9$ sones is a reduction of only 20 percent from the original loudness; the treated sound would be as loud as a 1000-Hz tone at 89 dB. It should be evident that a significant reduction in loudness could be achieved only if the sources associated with the 1000-Hz and 500-Hz octave bands are also considered for treatment.

When it is necessary to determine only the loudness *ranking* of the octave bands and not the subjective loudness itself, the expedient method illustrated in Table L2.5b works very well:

Table 2-1 Band-level conversion to loudness index

Band level, dB	i31.5	63	125	250	500	1000	2000	4000	8000	Loudness, sones	Loudness level, phons
			Band loudness index								
20						.18	.30	.45	.61	.25	20
21						.22	.35	.50	.67	.27	21
22					.07	.26	.40	.55	.73	.29	22
23					.12	.30	.45	.61	.80	.31	23
24					.16	.35	.50	.67	.87	.33	24
25					.21	.40	.55	.73	.94	.35	25
26					.26	.45	.61	.80	1.02	.38	26
27					.31	.50	.67	.87	1.10	.41	27
28				.07	.37	.55	.73	.94	1.18	.44	28
29				.12	.43	.61	.80	1.02	1.27	.47	29
30				.16	.49	.67	.87	1.10	1.35	.50	30
31				.21	.55	.73	.94	1.18	1.44	.54	31
32				.26	.61	.80	1.02	1.27	1.54	.57	32
33				.31	.67	.87	1.10	1.35	1.64	.62	33
34			.07	.37	.73	.94	1.18	1.44	1.75	.66	34
35			.12	.43	.80	1.02	1.27	1.54	1.87	.71	35
36			.16	.49	.87	1.10	1.35	1.64	1.99	.76	36
37			.21	.55	.94	1.18	1.44	1.75	2.11	.81	37
38			.26	.62	1.02	1.27	1.54	1.87	2.24	.87	38
39			.31	.69	1.10	1.35	1.64	1.99	2.38	.93	39
40		.07	.37	.77	1.18	1.44	1.75	2.11	2.53	1.00	40
41		.12	.43	.85	1.27	1.54	1.87	2.24	2.68	1.07	41
42		.16	.49	.94	1.35	1.64	1.99	2.38	2.84	1.15	42
43		.21	.55	1.04	1.44	1.75	2.11	2.53	3.0	1.23	43
44		.26	.62	1.13	1.54	1.87	2.24	2.68	3.2	1.32	44
45		.31	.69	1.23	1.64	1.99	2.38	2.84	3.4	1.41	45
46	.07	.37	.77	1.33	1.75	2.11	2.53	3.0	3.6	1.52	46
47	.12	.43	.85	1.44	1.87	2.24	2.68	3.2	3.8	1.62	47
48	.16	.49	.94	1.56	1.99	2.38	2.84	3.4	4.1	1.74	48
49	.21	.55	1.04	1.69	2.11	2.53	3.0	3.6	4.3	1.87	49
50	.26	.62	1.13	1.82	2.24	2.68	3.2	3.8	4.6	2.00	50
51	.31	.69	1.23	1.96	2.38	2.84	3.4	4.1	4.9	2.14	51
52	.37	.77	1.33	2.11	2.53	3.0	3.6	4.3	5.2	2.30	52
53	.43	.85	1.44	2.24	2.68	3.2	3.8	4.6	5.5	2.46	53
54	.49	.94	1.56	2.38	2.84	3.4	4.1	4.9	5.8	2.64	54
55	.55	1.04	1.69	2.53	3.0	3.6	4.3	5.2	6.2	2.83	55
56	.62	1.13	1.82	2.68	3.2	3.8	4.6	5.5	6.6	3.03	56
57	.69	1.23	1.96	2.84	3.4	4.1	4.9	5.8	7.0	3.25	57
58	.77	1.33	2.11	3.0	3.6	4.3	5.2	6.2	7.4	3.48	58
59	.85	1.44	2.27	3.2	3.8	4.6	5.5	6.6	7.8	3.73	59
60	.94	1.56	2.44	3.4	4.1	4.9	5.8	7.0	8.3	4.00	60
61	1.04	1.69	2.62	3.6	4.3	5.2	6.2	7.4	8.8	4.29	61
62	1.13	1.82	2.81	3.8	4.6	5.5	6.6	7.8	9.3	4.59	62
63	1.23	1.96	3.0	4.1	4.9	5.8	7.0	8.3	9.9	4.92	63
64	1.33	2.11	3.2	4.3	5.2	6.2	7.4	8.8	10.5	5.28	64
65	1.44	2.27	3.5	4.6	5.5	6.6	7.8	9.3	11.1	5.66	65
66	1.56	2.44	3.7	4.9	5.8	7.0	8.3	9.9	11.8	6.06	66
67	1.69	2.62	4.0	5.2	6.2	7.4	8.8	10.5	12.6	6.50	67
68	1.82	2.81	4.3	5.5	6.6	7.8	9.3	11.1	13.5	6.96	68
69	1.96	3.0	4.7	5.8	7.0	8.3	9.9	11.8	14.4	7.46	69
70	2.11	3.2	5.0	6.2	7.4	8.8	10.5	12.6	15.3	8.00	70
71	2.27	3.5	5.4	6.6	7.8	9.3	11.1	13.5	16.4	8.6	71
72	2.44	3.7	5.8	7.0	8.3	9.9	11.8	14.4	17.5	9.2	72
73	2.62	4.0	6.2	7.4	8.8	10.5	12.6	15.3	18.7	9.8	73
74	2.81	4.3	6.6	7.8	9.3	11.1	13.5	16.4	20.0	10.6	74

Table 2-1 (Continued)

Band level, dB	Band loudness index									Loudness, sones	Loudness level, phons
	31.5	63	125	250	500	1000	2000	4000	8000		
75	3.0	4.7	7.0	8.3	9.9	11.8	14.4	17.5	21.4	11.3	75
76	3.2	5.0	7.4	8.8	10.5	12.6	15.3	18.7	23.0	12.1	76
77	3.5	5.4	7.8	9.3	11.1	13.5	16.4	20.0	24.7	13.0	77
78	3.7	5.8	8.3	9.9	11.8	14.4	17.5	21.4	26.5	13.9	78
79	4.0	6.2	8.8	10.5	12.6	15.3	18.7	23.0	28.5	14.9	79
80	4.3	6.7	9.3	11.1	13.5	16.4	20.0	24.7	30.5	16.0	80
81	4.7	7.2	9.9	11.8	14.4	17.5	21.4	26.5	32.9	17.1	81
82	5.0	7.7	10.5	12.6	15.3	18.7	23.0	28.5	35.3	18.4	82
83	5.4	8.2	11.1	13.5	16.4	20.0	24.7	30.5	38.	19.7	83
84	5.8	8.8	11.8	14.4	17.5	21.4	26.5	32.9	41.	21.1	84
85	6.2	9.4	12.6	15.3	18.7	23.0	28.5	35.3	44.	22.6	85
86	6.7	10.1	13.5	16.4	20.0	24.7	30.5	38.	48.	24.3	86
87	7.2	10.9	14.4	17.5	21.4	26.5	32.9	41.	52.	26.0	87
88	7.7	11.7	15.3	18.7	23.0	28.5	35.3	44.	56.	27.9	88
89	8.2	12.6	16.4	20.0	24.7	30.5	38.	48.	61.	29.9	89
90	8.8	13.6	17.5	21.4	26.5	32.9	41.	52.	66.	32.0	90
91	9.4	14.8	18.7	23.0	28.5	35.3	44.	56.	71.	34.3	91
92	10.1	16.0	20.0	24.7	30.5	38.	48.	61.	77.	36.8	92
93	10.9	17.3	21.4	26.5	32.9	41.	52.	66.	83.	39.4	93
94	11.7	18.7	23.0	28.5	35.3	44.	56.	71.	90.	42.2	94
95	12.6	20.0	24.7	30.5	38.	48.	61.	77.	97.	45.3	95
96	13.6	21.4	26.5	32.9	41.	52.	66.	83.	105.	48.5	96
97	14.8	23.0	28.5	35.3	44.	56.	71.	90.	113.	52.0	97
98	16.0	24.7	30.5	38.	48.	61.	77.	97.	121.	55.7	98
99	17.3	26.5	32.9	41.	52.	66.	83.	105.	130.	59.7	99
100	18.7	28.5	35.3	44.	56.	71.	90.	113.	139.	64.0	100
101	20.3	30.5	38.	48.	61.	77.	97.	121.	149.	68.6	101
102	22.1	32.9	41.	52.	66.	83.	105.	130.	160.	73.5	102
103	24.0	35.3	44.	56.	71.	90.	113.	139.	171.	78.8	103
104	26.1	38.	48.	61.	77.	97.	121.	149.	184.	84.4	104
105	28.5	41.	52.	66.	83.	105.	130.	160.	197.	90.5	105
106	31.0	44.	56.	71.	90.	113.	139.	171.	211.	97.	106
107	33.9	48.	61.	77.	97.	121.	149.	184.	226.	104.	107
108	36.9	52.	66.	83.	105.	130.	160.	197.	242.	111.	108
109	40.3	56.	71.	90.	113.	139.	171.	211.	260.	119.	109
110	44.	61.	77.	97.	121.	149.	184.	226.	278.	128.	110
111	49.	66.	83.	105.	130.	160.	197.	242.	298.	137.	111
112	54.	71.	90.	113.	139.	171.	211.	260.	320.	147.	112
113	59.	77.	97.	121.	149.	184.	226.	278.	343.	158.	113
114	65.	83.	105.	130.	160.	197.	242.	298.	367.	169.	114
115	71.	90.	113.	139.	171.	211.	260.	320.		181.	115
116	77.	97.	121.	149.	184.	226.	278.	343.		194.	116
117	83.	105.	130.	160.	197.	242.	298.	367.		208.	117
118	90.	113.	139.	171.	211.	260.	320.			233.	118
119	97.	121.	149.	184.	226.	278.	343.			239.	119
120	105.	130.	160.	197.	242.	298.	367.			256.	120
121	113.	139.	171.	211.	260.	320.				274.	121
122	121.	149.	184.	226.	278.	343.				294.	122
123	130.	160.	197.	242.	298.	367.				315.	123
124	139.	171.	211.	260.	320.					338.	124
125	149.	184.	226.	278.	343.					362.	125

Source: A. P. G. Peterson and E. E. Gross, *Handbook of Noise Measurement*, 7th ed., General Radio Company, Concord, Mass., 1972, pp. 25–26.

Table L2.5 Determination of subjective loudness from octave-band readings

(a) Using band loudness index S_i from Table 2.1

	Center frequency, Hz								
	31.5	63	125	250	500	1000	2000	4000	8000
Band level, dB	60	60	76	76	80	80	60	60	73
Band loudness index, S_i (see Table 2.1)	0.94	1.56	7.4	8.8	13.5	16.4	5.8	7.0	18.7
Ranking	9	8	5	4	3	2	7	6	1

$S_{total} = \Sigma S_i = 80.1$; $S_{max} = 18.7$ (at 8000 Hz)

Loudness $S = 0.7 \times (18.7) + 0.3 \times (80.1) = 37.12 \sim 37$ sones

Loudness level = 92 phons

(b) Using expedient method (for ranking only)

	Center frequency, Hz								
	31.5	63	125	250	500	1000	2000	4000	8000
Band level, dB	60	60	76	76	80	80	60	60	73
Adjustment	0	+3	+6	+9	+12	+15	+18	+21	+24
Ranking level	60	63	82	85	92	95	78	81	97
Ranking	9	8	5	4	3	2	7	6	1

add 0, 3, 6, . . . , 24 to the readings in the 31.5-, 63-, 125-, . . . , 8000-Hz octave bands, respectively. The ranking of the adjusted readings will correspond closely to the ranking obtained by comparing loudness indices. Note that the ranking is identical with that obtained in L2.5a from the same octave-band data.

Evaluating speech interference and annoyances Experiments have shown that sound in the 500-, 1000-, and 2000-Hz octave bands has the greatest influence on speech perception. Consequently, the expected speech interference of a sound environment is estimated by computing the so-called PSIL (three-band preferred speech-interference level) from the average of the 500-, 1000-, and 2000-Hz octave-band levels. The resulting figure is compared with empirical evidence (Chap. 2) to evaluate the sound field's acceptability. In a similar manner, the annoyance potential of a sound environment for a particular human activity is determined from octave-band data using the NC (noise criteria) rating procedure outlined in Chap. 7. Other procedures, experimentally determined and described in specific detail, are used to evaluate community response, privacy, etc. The user should attempt to determine the most suitable procedure and make measurements accordingly.

L2.5 Experiment

To begin the exercise, the reader should carefully obtain overall, A-weighted, and octave-band levels at a typical listener's position in a sound environment. The environment should be produced by two or more combined sources with a wide range of frequencies. Techniques developed in Lab 1 should be used to obtain these readings. Note that a sound-level meter with an octave-band filter set is needed to carry out this experiment. A period of familiarization may be needed if the filter set is being used for the first time, but the procedure is basically the same as that used to select weighting (A, B, C) networks. Once the data are obtained, they will be used to:

1. Estimate the subjective loudness of the environment
2. Estimate the overall and A-weighted sound-pressure levels from octave-band readings (these can be compared with the direct readings)
3. Estimate the speech-interference level of the environment
4. (Very important) predict the effects on these subjective measures of removing sources. Verify by turning off sources.

A suggested calculation scheme is shown in Table L2.6.

The reader can estimate the potential effects of environmental changes by ignoring selected octave-band levels in Table L2.6 and repeating the loudness, PSIL, and dBA estimates. From these evaluations, it can be determined that:

1. Noise treatments are most effective if directed toward the greatest contributors first. Treating the lesser contributor is practically useless until after the larger contributor has been reduced to the level of the lesser contributor.
2. Nearly equal contributors must be reduced together in order to realize a benefit.

If only a Type 2 sound-level meter is available, modified criteria based on A-weighted levels may be employed to evaluate loudness and speech interference (see Fig. 2.13). Combined sound fields can be created by using multiple noise sources. Note that two or more levels can be properly combined and compared only if they are obtained through the same weighting network (A, B, C, D, or linear). It is not correct to combine two levels obtained through different weighting networks—for example; 70 dBA + 70 dBC $\neq$ 73 dB(?).

Table L2.6 Tabulation scheme for Lab 2

Octave band, Hz	Overall level		Loudness		Loudness Ranking			A-weighted level			PSIL
	Level, dB	Combinations	Loudness index, sones	Rank	Adjustment, dB	Modified level, dB	Rank	Adjustment dB	Adjusted band level, dB	Combinations	Band level, dB
31.5					0			−39.4			X
63					3			−26.2			X
125					6			−16.1			X
250					9			−8.6			X
500					12			−3.2			
1000					15			±0			
2000					18			+1.2			
4000					21			+1.0			X
8000					24			−1.1			X
16000					—			—			X

S_{max} = _____ sones

S_{total} = _____ sones

$S = 0.75 S_{max} + 0.3 S_{total}$ = _____ sones

$PSIL = \dfrac{L_{p500} + L_{p1000} + L_{p2000}}{3}$ = _____ dB

Weighting	Level, dB
A	
B	
C	
D	
Linear	

LAB 3 FIELD MEASUREMENTS OF ROOM ABSORPTION AND REVERBERATION TIME

L3.1 Prediction of Sound Levels in Enclosures

It was shown in Chap. 4 that the sound field produced in a room by a given source is dependent not only upon the acoustic power and directivity of the source but also on the absorption properties of the room itself. The equation commonly used to predict the sound-pressure level in a typical room has been shown to be:

$$L_p = L_w + 10 \log_{10}\left(\frac{Q}{4\pi r^2} + \frac{4}{a}\right) \quad \text{dB} \tag{L3.1}$$

where L_p = sound-pressure level at a distance r from the source, dB Re 2×10^{-5} N/m^2

L_w = sound-power level of the source, dB Re 10^{-12} W

Q = source directivity in its proposed configuration

a = room absorption, m^2 (sabins)

r = distance from source, m

The acoustic power L_w of the source may be provided by the manufacturer. The term $Q/4\pi r^2$ describes the square-law reduction of the direct-sound field as the observer moves away from the source; the term $4/a$ is dependent on room absorption and is usually assumed independent of position in the room. The room absorption a can be estimated using the equation derived in Chap. 4 and a knowledge of the absorption properties of the room materials:

$$a = \sum_{i=1}^{n} \alpha_i S_i = \bar{\alpha} S \tag{L3.2}$$

where n = number of different absorbing surfaces in the room

S_i = area of the ith absorbing surface

α_i = absorption coefficient of ith surface

$\bar{\alpha}$ = room-averaged sound absorption coefficient

S = total room area

Alternatively, the room absorption can be determined from the measured reverberation time T of the room

$$a = \frac{0.16V}{T} \tag{L3.3}$$

where V is the room volume in cubic meters and T is the reverberation time in seconds required for the sound intensity to decay 60 dB after the source is shut off. The latter method for determining the room absorption is preferred, since the reverberation time is characteristic of the actual response of the room.

In practice, the reverberation time is determined at each octave-band center frequency, and the octave-band sound level is then predicted from the manufacturer's data on octave-band power levels of the source using Eqs. (L3.1) and (L3.3). Properly combining the octave-band levels as described in Sec. L2.3 then leads to predicted A-weighted levels in the enclosure. Third-octave-band levels could also be estimated in this way, but at considerably greater expense.

L3.2 Practical Aspects of Measuring Reverberation Times

The procedure for evaluating reverberation time is basically very simple: a sound is generated in the enclosure or room and then cut off abruptly. The sound-pressure level is measured and (preferably) recorded as it decays. The reverberation time is computed by extrapolating the decay curve of the sound-level history to a 60-dB drop and measuring the time required for that drop. Figure L3.1 illustrates this procedure. Since Eq. (L3.1) assumes that a diffuse reverberant sound field exists in a large room, several practical requirements must be met in order to satisfy the premises of these equations:

1. *The sound field must be diffuse*—the intensity should be uniform throughout the room and sound should approach the microphone uniformly from all directions. Since sound reflected from an absorbing wall cannot have the same intensity as sound from other directions, it is evident that this condition cannot be met near absorbing surfaces. Therefore, all measurements used in Eq. (L3.1) must be made at least 1/3 wavelength from walls, ceilings, floors, and other large obstacles. Since standing waves can occur with continuous pure-tone sources, the intensity may not be uniform throughout the room unless measures are taken to better distribute the sound energy over the room volume—for example:
   (*a*) Warble tones or random noise sources may be used, rather than pure tones, to reduce standing-wave differences.
   (*b*) Gunshots, popping balloons, or other impulsive sources may be employed; standing waves, being steady-state phenomena, do not have sufficient time to develop.

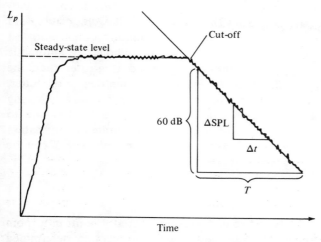

Figure L3.1 Typical sound-pressure level history during a reverberation time test.

(c) Rotating reflectors may be placed in the room to improve the diffusing of sound throughout the room.

2. *The room must be large*—so that the reverberation time will not be dependent upon the positions of the source and the microphone. A room can be considered large when both of the following conditions are satisfied:

$$V > 4\lambda^3 \quad \text{and} \quad l > 1.5\lambda$$

where V and l are the volume and shortest major dimension of the room, respectively, and λ is the longest wavelength being considered. When the room is not large, care must be taken to locate the source and the microphone in the zones of the expected major source and receiver, and the sound field should be sampled over a volume of at least $\lambda/2$ diameter in order to determine average reverberation time.

3. *The test source must be powerful enough to permit an accurate extrapolation of the decay.* The sound-pressure level should be raised at least 30 dB above ambient level so that at least 20 dB of decay can be used to establish the decay slope. If a speaker is used as the noise source, the electrical signal can be filtered to concentrate the acoustic energy in the frequency band of interest and raise the sound level in that frequency range. Warble tones can also achieve this concentration without filtration. If the background level is too high because of duct noise or operating equipment, it may also be necessary to filter the microphone output to suppress sound outside the frequency range of interest. If both source and microphone are filtered, the filters should cover the frequency range of interest, with the microphone filter narrower than the source filter, if possible.

4. *Human measurement errors should be reduced*—by plotting sound-pressure-level history automatically, rather than relying on a stopwatch and sound-level-meter reading. At least three runs should be made at each position and frequency of interest. The microphone should be omnidirectional, and test equipment should not be located close to the microphone. If automatic plotting is used, make certain that the writing speed is greater than the expected decay rate. Typical decay curves exhibit a certain degree of flutter, as sound energy reaches the microphone in bursts from faraway reflecting surfaces. A smooth decay curve implies that the writing speed is too slow to catch these variations and may be too slow to permit accurate determination of reverberation time. In this case, accurate decay measurements can be obtained only if the writing speed is increased.

L3.3 Experiment

The reader will predict and verify the sound-pressure level at a point in a room arising from a source of known acoustic power, using absorption determined from reverberation-time measurements.

Familiarization This experiment requires a considerable amount of equipment. The *sound-generation* system should produce either an impulsive or continuous random signal and should be capable of being shut off within milliseconds. A speaker-amplifier combination, driven by a signal generator with a push-button shut-off, will satisfy this requirement. In a typical room of classroom size, a 30- to 50-W system will suffice. The *sound-measurement* system should consist of a sound-level meter with octave-band filter and readout into a strip-chart recorder. The recorder should be fast enough to track the decaying signal. The scale should be compatible with the signal from the sound-level meter: preferably the *level* should be plotted on a linear scale, so that the decay curve will be linear with respect to time. To check the charting speed, abruptly disconnect the cable leading into the recorder terminal and note the slope of the recorder's return to zero. Sound-decay plots which seem to have the same slope are not being properly tracked by the recorder, and an increase in charting speed is necessary. Familiarization should start with the sound-generation and sound-measurement systems operating separately, then together.

Reverberation-time measurements The sound-generating and recording systems (assuming a speaker source) should be set up in a room and connected as shown in Fig. L3.2. The sound source should be turned on to generate sound in the room and then abruptly turned off. The strip-chart record of the sound-level decay will provide the information needed to determine the reverberation time. (Refer to Sec. 6.1 for further discussion on measurement of reverberation times.)

1. Determine reverberation times in the room at 125-, 150-, 500-, 1000-, 2000-, and 4000-Hz center frequencies, using at least three sample sound-decay runs per frequency. If the room can be considered small at the lower frequencies, place the source, speaker, and receiver microphone at typical positions and make note of this fact on the data sheet.
2. Compare the measured value of reverberation time at 500 Hz with the range of values recommended in Fig. 6.2 for the same type of room.

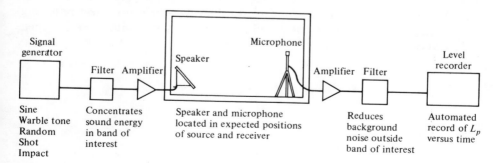

Figure L3.2 Experiment for determining room absorption from reverberation time or L_p decay slope.

Room absorption estimates

1. Compute the effective room absorption a in square meters from the reverberation times calculated above. Note that the absorption is a function of frequency.
2. Estimate the effective room absorption from Eq. (L3.2) using values for α_i from Tables 8.2–8.6. Compare the estimated values with those computed in part 1 from reverberation-time measurements.
3. Compute the average room absorption $\bar{\alpha}$:
   (a) Using the value of a computed in part 1.
   (b) Using the value of a computed in part 2.
4. How much should the absorption be increased or reduced to produce the recommended reverberation time at 500 Hz (Fig. 6.2)?

Sound-level predictions

1. If a sound source of known band-power levels is available, use the room absorption values computed above to predict the 500-Hz and 1000-Hz octave-band sound levels which would be produced at three different locations in the room.
2. Place the known source at a fixed position in the room (preferably the speaker location of the reverberation-time experiment), and measure the actual sound level produced at each of the three positions. Compare these levels with the predicted levels. See Sec. 4.5 when estimating the directivity Q.

Sound-power estimates If a sound source with known sound-power levels is not available, place an arbitrary sound source at a location near the center of the room.

1. Measure the octave-band sound levels at a convenient microphone location.
2. Using these levels, plus the computed room absorption, estimate the acoustic-power levels in several octave bands for the unknown source.
3. Repeat 1 and 2 with the source placed near an edge (or corner) of the room. Adjust the value of Q to account for placement of the source near reflecting surfaces, and compare the computed sound-power levels with those obtained in 2 above.

LAB 4 FIELD MEASUREMENTS OF TRANSMISSION LOSS AND NOISE REDUCTION

L4.1 Prediction of Noise Reduction through Partitions

It is good engineering practice to separate noisy equipment from areas requiring relatively quiet backgrounds, by either enclosing the source or removing the source to another room. When separating the source from the receiver by a partition, it is important to be able to estimate the sound level expected in the receiving room during operation of the source in the adjoining room (source room). Consider two adjoining rooms (Fig. L4.1) separated by a partition of area S_{12}. If careful measures are taken to intercept or block all flanking paths, the wall provides the only path for sound to pass from the source in room 1 to the receiver in room 2. The sound-pressure level L_{p2} in room 2 will then depend to a large degree on the level L_{p1} in room 1 and the ability (TL) of the wall to act as a barrier. To a lesser degree the absorption a_2 in the receiver room will modify and tend to reduce the resulting steady-state level L_{p2} in the receiver room.

The sound level L_{p2} is estimated from knowledge of L_{p1}, TL, and a_2, using the formula:

$$L_{p2} = L_{p1} - TL + 10 \log_{10}\left(\frac{S_{12}}{a_2}\right) \qquad \text{dB} \qquad (\text{L4.1})$$

where the partition area S_{12} and room absorption a_2 are expressed in the same area units. The room absorption a_2 and the source level L_{p1} can be calculated or measured using techniques and equations described in Lab. 3; the transmission loss TL can be estimated using tabulated data obtained under laboratory test conditions. Laboratory estimates of transmission loss are usually higher than those realized under field conditions, since in the laboratory the test partition is carefully fabricated and sealed against flanking paths and leaks, while the field

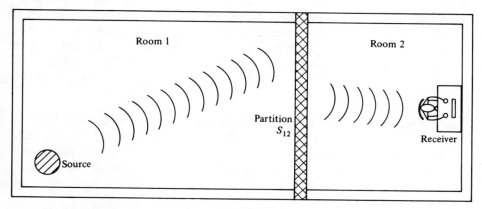

Figure L4.1 Sound transmission through a separating partition.

version of the same partition usually contains openings for wiring, pipes, vents, seams, etc., and is installed with relatively little concern for flanking paths, unless rigidly specified otherwise.

The transmission loss TL is a property of a partition's construction, while the total noise reduction NR($= L_{p1} - L_{p2}$) is dependent not only on the partition (TL) but also on the absorption (a_2) of the receiving room. At a field installation, the noise reduction NR, defined by

$$NR = L_{p1} - L_{p2} \qquad (L4.2)$$

is relatively easy to determine by testing, and it leads directly to estimates of TL by the equation

$$NR = TL - 10 \log_{10}\left(\frac{S_{12}}{a_2}\right) \qquad (L4.3)$$

Both the transmission loss TL and noise reduction NR are functions of frequency. Once the band levels L_{p1} and transmission loss TL or noise reduction NR are determined in each band over the frequency range of interest, the band levels L_{p2} in the receiving room can be estimated using (L4.1) or (L4.2). These band levels can then be combined to estimate weighted levels, using techniques illustrated in Lab 2.

L4.2 Practical Aspects of Measuring Transmission Loss or Noise Reduction

The American National Standards Institute (ANSI) prescribes a standard method for evaluating transmission loss. However, the procedure is tedious, requiring measurements in each 1/3-octave band of the spectrum. Information usable to a plant engineer can still be obtained from a simpler procedure, requiring octave-band measurements, provided the premises of Eqs. (L4.1) and (L4.2) are met in the sound field. The basic procedure suggested by Eqs. (L4.1) and (L4.2) is straightforward: a continuous sound is generated on one side of a partition between two rooms. The space-averaged band levels are measured in each room, and the noise reduction NR is computed for each center frequency using Eq. (L4.2). The transmission loss TL is then computed from each NR figure using Eq. (L4.3) and estimated room absorption a_2 at each center frequency. Since Eqs. (L4.1) and (L4.2) assume that a diffuse field exists in both rooms, the limitations and requirements laid out in Lab 3 also apply to the measurement of partition properties:

1. *Both sound fields must be diffuse*—the intensity should be uniform in both rooms, and measurements should be taken at least 1/3 wavelength from walls and obstacles to ensure this condition. Since standing waves may occur with pure-tone components, the intensity may not be uniform in either room. Special measures may be taken to ensure the diffuseness conditions, for example:
   (a) Warble tones or random noise sources may be used to reduce standing waves.

(*b*) Rotating reflectors may be used to improve diffusion.

(*c*) Measurements should not be taken in the direct field, nor should the direct component be dominant near the partition in the source room.

2. *Both rooms must be large* relative to the longest wavelength of interest. A room is considered large when both of the following conditions are satisfied:

$$V > 4\lambda^3 \quad \text{and} \quad l > 1.5\lambda$$

where V and l are the volume and shortest major dimension of the room, respectively, and λ is the longest wavelength being considered (corresponding to octave-band center frequency).

3. *The sound power of the source* must be sufficient to raise the band level L_{p2} in the *receiver* room at least 10 dB above the ambient level. It may be necessary to filter both the source signal and the receiver microphone output in order to achieve this increase in the frequency bands of interest, particularly if the partition is a good barrier (a 50- to 100-W speaker-amplifier system will serve well as a source in many practical cases).

4. *Space-averaged sound levels must be determined.* Since Eq. (L4.1) is derived from a power balance, levels L_{p1} and L_{p2} must be averaged from numerous readings over the room volumes. Microphone readings must be taken from positions no less than 1/2 wavelength apart, to ensure independence of the readings. Given M readings from M points distributed over the volume of the room, the space-averaged sound-pressure level $L_{\bar{p}}$ is obtained from the average intensity in the room:

$$L_{\bar{p}} = 10 \log_{10}\left[\left(\frac{p_1^2}{p_{\text{ref}}^2} + \frac{p_2^2}{p_{\text{ref}}^2} + \cdots + \frac{p_M^2}{p_{\text{ref}}^2}\right) \Big/ M\right] \quad (L4.4)$$

or

$$L_{\bar{p}} = 10 \log_{10}\left[\frac{p_1^2}{p_{\text{ref}}^2} + \frac{p_2^2}{p_{\text{ref}}^2} + \cdots + \frac{p_M^2}{p_{\text{ref}}^2}\right] - 10 \log_{10}(M) \quad (L4.5)$$

where the first term can be determined by combining the M levels as if they came from separate sources.

The estimate of space-averaged sound-pressure level improves as the number M of microphone positions is increased. A relatively large number of measurements is required when the source has pure-tone components, while considerably fewer are required when a random source is used and a diffuse field is produced by means of diffusors. Figure L4.2 presents a plot of the probabilities that the estimated space-averaged sound-pressure level, determined from sampling M microphone positions at least $\lambda/2$ apart, will fall within $\pm 1/2$, ± 1, or ± 2 dB of the true space-averaged sound-pressure level. For example, the dashed lines on this figure illustrate that 40 microphone positions spaced at least 1/2 wavelength apart will produce an estimate within ± 2 dB at 99 percent probability (or within ± 1 dB at 87 percent probability) in a field generated by a pure-tone source. If a random source is used and diffusers employed, as few as four ($M/10 \doteq 4$) positions may suffice. Note that if only one microphone

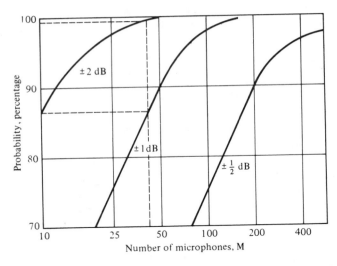

Figure L4.2 Criterion for determining the number of microphone positions needed to estimate the true space-averaged sound-pressure level. The number of microphone positions (M) is determined for pure tones. Divided M by up to 10 if diffusers are used and the source produces random noise.

position is used, the probability of estimating the true space-averaged level within ± 1 dB is too low to justify the procedure for any source.

In general, it is incorrect to use the *numerical* average of the readings; the numerical average is always lower than the true average, with the discrepancy worsening as the difference between the highest and lowest readings increases. On the other hand, when the difference between upper and lower readings is 5 dB or less, and the readings occur with more or less equal probability, the discrepancy between true and numerical averages is insignificant for field measurements.*

L4.3 Experiment

The reader will predict and verify sound-pressure levels in a receiving room while a noise source operates in an adjoining source room, using noise-reduction or transmission-loss data to characterize the partition effects.

Site and equipment The reader should select two rooms separated by one adjoining wall, similar to the arrangement depicted in Fig. L4.1. The wall should be checked carefully to ensure that no ductwork or plenum connects the two rooms in the space above the ceiling, and ideally the wall should contain no windows (unless of special acoustical design). It is important that the wall be

---

* H. Cox, "Linear versus Logarithmic Averaging," *J. Acoust. Soc. Amer.* **39**:688–690 (1966).

homogeneous and provide no air paths between the rooms. Any doorway in the wall should be closed and cracks caulked while making measurements.

The test source should produce random noise and should be situated well away from the wall, so that a reverberant field will predominate within several wavelengths of the wall in both rooms. A 50- to 100-W loudspeaker-amplifier combination, with the loudspeaker facing into a far corner, will normally be adequate for residential rooms or small classrooms. If an engine or other vibrating source is used, it should be isolated from the floor and walls to reduce the possibility of the "flanking" of vibration energy into the receiver room via the building structure.

Preliminary determinations The number of required measurement positions should be estimated for each room, using Fig. L4.2 and aiming for ± 1 dB precision in the estimate. For a random source, at least four positions should be used. The extent of the reverberant field in the source room should be determined, either from observing the sound level as the microphone moves away from the source or by estimation. The measurement stations should then be located at least $\lambda/2$ apart, uniformly distributed through the volume of the reverberant field in each room, taking care to stay at least 1/3 wavelength from the walls, ceilings, floors, and large reflectors, and varying the height, as well as plan, position. A chalk or tape marker can be used to mark each point and indicate measuring height. The longest wavelength of interest should be computed from volume and room dimensions. The absorption of the receiver room should be determined experimentally, or calculated from tabulated absorption coefficients at each center frequency of interest, or estimated assuming $\bar{\alpha} \doteq 0.20$ for common rooms.

Before making measurements, it is desirable that the source raise the measured level in the receiver room by at least 10 dB above the measured ambient level *in the octave band of interest*. If a speaker is used, it may be necessary to concentrate its output by passing the signal through the desired octave filter before amplification. If octave-band-filtered noise is used, the space-averaged levels can be determined using any weighting network (A, B, C, flat, octave-band), provided the same weighting network is used in both rooms.

1. Determine the noise reduction NR of the configuration in the 125-, 250-, 500-, 1000-, 2000-, and 4000-Hz octave bands, if possible, applying the measured space-averaged levels to Eq. (L4.2).
2. Compute partition transmission loss TL in each octave band, employing room absorption a_2 and Eq. (L4.3).
3. Compare the TL with published values for a wall of similar construction. What construction features contribute to the discrepancies, if any? Significant leaks in the partition can be detected by "scanning" the microphone near the wall, particularly in corners, near edges, and at receptacles. Sharp rises in level indicate sources radiating at higher power than that predicted for the theoretical homogeneous wall.

4. Using the experimental TL values, estimate the actual sound transmission class (STC) of the partition. Compared with tabulated values of preferred STC, how well does the wall perform its intended function?

5. Using a different source, measure the space-averaged level L_{p1} in the source room and estimate the expected level L_{p2} in the receiver room, using previously measured values of NR. This need be done for only a few octave-band levels.

6. Measure the actual levels in the receiver room, correct for ambient background if necessary, and compare with the estimated levels. Explain discrepancies, if any.

When only a Type 2 meter is available, the reader can still perform the above experiments if the speaker source is filtered through the necessary octave-band filters before amplification. Even if the source is unfiltered, the reader can still experimentally determine NR for A- or C-weighted levels in step 1, and then estimate A- or C-weighted levels in steps 5 and 6. Unless the spectra of the two sources have radically different shapes, the estimates would still be reasonable for preliminary estimations.

A simplified sampling method, in which a single reading is taken at a one-third point on one of the four room diagonals, can provide reasonable, quick estimates of space-averaged levels. The selected measuring point should be the one nearest to both the partition and the more reflective adjacent surface, and it should not be close to the source.

7. The reader may wish to check the one-third-diagonal proposition by including this point among the measurement points in parts 1 to 6 and comparing results with those obtained from the third-diagonal point alone. (For example, a discrepancy of 3 to 5 in STC would not be considered serious, in view of the uncertainty of human response.)

LAB 5 PLANT NOISE SURVEYS

L5.1 Introduction

An effective program for plant noise control generally consists of hazard identification, monitoring of worker exposure, reduction of hazards, audiometric testing, and education of plant personnel (Chap. 11). The noise survey is an indispensable element of this program, since it provides the data needed to evaluate both the work environment and the changes brought about by modifications. If properly conducted, the plant noise survey also provides important information needed for hazard identification, source and path identification, and selection of feasible control methods. Although experience is an important asset in the conduct of noise surveys, the reader will find that a few basic measuring instruments, applied with common sense, will enable even the newcomer to noise control engineering to obtain the data base needed to initiate a noise control program.

L5.2 Conduct of Noise Surveys

Initial considerations An attempt should be made to collect all available background information about a noise problem before beginning a survey. This information can often be obtained by reading plant layouts and discussing the potential problems with appropriate supervisory and shop personnel. Background investigation should consider suspected problem areas, associated noise regulations, and appropriate measuring techniques before committing time and resources to a full-scale plant survey. In particular, the reader should establish the following information beforehand [2]:

1. *Why is the survey being made?* Is the problem one of community annoyance, speech impairment, hearing damage?
2. *What regulations, criteria, or standards apply to the problem?* These are usually documented in sufficient detail to determine the measurement techniques needed to evaluate the environment. They should be reviewed before the plant survey is conducted.
3. *What are probable sources of noise and vibration?* What operational features produce the objectionable sound? What are their duty cycles? Where can measurements be taken? The use of plant layouts, personal visits, and the telephone can produce valuable information.
4. *What are the characteristics of the sound?* Is it intermittent, impulsive, periodic, pure-tone, random, continuous? These characteristics may govern the choice of instrumentation and measurement procedures.
5. *Where are the affected personnel?* What are their exposures? Are there

conditions such as humidity, temperature, or flying particles which preclude or modify the use of some instruments?

A plant engineer may already know the answers to many of these questions. Decisions on the selection and use of instrumentation, and the plan for their deployment, can usually be settled quickly once this information is available.

Equipment When selecting equipment for field measurements, a premium is placed on size, weight, and convenience of use. A basic system for field measurements should consist of a portable sound-level meter and calibrator. These should be rugged, battery-operated, and reasonably lightweight, and the sound-level meter should conform to American National Standards Institute Standard ANSI S1.4-1971, "Sound-Level Meters." Whenever sound sources are to be analyzed at the site and perhaps modified, an octave-band filter set or analyzer should also be included. If detailed narrow-band analysis is to be performed, or if more sophisticated signal analysis is to be conducted in a laboratory, a tape recorder may be needed to bridge the gap between field measurements and laboratory analysis. The tape recorder must have uniform gain over the frequency range of interest; accurate speed control, with low distortion, flutter, and wow; and a dynamic range wide enough to capture both the highest- and lowest-intensity signals of significance.

It is important to become familiar with the instruments *prior to* making field measurements. In fact, it is good practice to assemble and operate the selected instruments in your shop or laboratory before using them in the field. This ensures that batteries, cables, and connectors are available and functioning, and that the selected system will perform the job. This "rehearsal" provides a refamiliarization with instrument operation and can save time and money in the long run by avoiding costly delays. Wherever necessary, the operator should also reread the instruction manuals to ascertain the following:

1. What is the principle of operation? Does the meter read peak, rms, or average level?
2. Are precautions needed to prevent overload?
3. What is the usable frequency range of the combined measuring system? What is the dynamic range?
4. How is the system to be calibrated (manufacturer's recommendations should be followed to the letter)?
5. How will interconnection affect the instruments' performance? Will an extension cable affect overall readings?
6. Should the microphone be hand-held or placed on a stand?
7. What is the electrical noise floor in each frequency bandwidth (this places a limit on sensitivity)?
8. Will the expected environment (humidity, wind, radio signals, magnetic fields, barometric pressure) affect the readings significantly?

It is good practice to prepare a checklist to ensure that the instruments perform properly in the plant. A simple checklist is listed below:

____Visually inspect instruments for in-transit damage.

____Recheck batteries. Will they last?

____Calibrate the sound-level meter. Indicate time and calibration level. If a ±0.5-dB change is noted, in-transit damage may have occurred.

____Check electrical noise floor. For a sound-level meter, octave-band readings can be made with an acoustic calibrator placed as a shield over the microphone, but not operating. The noise-floor levels represent the lower bound on readings. Meaningful band levels should exceed the noise floor by at least 10 dB in each octave band.

____Check for shorts or breaks in the cables by flexing the cables near the connectors. Violent fluctuations in needle movement may indicate problems in the cables.

Measurements in the plant Measurement positions can often be selected from plant layouts, but it is still good practice to take a quick tour through the plant, using one's eyes, ears, and a few measurements to verify (or revise) the choice of measuring positions. This also provides the opportunity to observe the movement of personnel, to ask questions of and receive suggestions from the supervisor, to tentatively identify sources and paths, etc., before becoming too involved in the measurements themselves. After this quick tour, the observer is in a better position to decide which locations should receive more attention and which type of measurements should be taken.

Since the microphone can be quite directional at high frequencies, its orientation must be selected to get the most useful results. If omnidirectionality is required, a small-diameter microphone or a random-incidence corrector must be used. Usually, no attempt is made to alter the reflection of sound from nearby objects since these reflections are a part of the sound field in the plant. But, in cases where a particular source must be isolated and analyzed, the microphone should be placed near the source and sound-absorbing material placed on reflecting surfaces to reduce their contribution. If possible, the background sound should be evaluated by turning off the source and then reading octave-band and overall levels. If the overall level exceeds the background level by 10 dB or more, the overall level may be ascribed to the source being studied. If the difference is less than 3 dB, the background sound is dominant, and the source cannot be accurately evaluated. Table L5.1 summarizes corrections that can be subtracted from overall levels to get source levels when the background sound has already been evaluated. (See also Fig. 1.7.)

Meter-reading techniques depend on the sound field being evaluated. The microphone must always be held at least 2 ft from the body, and the hands must not be placed near the microphone when making measurements of any kind.

Table L5.1 Correction for background noise (to be applied separately for each band level)

dB difference between total noise level and background noise level	dB to be subtracted from total noise level to get the noise level owing to the source
8–10	0.5
6–8	1.0
4.5–6	1.5
4–4.5	2.0
3.5	2.5
3	3.0

While taking readings, always take note also of what can be *heard*, since numbers alone cannot convey this information:

1. *Steady noise*—meter reading does not vary more than 3 dB on slow meter response. The average reading over a 10-s interval is taken. If a level in one octave band exceeds adjacent bend levels by more than 5 dB, an audible pure tone may exist. In this case it may be necessary to move the microphone over a volume at least 1/2 wavelength in diameter and to use the average reading over this volume. This event should be noted on the data sheet.
2. *Fluctuating noise*—meter fluctuates over a 3- to 10-dB range on slow meter response. In this case it is more useful to record the high and low readings rather than some "average" reading. In some evaluations where the true average level must be determined, it can be shown that it is usually within 3 dB of the higher reading (slow meter response), regardless of the lower reading. Table L5.2 summarizes this effect.
3. *Nonsteady noise*—meter readings fluctuate more than 10 dB on slow response. In most cases the maximum and minimum levels, along with a statistical description (such as a histogram) of their occurrence, would be

Table L5.2 Obtaining true average reading from uniformly fluctuating levels

Difference between high and low reading	High reading minus true average reading
0	0
3	1
5	2
10	2.5
20	3

appropriate. The events corresponding to the maximum and minimum levels should be carefully noted on the data sheet, and it may be desirable to record the signal along with voice commentary on magnetic tape for laboratory analysis.

4. *Impulsive noise*—in this case the unfiltered peak sound-pressure level, rise time, and duration are usually desired. For evaluating potential hearing damage, a sound-level meter with true-peak-reading capability is needed. If this is not available, an oscilloscope and Polaroid camera may be employed. "Audio" tape recorders will normally be unable to record the impulse well enough to preserve the peak pressure. If in doubt, consult the recorder manufacturer with details of the signal's expected duration and amplitude before attempting use of the tape recorder.

The number of measurements taken around a source will depend on the distribution of the sound field. In plant measurements, the most important locations are the operators' positions at head level. For additional measurements, an imaginary rectangular box should be drawn around the source. Measurements can then be taken at distances of 1 m or four source dimensions (whichever is smaller) from the boundaries, at heights typical of the operator's head position.

L5.3 Records and Accessories

All plant noise measurements should be recorded on standard data forms. Although it requires time to develop and copy a standard form, it is the best means of ensuring that all important data are recorded in a way that is uniform and can be consistently interpreted by everyone in an organization. Moreover, it serves as a checklist which reminds the user to calibrate, check ambient conditions, record instrument descriptions, etc. If many surveys are to be made, the time saved by using a standard form will be considerable.

Sample data forms are shown in Fig. L5.2. Although they may not be completely adequate for the reader's first noise survey, they can provide a starting point. It should be updated and improved continually, as experience dictates; its format must not be allowed to impede judgment, since they should be considered as *guides*, not *rules*, for data recording. The following list presents important features of the data form:

1. *Heading.* Description of conditions that persist throughout testing:
   - Identification of equipment and instruments used
   - Observers, time, and date
   - Calibration levels and check times
   - Pertinent ambient conditions
   - Sheet number and total number of sheets

SOUND-LEVEL SURVEY

DATE_____ SHEET_____ OF____. PROJECT NO._____ ENGINEER_____

Client_____
Project_____
Observers_____

Primary noise source_____
Manufacturer's name and machine_____
designations_____
Operating conditions_____

Secondary sources_____
Manufacturer's name and machine_____
designations_____
Operating conditions_____

INSTRUMENTS
SLM type_____ Ser. No._____
Microphone type_____ Ser. No._____
Filter type_____ Ser. No._____
Calibrator type_____ Ser. No._____
Other type_____ Ser. No._____
Type_____

BLOCK DIAGRAM

Time	Calibra- tion, dB	°F DB	°F WB	% RH	mm Hg.	Wind, mph	Wind direction	Other

Test number	Time, h	POSITION OR SYMBOL (SHOW ON SKETCH)	Conditions of Operation & Measurement	A	OVER ALL	Sound Pressure Level, dB re 2×10^{-5} N/m^2 Octave-Band Center Frequency, Hz								
						31.5	63	125	250	500	1K	2K	4K	8K

COMMENTS & RECOMMENDATIONS (CONTINUE ON REVERSE SIDE)_____

(ATTACH SKETCHES)

Figure L5.2 Sample data sheets—source noise survey. (*See Fig 11.1, p. 328, for plant noise survey form.*)

2. *Descriptions.* Explanation of sources, environment, and apparatus, sufficiently detailed to enable a *colleague* to interpret and use:
   - Measurement areas and microphone locations (see plant layout)
   - Source characteristics, size, speed, operation mode
   - Secondary sources
   - Worker locations
   - Measuring equipment deployment, schematic
3. *Measurements and observations.* List of data needed to evaluate sound fields or sources:
   - Background levels (band or weighted)
   - Meter response (slow or fast)
   - Levels during operation (band or weighted)
   - Weighting network used
   - Observations made during the readings regarding sources, character of sound, operation discrepancies (what do you *hear?*)

Any sketches or observations not already covered should be entered somewhere on the front or back of the form, or on an attached sheet. All impressions and observations should be written down immediately; they can be evaluated later in the quiet of office or work area. Once a set of measurements is completed, attach all pages together and never separate them again. Requests for data should be met with copies, never the original, of the data sheets. As a rule, only raw data (readings) should be entered on the form. Subsequent analysis and conclusions can be performed later, under more relaxed conditions and on more suitable worksheets. Attempting to analyze data on the form itself can lead to loss of data, confusion of information, and even incorrect conclusions.

Useful accessories during plant surveys may include: camera, tape measure, stopwatch, clipboard, crayon or chalk for marking positions, spare batteries and cables, ear protectors, stethoscope, pliers, screwdrivers. An earphone can be connected to the sound level meter to monitor the sound being measured. Noise or "popping" is evidence of trouble which must be remedied before continuing. *Note that calibration checks should be made before and after each important block of readings.*

References

1. *Primer of Plant Noise Measurement and Hearing Test:..g*, General Radio Company, Concord, Mass., 1971.
2. Bruce, R. D., "Field Measurements: Equipment and Techniques," in L. L. Beranek (ed.), *Noise and Vibration Control*, McGraw-Hill, 1971.
3. Peterson, A. P., and E. E. Gross, *Handbook of Noise Measurement*, 7th ed., General Radio Company, Concord, Mass., 1974.

L5.4 Experiment

If possible, the reader should arrange to visit an actual plant site, preferably one containing sources of steady, fluctuating, nonsteady, and impulsive noise. If this experiment is part of a first course in noise control, or if the participant is proceeding on a self-study basis and has had limited experience in noise surveys, an OSHA survey should be conducted.*

For an OSHA survey, this experiment will have two objectives:

1. Identify potentially hazardous areas and work environments in the plant
2. Estimate noise exposure of personnel in the hazardous areas

The reader should review Sec. 11.2 before proceeding with this experiment.

Selection of equipment This is based upon assessment of source types and requirements of the governing regulations or standards. For the OSHA survey, a Type 2 general-purpose sound-level meter and calibrator are primary requirements. If impulsive sounds are present, a meter with a peak-hold capability is needed to evaluate peak levels. At work sites where fluctuating levels in excess of 90 dBA (slow meter response) exist, a noise dosimeter would be helpful to determine total exposure either at a work station or for a particular worker moving between work stations. It may be necessary to pay a preliminary visit to the plant to get an idea of the measurement problems.

Measurements in the plant This task should preferably be conducted with a partner so that ideas can be exchanged. The headings and description on the selected data sheets should be completed and checked before going to the site. At each measuring position, the primary sources contributing to the measured sound should be noted, verifying observations with plant personnel if necessary. If several operating modes are possible, the applicable mode should be noted. In work areas experiencing levels in excess of 90 dBA, it may be necessary to identify specific sources and contributions by turning sources off and on, in sequence, and evaluating changes. Background levels should be established, if possible, during lulls in operation, during breaks, or during periods of relative quiet generated by turning production equipment off. If a plant layout is available, it is extremely useful to write the measured levels at the appropriate locations on the layout. In the OSHA survey, it may also be necessary to indicate the number of people exposed at the measuring position and to determine the approximate exposure time at the indicated level.

Evaluation of data Evaluation should take place after the raw data are recorded and before leaving the plant, making computations on separate paper to avoid defacing the original data sheets. Sites in violation of noise regulations should be identified, and major sources and paths of noise should be determined along with the extent of the violation. If possible, data sheets should be exchanged

---

* The authors have found that many companies, when contacted, will participate in such an experiment in exchange for a brief, confidential report evaluating the work environment in light of the OSHA noise regulation.

between participants to identify deficiencies in the data. Deficiencies in data should be corrected as soon as possible, either through debriefing with plant personnel (or the instructor) or by returning to work sites for additional measurements. If noise reduction measures are planned, it may be necessary to determine whether the measurement is in the direct or reverberant field of major sources, and to attempt assessment of possible changes.

Any deficiencies in the data sheets' format should be corrected and the data sheets later redrawn for subsequent plant surveys.

LAB 6 IDENTIFICATION OF SOURCES

L6.1 Components of Combined Sound Fields

The sound fields encountered in most industrial and community environments usually result from many sources acting either (a) independently, for example, a line of punch presses or traffic at an intersection; or (b) interdependently, for example, the components of a diesel engine or the components of a turbofan engine. The sound-pressure level measured at an observer's position in these combination environments may reflect the contribution from each of the possible sources, but the measurement alone offers no information regarding the major (or minor) contributors to the sound field. In the interest of economy, it is important both to identify the sources of the sound field and to rank these sources in order of their contributions to the total sound field (or the descriptor) to be controlled. The ranking of major sources, coupled with an understanding of the mechanisms by which each source creates its sound, permits development of straightforward, economical noise reduction strategies.

It has been emphasized in Chap. 9 that, for optimum effectiveness, major contributors must be treated *first*; equal contributors must be reduced *together*. Deviations from this strategy can increase the cost of a noise reduction program. It can be a serious error to treat minor sources just because their treatments may be inexpensive while neglecting major sources whose treatments may be relatively expensive. Another type of error is to *overtreat* major sources while ignoring what appear to be relatively minor sources. For example, consider three independent sources producing 85, 80, and 79 dBA at a particular location, which will produce 87 dBA in combination. A 15-dBA reduction in the first source alone would result in an 83-dBA combined level because the second and third sources become dominant after the treatment. An idealized strategy would be to (a) reduce the first source to the next lower level (80 dBA); then (b) reduce the two sources together to the third level (79 dBA); then (c) reduce all three sources together to produce the desired overall level. An overall reduction to 83 dBA would then require reduction of only 7, 2, and 1 dBA, respectively. Reductions of 1 and 2 dBA are usually easy to achieve, but the difference between a 7-dBA and a 15-dBA reduction for the first source could mean a considerable savings in costs.

Source identification is somewhat of an art, in the sense that an understanding of mechanisms and processes must be coupled with knowledge of measurement techniques in order to identify the sources and to quantify their contributions. Both direct and comparative techniques are used to identify sources. The direct methods can often be implemented with a sound-level meter alone, while comparative techniques usually require the use of a spectrum analyzer to obtain quantitative results.

L6.2 Direct Methods of Identification

Most of the direct methods, in which the contribution of each source is determined directly from measurements, are based on the fact that the overall intensity I at any point in a sound field is equal to the sum of intensities associated with each source in the field, where there are m identifiable sources which can be controlled, i.e.,

$$I = I_1 + I_2 + \cdots + I_m + I_n \tag{L6.1}$$

where $m=$ the number of identifiable sources which can be controlled

$I_i=$ the intensity associated with the ith identifiable source

$I_n=$ the intensity associated with the remaining unidentified or uncontrolled sources

When the sources are uncorrelated, the net mean square pressure p^2 can be determined from Eq. (L6.2):

$$\frac{p^2}{p_r^2} = \frac{p_1^2}{p_r^2} + \frac{p_2^2}{p_r^2} + \cdots + \frac{p_m^2}{p_r^2} + \frac{p_n^2}{p_r^2} \tag{L6.2}$$

where $p^2/p_r^2 = 10^{L_p/10}$ and $p_r = 20 \ \mu N/m^2$. Whenever a source is deactivated or modified, the net mean square pressure p^2 is changed in accord with its effect on Eq. (L6.2).

The direct methods of identification require selective activation and/or deactivation of candidate sources. The measured changes in net levels are then used to obtain numerical measures of the source contributions. Three commonly employed procedures can be described on the basis of Eq. (L6.2).

Individual Activation of Sources

This is the most direct approach but often difficult to carry out in practical situations. Each source is activated by itself; the measured level is (obviously) the level contributed by that source alone, plus the "ambient" or "background" noise which exists when all identifiable sources are turned off. It is instructive to illustrate the procedure as follows:

Test 1:
$$\left(\frac{p^2}{p_r^2}\right)_1 = \frac{p_1^2}{p_r^2} + 0 + 0 + 0 + \frac{p_n^2}{p_r^2} = 10^{L_{p1}/10}$$

Test 2:
$$\left(\frac{p^2}{p_r^2}\right)_2 = 0 + \frac{p_2^2}{p_r^2} + 0 + \frac{p_n^2}{p_r^2} = 10^{L_{p2}/10}$$

Test M:
$$\left(\frac{p^2}{p_r^2}\right)_m = 0 + 0 + \cdots + \frac{p_m^2}{p_r^2} + \frac{p_n^2}{p_r^2} = 10^{L_{pm}/10}$$

All sources off:
$$\left(\frac{p^2}{p_r^2}\right)_n = 0 + 0 + \cdots + 0 + \frac{p_n^2}{p_r^2} = 10^{L_{pn}/10}$$

where the ratio p_n^2/p_r^2 is produced by the uncontrolled background noise sources.

The contribution of the ith source is then

$$\left(\frac{p_i^2}{p_r^2}\right) = 10^{L_{pi}/10} - 10^{L_{pn}/10} \tag{L6.3}$$

This approach is convenient to use at worksites where several pieces of equipment operate independently, e.g., fans, furnaces, forklifts, and conveyors at a heat treatment facility. The computations are checked by recombining the individual levels and comparing against the measured overall level.

Sequential Activation of Sources

In using this approach, the sources are activated in sequence until all are operating. The overall level at each increment is recorded and compared with the previous level to evaluate the contribution of the added source. Sequential activation may be necessary whenever sources cannot operate individually. A motor-driven conveyor, dumping parts into a receiving hopper, would be tested by first activating the motor, then engaging the conveyor drive, and, finally, adding parts to the conveyor. The residual or background level would be obtained by deactivating the motor (and conveyor). The equations below describe this procedure.

Test 1:
$$\left(\frac{p^2}{p_r^2}\right)_1 = \frac{p_1^2}{p_r^2} + 0 + \cdots + 0 + \frac{p_n^2}{p_r^2} = 10^{L_{p1}/10}$$

Test 2:
$$\left(\frac{p^2}{p_r^2}\right)_2 = \frac{p_1^2}{p_r^2} + \frac{p_2^2}{p_r^2} + \cdots + 0 + \frac{p_n^2}{p_r^2} = 10^{L_{p2}/10}$$

Test M:
$$\left(\frac{p^2}{p_r^2}\right)_m = \frac{p_1^2}{p_r^2} + \frac{p_2^2}{p_r^2} + \cdots + \frac{p_m^2}{p_r^2} + \frac{p_n^2}{p_r^2} = 10^{L_{pm}/10}$$

All sources off:
$$\left(\frac{p^2}{p_r^2}\right)_n = \frac{p_n^2}{p_r^2} = 10^{(L_p)_n/10}$$

noting that

$$\left(\frac{p^2}{p_r^2}\right)_i = 10^{L_{pi}/10}$$

the contribution of the ith source is determined by subtraction:

$$\frac{p_i^2}{p_r^2} = \left(\frac{p^2}{p_r^2}\right)_i - \left(\frac{p^2}{p_r^2}\right)_{i-1}$$

or

$$\frac{p_i^2}{p_r^2} = 10^{L_{pi}/10} - 10^{L_{pi-1}/10} \tag{L6.4}$$

This approach is most effective if the sources are activated in *ascending order of strength*, so that overall levels increase sufficiently to evaluate the additional contributions. Only the most important sources need be considered, since the weaker sources can be ignored or lumped under the residual term p_n^2/p_r^2.

Sequential Deactivation of Sources

This approach is the reverse of the preceding one. Sources are sequentially deactivated and net levels recorded. The following equations describe this procedure:

Test 1:
$$\left(\frac{p^2}{p_r^2}\right)_1 = \frac{p_1^2}{p_r^2} + \frac{p^2}{p_r^2} + \cdots + \frac{p_m^2}{p_r^2} + \frac{p_n^2}{p_r^2} = 10^{L_{p1}/10}$$

Test 2:
$$\left(\frac{p^2}{p_r^2}\right)_2 = 0 + \frac{p_2^2}{p_r^2} + \cdots + \frac{p_m^2}{p_r^2} + \frac{p_n^2}{p_r^2} = 10^{L_{p2}/10}$$

Test M:
$$\left(\frac{p^2}{p_r^2}\right)_m = 0 + 0 + 0 + \frac{p_m^2}{p_r^2} + \frac{p_n^2}{p_r^2} = 10^{(L_p)_m/10}$$

All sources off:
$$\left(\frac{p^2}{p_r^2}\right)_n = \frac{p_n^2}{p_r^2}$$

The contribution of the ith source is determined by the relationship

$$\frac{p_i^2}{p_r^2} = 10^{L_{pi}/10} - 10^{L_{pi+1}/10} \qquad (\text{L6.5})$$

Successive deactivation is most effective if the sources are deactivated in *descending order of strength*. This technique may be more economical than the preceding one because the deactivation process can be discontinued when the combined level is judged close enough to the "ambient" level.

Limitations of Direct Methods

The direct method of source identification can be applied using not only overall or weighted levels but also bandlimited (e.g., octave or third-octave) levels. The application of these methods can become very tedious, but the logic of the direct methods is easily understood through Eq. (L6.2). Figures (1.6) and (1.7) for adding and subtracting levels can be used instead of Eq. (L6.3) through (L6.5) when applying the direct methods.

The major drawback of all the direct methods is that they do not lend themselves to cases where sources are interdependent and cannot be operated separately.

L6.3 Comparison Methods of Identification

The success of comparison methods depends upon the engineer's ability to recognize *similarities* between certain features of suspected sources and those of the combined sound field. These similarities may occur between acceleration and sound spectra, or in certain temporal patterns or in audible frequency characteristics. Comparison is often based on experience and becomes a matter of judgment. For example, during a plant survey the observer not only records the combined sound level but also attempts to identify what he or she hears during the measurement by careful aural and visual observations. The experienced auto mechanic uses a form of comparison (by ear) when identifying lifter noise among all the sounds produced by an automobile engine. Experience with the sources is an important factor in the application of comparison methods. Moreover, these methods can be applied even when sources cannot be activated or deactivated at will. Although techniques are available which can actually quantize source contributions, most comparison methods yield qualitative estimates which are nevertheless valuable for initiating control procedures. The underlying principles will be discussed to alert the reader to the potential of comparison methods.

L6.3.1 Comparison by Ear

The ear, when coupled with the human brain, is capable of recognizing many sound patterns to which it is exposed. Since the use of the logarithmic (decibel) scale was motivated by the perception characteristics of the ear, it proves generally true that sources most audible to the operator are likely to be significant contributors to the A-weighted level at the observer's ear. The ear's ability to recognize temporal patterns even permits detection of sources that do not contribute significantly to the overall sound level. By listening first in the near vicinity of suspected sources, and then at the measuring point, the observer can often identify associated sound patterns of the sources sufficiently to enable further study of quantitative features.

The signal detected by the sound-level meter can also be monitored through earphones. This form of monitoring permits comparison of the signal being measured against that heard without the monitor. A suspected source with known operating speeds can sometimes be detected by monitoring the signal filtered through an octave-band filter centered over the appropriate frequency range. The ear can also monitor accelerometer, or strain, signals taken from suspected vibrating surfaces. Comparing the "heard" acceleration against the heard sound pressure can provide useful insights because the acceleration signal is usually free of the extraneous sounds often present in a shop environment. In this case, the output can come from the accelerometer preamplifier or a taped record.

The obvious disadvantages of using the ear are that it cannot quantize the source contributions, nor can it detect sources masked by louder sources unless very distinctive patterns are present. Nevertheless, the ability of the ear to recognize patterns should not be discounted as a supplement to both direct and comparison methods.

L6.3.2 Comparison of Spectra

When a spectrum analyzer is available, the spectrum of the combined sound field can be compared against spectra of sound, vibration, strain, flow velocity, etc., produced by suspected sources. Special attention is paid to a spectral peak which appears at the same frequency in both the combined sound and source spectra, since this is evidence of a strong contribution by the suspected source.

Figure L6.1 depicts three spectra: (a) from the combined sound field; (b) from an accelerometer on a motor casing; and (c) from the sound produced in the near field of a suspected panel. Although not quantitative, Fig. L6.1 indicates a strong coincidence between major spectral peaks A and D of the overall sound spectrum and the accelerometer spectrum. Therefore, special attention should be paid to features of the motor which would produce vibrations in either frequency range, with particular emphasis on frequency range A. Further comparisons with spectrum c indicate that the panel may be contributing to frequency range B, though the panel is not the major contributor to the overall sound pressure. The smaller peaks in frequency ranges A, C, and D indicate that these contributions are probably coming from other sources and are being detected by the microphone even at the position near the panel. The important contribution in the frequency range C probably does not originate from either the motor casing or the panel: another source is present and has yet to be identified.

Figure L6.1c indicates the possible misinterpretation that can arise from comparing *sound* spectra. Although the changing of proximity revealed the panel as a probable source, this spectrum also contained extraneous contributions from the motor casing (and another source). Since accelerometers and strain gauges detect only the response of the underlying surface, they are less likely to respond to extraneous sound (except where it is intense enough to actually excite the surface being observed).

An octave-band filter is useful when detecting general trends in the spectrum, but the reader will find it usually lacks the definition needed to compare the positions of spectral peaks with known operating frequencies of suspected sources. Spectra of the type shown in Fig. L6.1 are normally obtained through 1/3-octave or narrower band filters.

Sophisticated computer-based digital techniques are also available for source detection. These techniques normally require simultaneous sampling of two or more signals, followed by statistical analysis to discard dissimilar features of the

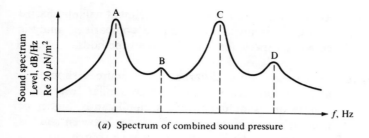

(*a*) Spectrum of combined sound pressure

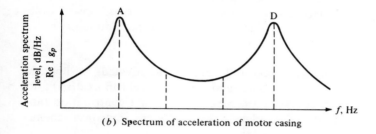

(*b*) Spectrum of acceleration of motor casing

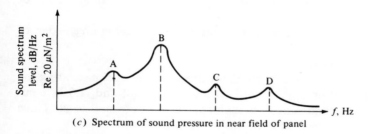

(*c*) Spectrum of sound pressure in near field of panel

Figure L6.1 Identification of sources by comparison of spectra.

signals. Procedures involving analysis in the time domain (correlation) and the frequency domain (coherence) have been developed to the point of being applicable to field environments. However, the electronics and mathematical background needed to effectively employ these techniques and interpret the computations extends well beyond the intended scope of this book. The reader who wishes to begin pursuing these advanced procedures is referred to Ref. [1] for an excellent review of the necessary background. Unlike the other comparison methods described, these techniques can provide quantitative measures of the contributions.

L6.4 Experiment

Direct methods can be employed using only a sound-level meter, while comparison methods may require additional equipment and a good knowledge of the physical characteristics of the candidate sources. This experiment will emphasize the direct methods, but the reader is urged to attempt a comparison analysis after he or she has achieved some experience with the direct methods.

L6.4.1 Independent Sources At least three different noise sources should be deployed in a room. Ideally, two sources should produce similar levels at a selected measuring point, while one should produce a significantly higher or lower level. This can often be achieved by changing distances between sources and measuring point. The reader should be able to activate each source independently. Although it is possible to use separate loudspeakers to achieve this, it is preferable that shop and laboratory equipment such as fans, power drills, routers, lathes, etc., be used. These sources should produce continuous rather than impulsive sound.

1. After measuring the ambient level (all sources deactivated), switch the sources on one by one, measuring the sound-pressure level (dB or dBA) after each change. Using Eqs. (L6.4) and (L6.5), compute the contribution (and range) of each source to the overall level. Three different activation schemes should be used, and the results tabulated:
   (a) Activate lesser contributors first, continuing in ascending order of strength.
   (b) Activate greater contributors first, continuing in descending order of strength.
   (c) Activate in arbitrary order.
2. With all sources operating, *de*activate the sources one by one, measuring the sound-pressure level after each change. Using Eqs. (L6.6) and (L6.7), compute the contribution (and range) of each source to the overall level. Three deactivation schemes should be used, with results tabulated:
   (a) Deactivate greater contributors first, continuing in descending order of strength.
   (b) Deactivate lesser contributors first, continuing in ascending order of strength.
   (c) Deactivate in arbitrary order.
3. Measure the level produced by each source operating alone. Compare each level against those computed in parts 1 and 2. How did activation order affect the predicted levels? Are the correct levels within the ranges computed in parts 1 and 2?

L6.4.2 Interdependent Sources A shop vacuum cleaner or a power mower possesses noise sources (motor, air intake, fan, etc.) which cannot be deactivated independently. Instead of deactivating sources individually, the sources must be permitted to operate and their outputs *reduced* using temporary treatments. Temporary reductions of some component sources can be achieved by means of lead-backed, foam-lined shrouds covering vibrating surfaces, or mufflers on air intakes, or isolation at mechanical connecting points, or removal of fan blades, or replacement of components. Ideally, the temporary treatments should reduce source contributions by at least 10 dB.

4. Measure levels as temporary treatments are applied to sources in suspected descending order. Estimate the contributions of sources, assuming the treatments are equivalent to deactivation. Do the estimated contributions "add up" to the total? How well does the assumption of 100 percent treatment effectiveness appear to apply? In what order should the sources be treated to achieve overall reductions of 5 dB? 10 dB? 15 dB? Can this be accomplished without degrading performance of the equipment?

L6.4.3 Comparison Methods

Comparison methods can be employed using either A, B, C, octave-band, or narrow-band weighting networks. Comparisons can be made not only between overall levels but also between *spectrum* or weighted levels, when made using the same weighting networks.

5. Using the independent sources of L6.4.1, determine the extent to which the sources can be identified using the ear, either alone or by monitoring the filtered or unfiltered sound level meter output:
   (*a*) At a stationary position near the microphone
   (*b*) By moving closer to suspected sources and comparing sensations against those heard at the microphone position
   (*c*) By modifying or covering suspected sources and listening to the effects of those changes is it possible to rank the sources by ear? Compare the qualitative ranking against the known ranking.
6. Readers with access to a spectrum analyzer, accelerometer-preamplifier, and a motor-driven fan or router can compare the acceleration spectrum of the motor casing with the sound spectrum produced during operation of the machine. Matching of spectrum peaks enables tentative identification of contributions of the casing to the sound. If the accelerometer signal can be made available from the preamplifier, a set of high-impedance (2000 Ω or greater) headphones will enable the reader to listen to the acceleration signal and compare qualitative features of the sound and acceleration signals. Generally, it is not good practice to monitor and measure signals simultaneously unless the system is specifically designed to allow this.

REFERENCE

1. Bendat, J. and A. Piersal, Random Data: Analysis and Measured Procedures, Wiley, New York, 1971.

LAB 7 DETERMINATION OF SOUND POWER LEVEL IN SEMIREVERBERANT ENVIRONMENTS

L7.1 Sound-Pressure Level in the Sound Field Surrounding a Source

If the acoustic power of the source and the absorption properties of the room shown in Fig. L7.1 are known, the sound-pressure level at any point in the far field of the source is usually estimated by the equation:

$$L_p(\vec{r}) = L_w + 10 \log_{10}\left[\frac{Q(\vec{\theta})}{4\pi r^2} + \frac{4}{R} \right] \tag{L7.1}$$

where $L_p(\vec{r}) =$ the sound-pressure level, dB re 20 μN/m^2, at the position $\vec{r}$ relative to the source center

$L_w =$ the sound power level of the source, dB re 10^{-12} W

$Q(\vec{\theta}) =$ the directivity of the source along the direction $\vec{\theta}$ from the source center to the observer

$R =$ the room absorption m^2, estimated from the room area S and average absorption coefficient $\bar{\alpha}$

$$R = \frac{S\bar{\alpha}}{1 - \bar{\alpha}} \doteq S\bar{\alpha} \tag{L7.2}$$

and r is the distance from the source center to the observer (always in the *far field* of the source).

When the source rests on a hard floor, the source center is located on the floor underneath the source. Normally, the computation proceeds by octaves or one-third octaves, using power and absorption data tabulated for each frequency band.

The room absorption R can be calculated from tabulated absorption properties of the room's surfaces, or it can be estimated from the room's measured

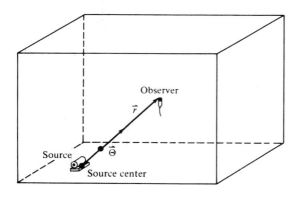

Figure L7.1 Estimation of sound level in an enclosure.

reverberation time T, i.e.,

$$\frac{1}{R} = \left(\frac{T}{0.16V} - \frac{1}{S}\right) \doteq \frac{T}{0.16V} \qquad (L7.3)$$

where V is the volume, m^3, of the room. The reader is referred to Lab 3 for practical aspects of evaluating the room absorption.

The acoustic power level L_w is normally a property of the source, while the directivity Q is a property of both the source and its location relative to adjacent reflective surfaces. Both power and directivity are independent of room absorption. The acoustic power, because of its complete independence of room properties, provides the best known basis for comparing the noise performance of sources. This laboratory deals with the practical aspects of determining sound power and directivity in the environments typically encountered in practice.

L7.2 Basic Equations Governing Techniques for Sound Power Determination

Many standards have been developed for determining sound power level under laboratory and field conditions. (A number of these are compiled in Appendix B.) These standards depend on sound-pressure measurements, and are based on the following relationship for the mean squared pressure $\overline{p_i^2}$, measured at a point i in the *far field* of a source:

$$\frac{\overline{p_i^2}}{\rho_0 c} = I_i + \left(\frac{4W}{R}\right)_i \qquad (L7.4)$$

where I_i = the intensity (W/m^2) of sound passing *directly* from the source through the measuring point

$\left(\frac{4W}{R}\right)_i$ = the acoustic energy density (W/m^2) of the *reverberant* field at the measuring point

W = the acoustic power (watts) of the source

$\rho_0 c$ = the characteristic impedance of the air (mks rayls)

At a measuring point in the *reverberant field*, the contribution $(4W/R)_i$ caused by the reverberant component exceeds the direct component I_i by at least one order of magnitude, so that

$$\frac{\overline{p_i^2}}{\rho_0 c} \doteq \left(\frac{4W}{R}\right)_i \qquad (L7.5)$$

Since the acoustic energy is not usually distributed uniformly through the field, a better estimate of the average acoustic energy density is obtained by averaging the mean squared pressure over many points in the reverberant field:

$$\left(\frac{4W}{R}\right) = \frac{1}{N}\sum_{i=1}^{N}\left(\frac{4W}{R}\right)_i = \frac{1}{N}\sum_{i=1}^{N}\frac{\overline{p_i^2}}{\rho_0 c} \qquad (L7.6)$$

from which follows the classical relationship between acoustic power level and space-averaged sound-pressure level $L_{\overline{ps}}$:

$$L_w = L_{\overline{ps}} - 10 \log_{10}(4/R) \tag{L7.7}$$

Since all measurements must be made in the reverberant field in order to use Eq. (L7.7), the directivity of the source cannot be evaluated by this technique.

At a measurement point in the *free field or semireverberant field*, the reverberant component is not large enough to dominate the pressure measurement, and the simplifications of (L7.5) leading to (L7.7) cannot be used. In this case, the source is assumed to be surrounded by an imaginary measurement surface which, in combination with adjacent solid surfaces, completely encloses the source. The total acoustic power passing *directly* from the source *through* the measurement surface is then determined by subdividing the measurement surface into M segments each of known area (ΔA_i), estimating the intensity (I_i) at each area by means of (L7.4) and a sound-pressure measurement (p_i^2), and summing the acoustic powers over the entire measurement surface:

$$W = \sum_{i=1}^{M} I_i \Delta A_i = \sum_{i=1}^{M} \left\{ \frac{\overline{p_i^2}}{\rho_0 c} - \left(\frac{4W}{R}\right)_i \right\} \Delta A_i \tag{L7.9}$$

This leads to the following relationship between the acoustic power level and the sound-pressure level averaged over the measurement surface:

$$L_w = L_{\overline{Pa}} - 10 \log_{10}\left(\frac{1}{A} + \frac{4}{R}\right) \tag{L7.10}$$

where L_w = the sound power level of the source, dB re 10^{-12} W

A = the total "transparent" area of the measuring surface m^2, excluding reflecting surfaces

$L_{\overline{Pa}}$ = the area-averaged sound-pressure level, defined by

$$L_{\overline{Pa}} = 10 \log_{10} \frac{1}{A} \sum_{i=1}^{M} \left(\frac{\overline{p_i^2}}{p_r^2}\right) \Delta A_i, \text{ dB re } 20 \ \mu\text{N}/\text{m}^2 \tag{L7.11}$$

with each pressure $\overline{p_i^2}$ measured on the surface

Since the reverberant component cannot be ignored, the directivity Q of the source cannot be evaluated exactly. But, it can be approximated from the data.

In a special case of (L7.11), when the measurement surface is entirely in the *free field*, the contribution I_i due to the direct component exceeds the reverberant component $(4W/R)_i$ by at least an order of magnitude. In this case the acoustic power level is simply related to the area-averaged sound-pressure level:

$$L_w = L_{\overline{Pa}} - 10 \log_{10}\left(\frac{1}{A}\right) = L_{\overline{Pa}} + 10 \log_{10} A \tag{L7.12a}$$

When all measurements are made in the free or direct field, the directivity $Q(\vec{\theta_i})$ of the source along the line from the source center to the ith area element is determined from the ratio of measured $(\overline{p_i^2})$ to averaged $(\overline{p_a^2})$ mean squared pressures:

$$Q(\vec{\theta_i}) = \frac{\overline{p_i^2}}{\overline{p_a^2}} \tag{L7.12b}$$

This number relates to the combined directivity of the source and the adjacent reflecting surfaces, and it could change if the source were mounted in a different part of the room.

The area-averaged sound-pressure level is particularly easy to compute if the measurement surface is divided into equal elements, each of sub-area A/M. Then the averaged sound-pressure level may be written:

$$L_{\overline{Pa}} = 10 \log_{10}\left[\frac{\overline{p_1^2} + \overline{p_2^2} + \cdots + \overline{p_m^2}}{Mp_r^2} \right]$$

$$= 10 \log_{10}\left[\frac{\overline{p_1^2}}{p_r^2} + \frac{\overline{p_2^2}}{p_r^2} + \cdots + \frac{\overline{p_m^2}}{p_r^2} \right] - 10 \log_{10}M \tag{L7.13}$$

where the first term in (L7.13) is computed by simply combining the M levels as if they came from separate sources.

L7.3 Practical Aspects of Sound Power Measurement

When the room's absorption can be estimated and the measurement surface properly defined, Eq. (L7.10) provides a basis for selecting the appropriate measurement technique: when the enclosure is very large compared with the room constant, a comparison of $1/A$ against $4/R$ may reveal that a *reverberant-field* technique may be used, even though the source is not located in a specially prepared reverberant chamber. On the other hand, when the enclosure is small or the room very absorptive, a comparison of $1/A$ against $4/R$ may indicate that a *free-field* technique could be employed, even though the source is not located outdoors nor in an anechoic chamber. When this comparison shows that neither field dominates, or when the nature of the field is uncertain, a *semireverberant-field* technique must be employed.

The success of determining sound power in either the reverberant or semireverberant field requires that several restrictions be observed. Some of these restrictions are independent of the approach chosen:

1. *Measurements can be made only in the far field of the source.* Only in the far field does the simple relationship (L7.4) hold true. Defining rf, m/s, as the product of source-microphone distance and octave (or third-octave) band center frequency, products of rf > 50 m/s or rf > 100 m/s will ensure the power-level estimation error to be less than 3 dB or 1 dB, respectively, if the source is a dipole. Higher products of rf > 120 m/s or rf > 250 m/s are needed to maintain errors less than 3 dB or 1 dB for more complex sources (e.g., quadrupole or higher). Powers computed (erroneously) from near-field measurements will always be *overestimates* of the actual power. A typical requirement is that an enclosing surface have a basic radius of at least two major source dimensions (and not less than 0.6 m) long, and extend at least four average source heights above the major reflecting plane. Measurements

taken within this enclosing volume should not be used in Eq. (L7.7), (L7.10), or (L7.12). Another typical approach is to first define a "reference surface"—the smallest parallelepiped which will enclose the source—then define the measurement surface at 1 m or farther from this reference surface.

2. *The number of measurement points must be sufficient to determine the averaged sound-pressure level,* whether it is space-averaged (reverberant field) or area-averaged. Most standards require at least five measurement points. A good rule of thumb (in the absence of explicit instructions) is that the number of measurements M should always exceed the difference in decibels between the highest and lowest readings, with a minimum of six measurements being taken. Errors incurred in free-field measurements over parallelepiped or hemispherical measurement surfaces can then be kept to within 1 dB for dipole and quadrupole sources. Errors incurred in reverberant-field measurements, where spatial averages are used, are described in Labs 3 and 4.

3. *Background levels must be at least* 10 dB *below the measured levels.* The presence of background noise results in overestimates of power, unless corrections are made for each reading. Some standards permit corrections if background levels are 3 to 10 dB below measured levels, but confidence in the results will be poor unless the difference is greater than 6 dB.

4. *Measurement points must lie wholly in the reverberant field if using (L7.7), or in the free field if using (L7.12).* In semireverberant fields, errors can be incurred if the area-averaged sound-pressure level $L_{\overline{p_a}}$ does not provide a good estimate of the acoustic energy-density $(4W/R)$.

Testing in the *reverberant field* is subject not only to restrictions (1) through (4) but also to those restrictions associated with determining space-averaged sound-power level. These are discussed in Lab 4. It is particularly important that no measurement be closer than one-third wavelength from the room boundaries or major reflecting surfaces when using a reverberant-field technique.

Testing in the *free field* is subject not only to restrictions (1) through (4) but also to those restrictions associated with estimating the power flowing across the measuring surface:

5. *The measurement surface should be normal to the line of power flow everywhere around the source.* Figure L7.2 illustrates the effect. The component I_i of sound intensity actually passing *through* the area is smaller than the total intensity I of the power flow. Since the mean squared pressure corresponds to the total intensity I, the result is an overestimate of the power passing through the surface, and a net overestimate of acoustic power. For this reason, the enclosing measurement surface should be as simple as possible, preferably a hemisphere or a rectangular parallelepiped. The overestimate can be maintained to less than 2 dB or 1 dB if the angle subtended by the machine at the measurement point never exceeds 102° or 74°, respectively. This error can be further reduced if the measurement surface is hemispherical or cubic in shape.

6. *All radiated sound must pass only through the measurement surface.* Sound dissipated in absorbers located within the confines of the measurement surface will not be accounted for in the summing process, and the estimated power would be low in this case. Solid bounding surfaces, such as the walls or floor which complete the bounding surface, should be highly reflective so that energy is lost neither through nor on them. This also eliminates the need to take sound-level measurements over the solid bounding surfaces.

When determining directivity from free-field measurements, all absorbing and reflecting surfaces within the confines of the measuring surface should be considered part of the source. Any changes of position or orientation of the solid

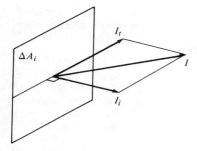

Figure L7.2 Surface oriented obliquely to the direction of power flow; intensity equals I.

bounding surfaces within this confine can change the apparent directivity of the source. For this reason, machines that will be operated near a wall or in a corner should be tested with similar bounding conditions to ensure that directivity is estimated with reasonable accuracy. As long as no absorption is introduced and the surfaces are isolated from the source, the total power level should be unaffected by such modifications.

When the sound field over the measurement surface is *semireverberant*, both direct and reverberant fields are present; ideally, all the restrictions described in (1) through (4), and those described in Labs 3 and 4 for reverberant fields, should be observed.

When it is impractical to determine the room absorption, several comparison techniques based on Eq. (L7.10) are available for determining power levels.

L7.4 Comparison Methods for Determining Sound Power Level in Semireverberant Fields

The semireverberant field is typically encountered in practice: plant enclosures are usually only lightly absorptive and space limits the size of the measurement surface so that neither component can be considered dominant near the measurement surface. In this case, the source directivity can be only estimated by (L7.12b), due to the reverberant component, though the sound power can still be evaluated using (L7.10):

$$L_w = L_{\overline{Pa}} - 10 \log_{10}\left(\frac{1}{A} + \frac{4}{R}\right) \tag{L7.10}$$

Comparison methods must be used when the absorption of the room is unknown. Basically, all comparison methods require at least two sets of measurements, the additional data being needed to eliminate the unknown absorption terms and determine the overall sound power level indirectly. This approach is inherently less precise than the so-called absolute methods because of the increased number of measurements and calculations required.

1. *Reference source method* A source of known power level L_{w1} is installed at a location similar (or identical) to that of the unknown source. The area-averaged sound-pressure level $L_{\overline{Pa1}}$ is determined over the measurement surface. The measurement is then repeated with

the unknown source operating and its area-averaged sound-pressure level $L_{\overline{Pa}}$ is determined. Since the measurement surface and room absorption are the same in both cases, the sound power level L_w of the unknown source is determined by manipulating Eq. (L7.10):

$$L_w - L_{w1} = L_{\overline{Pa}} - L_{\overline{Pa1}} \qquad (L7.14)$$

The reference source method works in principle for any type of sound field, since all terms related to the type of sound field have been eliminated in the derivation of Eq. (L7.14).

2. *Concentric surface method* Two concentric measurement surfaces are defined around the source, and area-averaged sound-pressure levels are determined over each surface. Denoting the two surfaces by the subscripts k and l, the Eq. (L7.10) can be written for each test:

$$L_w = L_{\overline{Pa}\,k} - 10\log_{10}\left(\frac{1}{A_k} + \frac{4}{R}\right) \qquad (L7.15a)$$

$$L_w = L_{\overline{Pa}\,l} - 10\log_{10}\left(\frac{1}{A_l} + \frac{4}{R}\right) \qquad (L7.15b)$$

Eliminating the absorption between the two equations leads to the acoustic power level:

$$L_w = L_{\overline{Pa}\,k} + 10\log_{10} A_k + 10\log_{10}\left(\frac{1 - f_{lk}}{1 - A_k/A_l}\right) \qquad (L7.16a)$$

where
$$f_{lk} = 10^{\,0.1(L_{\overline{Pa}\,l} - L_{\overline{Pa}\,k})} \qquad (L7.16b)$$

This method works most effectively if the difference between the two levels $L_{\overline{Pal}}$ and $L_{\overline{Pak}}$ is large. If the difference is too small to be considered significant, either the field is reverberant or the ratio of surface areas is too close to unity.

3. *Double-concentric-surface method* This is an extension of the concentric surface method. A third concentric surface, denoted j, is defined and a third area, averaged level $L_{\overline{Paj}}$, is determined. Assuming k is the middle surface, two sound power levels are computed:

$$L_w = L_{\overline{Pa}\,k} + 10\log_{10}\left(\frac{1 - f_{lk}}{1 - A_k/A_l}\right) + 10\log_{10} A_k \qquad (L7.16a)$$

$$L_w = L_{\overline{Pa}\,k} + 10\log_{10}\left(\frac{1 - f_{jk}}{1 - A_k/A_j}\right) + 10\log_{10} A_k \qquad (L7.17a)$$

where
$$f_{lk} = 10^{\,0.1(L_{\overline{Pa}\,l} - L_{\overline{Pa}\,k})} \qquad (L7.16b)$$

$$f_{jk} = 10^{\,0.1(L_{\overline{Pa}\,j} - L_{\overline{Pa}\,k})} \qquad (L7.17b)$$

The larger of the two power levels is taken as the source power level.

L7.5 Experiment

A variety of typical noise sources cannot be moved into special environments, nor are special anechoic or reverberant environments available to everyone. Thus, readers must be able to evaluate sound power sources in their own operating environments, in rooms which are neither highly absorptive nor completely reverberant. In this experiment, the reader will determine the acoustic power (and directivity, if possible) of a sound source in the "typical," semireverberant environment.

Site and Equipment The reader should select a relatively small, preferably portable, noise source which produces steady, broad-band noise without significant pure tones. The test room should have a hard floor and should be large enough that the microphone can be placed in the far field of the source without being within one-third wavelength of the room boundaries. A room of about 10 source dimensions on each edge will normally permit use of the double-concentric-surface technique. Avoid an unusually long or narrow room. If the proposed source vibrates, it should be isolated from the floor and walls. A precision sound level meter with an octave-band filter set is normally required. It should be fitted with a half-inch microphone to avoid microphone directionality effects above 2 kHz. Readers equipped with a Type II sound level meter may obtain "A-weighted" power levels by using the A-weighting network, but it must be recognized that the "power level" obtained relates only to rooms of similar absorptive properties and is subject to the errors inherent in Type II meters.

Preliminary Determinations The room constant R should be determined in several octave bands, preferably 63 Hz to 4 kHz inclusive. The restrictions pertaining to determination of R by means of the reverberation time T are outlined in Lab 3. These restrictions also apply, to a lesser degree, to sound power measurements made during this experiment. Alternatively, the room constant can be estimated from known area and tabulated absorption properties of the room surfaces.

The source should be placed on the floor, near the middle of the room, for easy access to measuring positions. While the source is operating, a rough sound level survey should be made along two horizontal traverses to identify the free, semireverberant, and (perhaps) the reverberant regions in the room. The extent of the near field can also be established, using the guidelines discussed in the text. Background levels should be at least 10 dB below all readings.

Ideally, the measurement surface should follow the source contours at a fixed distance, and always remain outside its near field. For simplicity, select a hemispherical or rectangular parallelepiped measurement surface which approximates this condition. Locate six to nine measurement points at equal spacing over its surface, perhaps using Fig. L7.3 as a guide. [These points are conveniently designated on the floor, by placing chalk or tape marks at the plan positions (X, Y) and noting the measurement height (Z) on the floor near each mark.] The reader should first concentrate on establishing a measurement surface in the semireverberant field, and then attempt to establish two more concentric measurement surfaces nearer to the free and reverberant fields, respectively.

In practical cases, it may be impossible to satisfy all the restrictions listed in the discussion. Nevertheless, the reader should attempt to satisfy the conditions underlying the governing equations as far as possible, and should carefully document the conditions which do not meet those restrictions for use later when evaluating and applying the results.

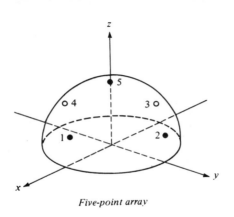

Five-point array

i	x	y	z
1	0.92	0	0.4
2	0	0.92	0.4
3	−0.92	0	0.4
4	0	−0.92	0.4
5	0	0	1

Six-point array

i	x	y	z
1	0.89	0	0.45
2	0.28	0.85	0.45
3	−0.72	0.53	0.45
4	−0.72	−0.53	0.45
5	0.28	−0.85	0.45
6	0	0	1

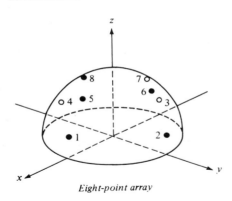

Eight-point array

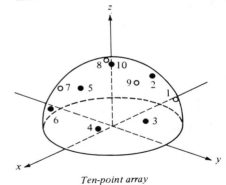

Ten-point array

i	x	y	z
1	0.97	0	0.25
2	0	0.97	0.25
3	−0.97	0	0.25
4	0	−0.97	0.25
5	0.63	0	0.78
6	0	0.63	0.78
7	−0.63	0	0.78
8	0	−0.63	0.78

i	x	y	z
1	−0.87	0.38	0.33
2	−0.33	0.58	0.75
3	0.13	0.93	0.33
4	0.75	0.58	0.33
5	0.67	0	0.75
6	0.75	−0.58	0.33
7	0.13	−0.93	0.33
8	−0.33	−0.58	0.75
9	−0.87	−0.36	0.33
10	0	0	1

(*a*) Hemispherical; radius equals 1 unit.

Figure L7.3 Typical measurement surfaces and arrays.

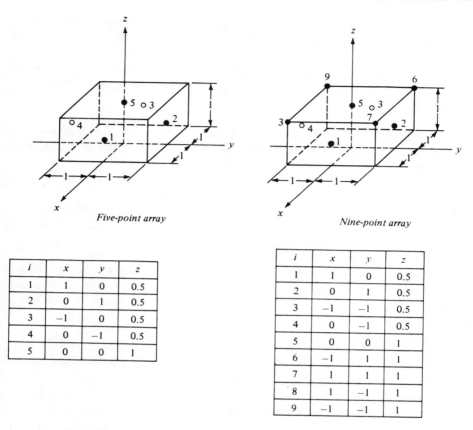

Five-point array

Nine-point array

i	x	y	z
1	1	0	0.5
2	0	1	0.5
3	−1	0	0.5
4	0	−1	0.5
5	0	0	1

i	x	y	z
1	1	0	0.5
2	0	1	0.5
3	−1	−1	0.5
4	0	−1	0.5
5	0	0	1
6	−1	1	1
7	1	1	1
8	1	−1	1
9	−1	−1	1

(*b*) Rectangular parallelepiped; dimensions equal 2 × 2 × 1 units.

Figure L7.3 (continued) Typical measurement surfaces and arrays.

Suggested Exercises

These exercises have been listed in priority order, with Exercise 1 being the most important. Exercises 6 through 8 require additional facilities and conditions that may be unavailable to the reader. If a large source is to be used, Exercises 1 and 5 should both be conducted.

1. Operate the source and determine sound power levels in at least two octave bands, using a measurement surface defined in the semireverberant field (L7.10). Assume the measurement surface area equally divided between the measurement points. Estimate the directivities (even though a reverberant component may exist).

2. Define a second concentric measurement surface having about twice the area of the surface used in Exercise 1. Estimate the acoustic power in the same octave bands, using the concentric-surface method (L7.16).

3. Determine power levels in the same octave bands, using the surface defined in the reverberant field (L7.7) and in the direct field (L7.12). Compare results with those of Exercise 1.
4. If possible, define a third surface and estimate the acoustic power using the double-concentric-surface method (L7.16, L7.17). Either of the surfaces defined in Exercise 3 may be used.

A draft ISO standard (ISO/DIS 3744) proposes that the measurement surface be located 1 m from the reference surface (the smallest hemisphere or parallelepiped which can enclose the machine).

5. Determine the sound power level using a rectangular measurement surface spaced 1 m from the reference surface. Use nine measuring points (see Fig. L7.3). Compare with the results of Exercise 1. For a large source, this technique will probably overestimate the power level. Why?

It is instructive to compare the power levels determined in (1) through (4) with levels obtained by other techniques. An important comparison can be made if a reference source of known acoustic power is available:

6. Repeat Exercise 1 using the reference source.
   a. How well do the measured and documented power levels agree?
   b. How accurately is the power of the unknown source determined using the reference-source method (L7.14)?
7. Repeat Exercise 3 using the reference source. Are the results obtained by the reference-source method actually independent of the test environment?

An anechoic half-space is approximated over a hard surface located outdoors. This is typically achieved in open parking lots, air fields, and so on, where buildings are well removed from the test site. Because of atmospheric attenuation, the measurement surface should not extend more than 15 m (50 ft) from the source.

8. If an outdoor test site is available, determine the power level and directivity of the source in the free field (L7.12). Compare with power level and directivity estimates made in Exercises 1 and 3. How reliable are the directivity estimates made in a semireverberant environment?

LAB 8 MEASUREMENT OF NORMAL INCIDENCE ABSORPTION COEFFICIENT IN A STANDING WAVE TUBE

L8.1 Sound Absorption Coefficients of Acoustical Materials

The performance of materials and structures used to dissipate acoustical energy is evaluated by means of an *absorption coefficient*. This quantity is the fraction of acoustic energy, incident upon the surface of a material or structure, that is dissipated (converted to minute amounts of heat) within the material or structure. Examples of acoustical absorbers are glass fiber, open-cell foams, and interlaced plant fibers, sometimes combined with a thin, impervious film, a perforated facing, or an air space. These materials have a weight density that ranges from $\frac{1}{2}$ to 20 lb per cubic feet, in thicknesses ranging from $\frac{1}{2}$ to 6 in. The most important physical requirement for an acoustical material is a series of interconnected pores or passages in which sound waves can propagate. Propagation, in turn, causes relative motion between the medium and the structure of the material; the relative motion causes viscous flow losses and, if the material is resilient, losses through internal friction of the fibers.

All acoustical materials and structures perform better at some frequencies than others. In other words, the absorption coefficients vary with frequency—the principal characteristics that determine this dependence are number, configuration and spacing of pores; material thickness; thickness of air space behind the material; and the type of facing employed. Because the absorption coefficient is frequency-selective, its value is usually measured over a range of frequencies (125 to 4000 Hz) that comprises the range of architectural interest.

Three types of absorption coefficient can be measured: the normal incidence absorption coefficient (α_n), the random incidence absorption coefficient (α_{st}), and the Sabine absorption coefficient (α_{sab}). The first is measured in a standing wave tube; the second is a theoretical quantity that assumes arrival of sound waves from all angles of incidence with equal probability; while the last is measured in a reverberation room where arrivals near grazing incidence are less likely than those at other angles of incidence. Usually, the α_n value at a given frequency is less than α_{sab}, which in turn is less than α_{st}.

L8.2 The Standing Wave Tube Method of Measuring Absorption Coefficients

Methods for estimating α_{st} from standing wave tube data are described in the literature. For this reason, a standing wave tube is an economical means for comparative evaluation of acoustical materials or for estimating their actual performance when installed.

At pure-tone frequencies with wavelengths greater than twice the tube diameter, plane acoustic waves propagate inside the tube (Fig. L8.1). A movable microphone probe measures the sound pressure at any desired location. At

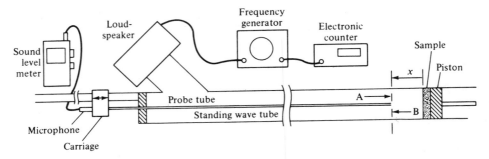

Figure L8.1 System for measuring normal incidence absorption coefficient.

distance x from the acoustical sample,

$$p(x, t) = A \sin \omega t + B \sin\left(\omega t - 2\frac{\omega}{c}x - \Theta\right) \quad \text{(L8.1)}$$

where $p(x, t)$ = total acoustic pressure at distance x
        A = amplitude of incident sound wave
        B = amplitude of reflected sound wave
        ω = frequency of sound wave, rad/s
        c = propagation velocity of sound waves
     $\frac{\omega}{c}x$ = phase angle correction due to distance $2x$
       Θ = phase angle between reflected and incident waves at surface of sample

The magnitude of the pressure wave is

$$|p(x, t)| = A^2 + B^2 + 2AB \cos\left(2\frac{\omega}{c}x + \Theta\right) \quad \text{(L8.2)}$$

The maximum value occurs at locations where $\cos(2\frac{\omega}{c}x + \Theta)$ equals $+1$:

$$P_{\text{max}} = \left[A^2 + B^2 + 2AB\right]^{1/2}$$
$$= |A + B| \quad \text{(L8.3)}$$

The minimum acoustic pressure occurs when $\cos(2\frac{\omega}{c}x + \Theta) = -1$:

$$P_{\text{min}} = \left[A^2 + B^2 - 2AB\right]^{1/2}$$
$$= |A - B| \quad \text{(L8.4)}$$

The intensity of the incident wave is given by $I_A = \dfrac{A^2}{2\rho c}$, where

$$\rho c = \text{characteristic impedance of medium} \quad \text{(L8.5)}$$

For the reflected wave,

$$I_B = \frac{B^2}{2\rho c} \quad \text{(L8.6)}$$

Under the assumption that no acoustic energy escapes from the tube,

$$\alpha_n = \frac{A^2 - B^2}{A^2}$$

After substituting for A and B from Eqs. L8.3 and L8.4:

$$\alpha_n = \frac{4 P_{max} P_{min}}{(P_{max} + P_{min})^2} \tag{L8.7}$$

Experiment

In this experiment the reader will qualify a standing wave tube and measure the normal incidence absorption coefficient of several acoustical structures over a range of frequencies.

Equipment The equipment required for this experiment consists of a standing wave tube, a signal generator and amplifier, a frequency counter, a sound level meter, and a variety of acoustical materials. The standing wave tube may be purchased or can be fabricated from plastic waste pipe and fittings*; a suitable loudspeaker and sample holder with adjustable air space must also be provided.

Reduction of data Calculation of the normal incidence absorption coefficient is straightforward if the microphone output voltage is recorded directly. The procedure is somewhat more complex when a sound level meter is used and decibel values corresponding to pressure maximum and minimum values are measured. In this case, the relation between maximum and minimum values is given by

$$Lp_{max} - Lp_{min} = 20 \log_{10} \frac{P_{max}}{P_{min}}$$

This relationship and Eq. L8.7 can be combined to yield an equation for α_n in terms of the "standing wave ratio," $L_{Pmax} - L_{Pmin}$. A graph of the relationship is shown in Fig. L8.2.

Qualification If the standing wave tube is terminated with a rigid piston, the magnitude of the absorption coefficient should equal 0 at all frequencies. As a practical matter, a measured absorption coefficient of 0.1 or less with a rigid termination is acceptable for evaluating acoustical materials with an absorption coefficient of 0.3 or greater. The tube should be qualified over the frequency range of architectural interest—this range normally spans the octave bands from 125 through 4000 Hz. However, the actual range of frequencies will be limited by the inside diameter and the length of the tube. The tube diameter determines the upper frequency limit: if the diameter is greater than a half wavelength, the

---

* See ASTM Standard C-384 for detailed specifications.

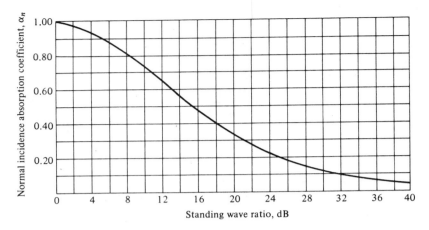

Figure L8.2 Values of α_n for various standing wave ratios.

traveling waves within the tube will no longer be plane. When this occurs, the absorption coefficient is not simply related to the maximum and minimum acoustic pressures. The lower frequency limit is determined by the tube length: the distance between adjacent minima equals one-half wavelength; when this distance exceeds the tube length, the necessary pressure maximum and minimum may not be present.

At frequencies much greater than the lower limit, a number of pressure minima may be present. To minimize the influence of attenuation produced by the tube walls, the pressure minimum closest to the termination should be selected.

Selection and preparation of acoustical samples An almost infinite variety of acoustical samples can be evaluated by combining available materials into different structures. Individual components include:

- Materials (glass fiber, foam, plant fibers) of varying thicknesses
- Impervious membranes of varying thicknesses
- Perforated covers with varying openings and percent-open areas
- Air spaces of varying lengths behind the sample

Each laboratory group should combine these components in a number of ways so that the effects of material, material facing, and air space can be evaluated. The accuracy and repeatability of measurements are highly dependent on a close fit between the sample and the tube wall. A tight seal is particularly important when an air space is present.

Additional measurements If the standing wave tube is equipped with a scale for measuring distances from the sample surface to a given pressure minimum, the phase angle between reflected and incident waves can be calculated. After this calculation, the acoustical impedance at the surface of the sample can be determined; procedures are described in Sec. 6.2.

The calculation of acoustic impedance is of value for indicating changes in an acoustical structure that will increase its random incidence absorption coefficient. Reference 4, Chap. 6, describes the required measurements and suggests guidelines for improving the performance of a given structure. A simpler procedure for transforming normal incidence absorption coefficients into their random incidence equivalents is described in Ref. 6, Chap. 6.

Measurement of the distance between pressure minima at a precisely known frequency f can be used to calculate the speed of sound to within 1 percent. The relevant equation is $c = f \cdot \lambda$, where λ = wavelength of sound at frequency f.

In Sec. 6.2 it is shown that the distance between adjacent minima is equal to a half wavelength. Note that the accuracy of the measurement can be improved by measuring the distance between several minima and dividing the result by the number of minima.

STANDARDS ORGANIZATIONS
AND STANDARDS DOCUMENTS

ACOUSTICAL AND BOARD PRODUCTS ASSOCIATION (ABPA)
Acoustical and Board Products Association
205 West Tuohy Avenue
Park Ridge, IL 60068

ACOUSTICAL SOCIETY OF AMERICA (ASA)
Back Number Dept., Dept. Std.
American Institute of Physics
333 East 45th Street
New York, NY 10017

ASA
STD1-1975
Method for the Measurement of Real-Ear Protection of Hearing Protectors and Physical Attenuation of Earmuffs.

ASA
STD3-1975
Test-Site Measurement of Noise Emitted by Engine-Powered Equipment.

ASA
STD4-1975
Method for Rating the Sound-Power Spectra of Small Stationary Noise Sources (ANSI S3.17-1975).

AIR-CONDITIONING AND REFRIGERATION INSTITUTE (ARI)
Air-Conditioning and Refrigeration Institute
1815 North Fort Myer Drive
Arlington, VA 22209

ARI
Standard 575
Standard for Method of Measuring Machinery Sound within equipment Rooms, (1973).

AIR DIFFUSION COUNCIL (ADC)
Air Diffusion Council
435 North Michigan
Chicago, IL 60611

AIR MOVING AND CONDITIONING ASSOCIATION (AMCA)
Air Moving and Conditioning Association
30 West University Drive
Arlington Heights, IL 60004

AMERICAN BOAT AND YACHT COUNCIL
American Boat and Yacht Council
15 East 26th Street
New York, NY 10010

AMERICAN GEAR MANUFACTURERS ASSOCIATION (AGMA)
American Gear Manufacturers Association
1330 Massachusetts Avenue, N.W.
Washington, D.C. 20005

AMERICAN NATIONAL STANDARDS INSTITUTE (ANSI)
American National Standards Institute
1430 Broadway
New York, NY 10018

ANSI
S1.11960
American National Standard Acoustical Terminology, (R1971).

ANSI
S1.2-1962
American National Standard Method for the Physical Measurement of Sound (partially revised by S1.13-1971 and by S1.21-1972).

ANSI
S1.4-1971
American National Specification for Sound-Level Meters.

ANSI S1.7-1970	Sound Absorption of Acoustical Materials in Reverberation Rooms, Method of Test for.
ANSI S1.13-1971	American National Standard Methods for the Measurement of Sound-Pressure Levels (partial revision of S1.2-1962).
ANSI S1.21-1972	American National Standard Methods for the Determination of Sound-Power Levels of Small Sources in Reverberation Rooms (revision of Section 3.5 of S1.2-1962).
ANSI S3.17-1975	Method for Rating the Sound-Power Spectra of Small Stationary Noise Sources.
ANSI S3.19-1974	Measurement of Real-Ear Protection of Hearing Protectors and Physical Attenuation of Earmuffs, Method for the (revision and redesignation of Z24.22-1957) (ASA Std. 1-1975).
ANSI S6.4-1973	Computing the Effective Perceived Noise Level for Flyover Aircraft Noise, Definitions and Procedures for.
ANSI S1.23-197X	Method for Designating the Sound Power Emitted by Machinery and Equipment.
ANSI S3.15	Method for Measurement of Community Noise, ANSI S3.15.

AMERICAN SOCIETY OF HEATING, REFRIGERATING, AND AIR-CONDITIONING ENGINEERS (ASHRAE)

American Society of Heating, Refrigerating, and
Air-Conditioning Engineers
345 East 47th Street
New York, NY 10017

AMERICAN SOCIETY FOR TESTING AND MATERIALS (ASTM)

American Society for Testing and Materials
1916 Race Street
Philadelphia, PA 19103

ASTM 384-58	Standard Method of Test for Impedance and Absorption of Acoustical Materials by the Tube Method, (Reapproved 1972).
ASTM C423-66	Standard Method of Test for Sound Absorption of Acoustical Materials in Reverberation Rooms (ANSI S1.7-1970), (Reapproved 1972).

ASTM E90-75	Standard Recommended Practice for Laboratory Measurement of Airborne Sound Transmission Loss of Building Partitions.

ASTM E336-71	Standard Recommended Practice for Measurement of Airborne Sound Insulation in Buildings.

ASTM E413-73	Standard Classification for Determination of Sound Transmission Class.

ASTM E492-73T	Tentative Method of Laboratory Measurement of Impact Sound Transmission through Floor-to-Ceiling Assemblies Using the Tapping Machine (1971).

AMERICAN TEXTILE MACHINERY ASSOCIATION (ATMA)
American Textile Machinery Association
1730 M St. N.W.
Washington, D.C. 20036

ANTI-FRICTION BEARING MANUFACTURERS ASSOCIATION (AFBMA)
Anti-Friction Bearing Manufacturers Association
60 East 42nd Street
New York, NY 10017

ASSOCIATION OF HOME APPLIANCE MANUFACTURERS (AHAM)
Association of Home Appliance Manufacturers
20 North Wacker Drive
Chicago, IL 60606

CALIFORNIA REDWOOD ASSOCIATION
California Redwood Association
617 Montgomery Street
San Francisco, CA 94111

COMPRESSED AIR AND GAS INSTITUTE (CAGI)
Compressed Air and Gas Institute
2130 Keith Building
Cleveland, OH 44115

DIESEL ENGINE MANUFACTURERS ASSOCIATION (DEMA)
Diesel Engine Manufacturers Association
2130 Keith Building
Cleveland, OH 44115

ELECTRONIC INDUSTRIES ASSOCIATION (EIA)
Electronic Industries Association
2001 Eye Street, N.W.
Washington, D.C. 20006

ELECTROTECHNICAL COMMISSION
(Available from ANSI)

FACTORY MUTUAL SYSTEMS
Factory Mutual Systems
184 High Street
Boston, MA 02110

FEDERAL CONSTRUCTION GUIDE SPECIFICATION (FCGS)
General Services Administration
Public Building Service
Office of Construction Management
Criteria and Research Branch
19th and F Street, N.W.
Washington, D.C. 20405

FEDERAL SPECIFICATIONS
Specification Sales (3FRDS)
Building 197, Washington Navy Yard
General Services Administration
Washington, D.C. 20407

GENERAL SERVICES ADMINISTRATION
General Services Administration
Washington, D.C.

HEARING AID INDUSTRY CONFERENCE, INC.
Hearing Aid Industry Conference, Inc.
75 East Wacker Dr.
Chicago, IL 60001

HOME VENTILATING INSTITUTE (HVI)
Home Ventilating Institute
230 North Michigan Ave.
Chicago, IL 60601

INDUSTRIAL SILENCER MANUFACTURERS ASSOCIATION (ISMA)
R. J. Yeager, ISMA
c/o Burgess Industries
P.O. Box 47146
Dallas, TX 75247

ISMA
Test Procedure
Standard Laboratory Test Procedure for Insertion Loss Measurement of Intake and Exhaust Silencers for Reciprocating Engines, (1974).
Insertion Loss of Pressure Reduction and Regulator Valve Silencers.

INSTITUTE OF ELECTRICAL AND ELECTRONIC ENGINEERS (IEEE)
Institute of Electrical and Electronic Engineers
445 Hoes Lane
Piscataway, NJ 08854

INSTRUMENT SOCIETY OF AMERICA (ISA)
Instrument Society of America
400 Stanwix Street
Pittsburgh, PA 15222

INTERNATIONAL CONFERENCE OF BUILDING OFFICIALS (ICBO)
International Conference of Building Officials
5360 South Warkman Mill Road
Whittier, CA 90601

STC
UBC35-1
Laboratory Determination of Airborne Sound Transmission Class (STC).

INTERNATIONAL ELECTROTECHNICAL COMMISSION (IEC)
American National Standards Institute
1430 Broadway
New York, NY 10018

IEC 123   Recommendations for Sound-Level Meters, (1961).
IEC 179   Precision Sound-Level Meters, (1973).

INTERNATIONAL ORGANIZATION FOR STANDARDIZATION (ISO)

American National Standards Institute
1430 Broadway
New York, NY 10018

ISO
R140-1960   Field and Laboratory Measurements of Airborne and Impact Sound Transmission.

ISO
R354-1963   Measurement of Absorption Coefficients in a Reverberation Room.

ISO
532-1975   Acoustics—Method for Calculating Loudness Level.

ISO
R1996-1971   Acoustics—Assessment of Noise with Respect to Community Response.

ISO
R2204-1973   Guide to the Measurement of Acoustical Noise and Evaluation of its Effect on Man.

ISO
3741-1975   Acoustics—Determination of Sound-Power Level of Noise Sources—Precision Methods for Broadband Sources in Reverberation Rooms.

ISO
DIS 3743   Acoustics—Determination of Sound-Power Level of Noise Sources—Engineering Methods for Special Reverberation Test Rooms.

ISO
DIS 3744   Acoustics—Determination of Sound-Power Levels of Noise Sources—Engineering Methods for Free-Field Conditions over a Reflecting Plane.

ISO
DIS 3746   Acoustics—Determination of Sound-Power Levels of Noise Sources, Survey Methods.

MILITARY SPECIFICATIONS

Commanding Officer
Naval Publications and Forms Center
5801 Tabor Avenue
Philadelphia, PA 19120

NATIONAL ELECTRICAL MANUFACTURERS ASSOCIATION (NEMA)
National Electrical Manufacturers Association
815 15th Street, Ste. 438
Washington, D.C. 20005

NATIONAL FLUID POWER ASSOCIATION (NEPA)
National Fluid Power Association
3333 N. Mayfair Road
Milwaukee, WI 53222

NATIONAL MACHINE TOOL BUILDERS ASSOCIATION (NMTBA)
National Machine Tool Builders Association
7901 West Park Drive
McLean, VA 22101

NATIONAL SCHOOL SUPPLY AND EQUIPMENT ASSOCIATION (NSSEA)
National School Supply and Equipment Association
Folding Partition Subsection
1500 Wilson Boulevard
Arlington, VA 22209

POWER SAW MANUFACTURERS ASSOCIATION (PSMA)
Power Saw Manufacturers Association
Box 7256
Belle View Station
Alexandria, VA 22307

PUBLIC BUILDING SERVICE (PBS)
General Services Administration
Public Building Service
Office of Construction Management
Criteria and Research Branch
GSA Building
19th and F Street, N.W.
Washington, D.C. 20405

RADIO MANUFACTURERS ASSOCIATION

Radio Manufacturers Association
1317 F Street N.W.
Washington, D.C. 20004

SOCIETY OF AUTOMOTIVE ENGINEERS (SAE)

Society of Automotive Engineers
400 Commonwealth Drive
Warrendale, PA 15096

SAE J331a	SAE Recommended Practice, Sound Levels for Motorcycles, (1975).
SAE J986a	SAE Standard, Sound Level for Passenger Cars and Light Trucks (ANSI S6.3-1973), (1972).
SAE ARP 1071	SAE Aerospace Recommended Practice, Definitions and Procedures for Computing the Effective Perceived Noise Level for Flyover Aircraft Noise, (1973).

STEEL DOOR INSTITUTE (SDI)

Steel Door Institute
2130 Keith Building
Cleveland, OH 44115

WOODWORKING MACHINERY MANUFACTURERS ASSOCIATION (WMMA)

Woodworking Machinery Manufacturing Association
1900 Arch Street
Philadelphia, PA 19103

SUMMARY OF FEDERAL REGULATIONS

Department of Labor Occupational Noise Exposure Standard, Title 29, Code of Federal Regulations, Chapter XVII, Part 1910, Subpart G, 36 FR 10466, May 29, 1971.

Department of Housing and Urban Development Circular 1390.2, Noise Abatement and Control: Departmental Policy, Implementation Responsibilities and Standards, August 4, 1971.

Department of the Interior Noise Standard Issued under the Federal Coal Mine Health and Safety Act, Title 30, Code of Federal Regulations, Chapter I, Parts 70 and 71, 35 FR 5544, April 3, 1970; 36 FR 12739, July 7, 1971: 37 FR 6368, March 18, 1972; 38 FR 18666, July 13, 1973.

General Services Administration, Public Buildings Service Construction Equipment and Practices, Par. 44.8 in Guide Specification PBS 4-01100, October 1973.

Federal Aviation Adminstration Noise Standards, Title 14, Code of Federal Regulations, Chapter I, Part 36, 34 FR 1864, November 18, 1969, as amended at 38 FR 29574, October 26, 1973.

Department of Transportation, Federal Highway Administration Vehicle Interior Noise Levels, Title 49, Code of Federal Regulations, Chapter III, Subchapter B, Part 393.94, 38 FR 30880, November 8, 1973.

Department of Transportation, Federal Highway Administration Highway Noise Control Standards and Procedures, Title 23, Code of Federal Regulations, Chapter I, Subchapter J, Part 772, 38 FR 15953, June 19, 1973, as amended at 39 FR 6696, February 22, 1974.

Environmental Protection Agency Final Noise Emission Standards, Motor Carriers Engaged in Interstate Commerce, Title 40, Code of Federal Regulations, Chapter I, Part 202, 39 FR 38208, October 29, 1974.

SELECTED STANDARDS FOR SOURCE EVALUATION (REF. 1, REF. 2)

INTERNATIONAL ORGANIZATION FOR STANDARDIZATION (ISO)

ISO.495	General Requirements for the Preparation of Test Codes for Measuring the Noise Emitted by Machines (1966).
ISO.1680	Test Code for the Measurement of the Airborne Noise Emitted by Rotating Electrical Machinery (1970).
ISO.3740	Determination of Sound Power Levels of Noise Sources—Guidelines for Use of Basic Standards and for Preparation of Noise Test Codes (Draft).
ISO.3741	Determination of Sound Power Levels of Noise Sources—Precision Method for Broad Band Sound Sources Operating in Reverberation Rooms (1975).
ISO.3742	Determination of Sound Power Levels of Noise Sources—Precision Methods for Discrete Frequency and Narrow Band Sound Sources Operating in Reverberation Rooms (1975).
ISO.3743	Determination of Sound Power Levels of Noise Sources —Engineering Methods for Special Reverberant Test Rooms.
ISO.3744	Determination of Sound Power Levels of Noise Sources —Engineering Methods for Free-Field Conditions over a Reflecting Plane (Draft).
ISO.3745	Determination of Sound Power Levels of Noise Sources—Precision Methods for Sources Operating In Anechoic Rooms (Draft).

ISO.3746   Determination of Sound Power Levels of Noise Sources—Survey Method (Draft).

ISO.2880   Determination of Sound Power Emitted by Small Noise Sources in Reverberation Rooms. Part 1: Broad Band Sources (Draft).

ISO.2946   Determination of Sound Power Emitted by Small Sources in Reverberation Rooms. Part 2: Discrete Frequencies and Narrow Band Sources.

EUROPEAN ECONOMIC COMMUNITY (EEC)

XI/28/75-E Rev. 2   Draft Proposal for a Council Directive on the Approximation of the Laws of Member States Relating to the Measurement of the Permissible Sound Levels of Grass Cutting Machines.

AUSTRIA

S5031   Determination of Sound Power Emitted by Small Noise Sources in Reverberation Rooms: Broad Band Sound Sources (1975).

S5034   Determination of Sound Power Emitted by Noise Sources: Field Measurement over a Reflecting Plane (1975).

FRANCE

S30-006   General Requirements for the Preparation of Test Codes for Measuring the Noise Emitted by Machines (1966).

S31-006   Test Code for the Measurement of the Airborne Noise Emitted by Rotating Electrical Machinery (1966).

S31-022   Determination of Sound Power Levels of Noise Sources.

S31-022   Precision Method for Broad Band Sound Sources Operating in Reverberation Rooms (1973), Part 1.

S31-023   Precision Methods for Discrete-Frequency and Narrow-Band Sound Sources Operating in Reverberation Rooms (1973), Part 2.

S31-024   Engineering Methods for Special Reverberant Test Rooms (1973), Part 3.

S31-025   Engineering Methods for Free-Field Conditions over a Reflecting Plane (1973), Part 4.

S31-026   Precision Methods for Sources Operating in Anechoic Rooms (1973), Part 5.

GERMANY

DIN 45632   Guidelines for the Measurement of the Noise Generated by Electrical Machines (DDR).

DIN 45635   Noise Measurements on Machines (DDR).

DIN 52218   Laboratory Measurements of the Noise Generated by Plumbing Equipment (DDR).

TGL 50-29034   Guidelines for the Measurement of the Noise Generated by Electrical Machines (DDR).

TGL 200-3110   Measurement of the Noise of Electrical Machines (DDR).

TGL 200-4505   Measurement of the Noise of Household Electrical Appliances (DDR).

UNITED KINGDOM

B.S. 4196   Guide to the Selection of Methods of Measuring Noise Emitted by Machinery.

B.S. 4999   General Requirements for Rotating Electrical Machines.
Part 50. (1972): Mechanical Performance—Vibration.
Part 51. (1973): Noise Levels.
Part 60. (1976): Tests.

UNITED STATES

ANSI. SI.21-1972   Methods for the Determination of Sound Power Levels of Small Sources in Reverberation Rooms.

ANSI. SI.23-1976   Method for the Designation of Sound Power by Machinery and Equipment.

ANSI. S3.17-1975   Method for Rating the Sound Power Spectra of Small Stationary Noise Sources.

ANSI. S5.1-1971   Test Code for the Measurement of Sound from Pneumatic Equipment.

ASA. STD 3-1975   Test-Site Measurement of Noise Emitted by Engine Powered Equipment.

ASA. STD 4-1975   Method for Rating the Sound Power Spectra of Small Stationary Noise Sources.

ASA. STD 5-1976   Method for the Designation of Sound Power Emitted by Machinery and Equipment.

ASHRAE STD 36-72   Methods of Testing for Sound Rating Heating, Refrigerating and Air-Conditioning Equipment.

IEEE 85   Test Procedure for Airborne Sound Measurements on Rotating Electric Machinery (1973).

SAE Standard J952b   Sound Levels for Engine Powered Equipment (1969).

ARI Standard 446   Standard for Sound Rating of Room Air-Induction Units (1968).

AMCA Standard 300-67 Test Code for Sound Rating (Of Air Moving Devices).

6

AMCA Bul. 303	Application of Sound Power Ratings for Ducted Air Moving Devices (1965).
AMCA Pub. 311-67	Certified Sound Ratings Program for Air Moving Devices.
AHAM Stand. NO. RAC 2SR	Room Air Conditioner Sound Rating (1971).
S5.1-1971 CAGI-PNEUROP	Test Code for the Measurement of Sound from Pneumatic Equipment.
HVI Test Procedure	Sound Test Procedure (for Domestic Ventilating Equipment) (1968).
PTI	Standard for the Measurement of Sound Emitted by Portable, Stationary and Fixed Electric Tools (Proposed ANSI S.10-1) (1974).

AUSTRALIA

| AS1217 | Methods of Measurement of Airborne Sound Emitted by Machines (1972). |

CANADA

| Z 107-3 | Methods for the Determination of Sound Power Levels of Small Sources in Reverberation Rooms (ANSI SI.21–1972) (1974). |

INDIA

| IS:6098 | Method of Measurement of the Airborne Noise Emitted by Rotating Electrical Machinery (1971) |
| IS:4758 | Methods of Measurement of the Noise Emitted by Machines (1968). |

U.S.S.R.

| Gost 11870-66 | Machines—Noise Characteristics and Methods for Their Determination. |
| Gost 11929-66 | Measurement of Noise Emitted by Electrical Rotating Machines and Transformers. |

REFERENCES

1. Acoustical Society of America, *Index to Noise Standards*, ASA STDS Index 1, 1976.
2. *Standards, Formula and Chart Handbook*, Brunel & Kjaer, Denmark.

INDEX

Page numbers in *italic* indicate illustrations or tables.